STOCHASTIC PROCESSES
IN
CHEMICAL PHYSICS

ADVANCES IN CHEMICAL PHYSICS
VOLUME XV

ADVANCES IN CHEMICAL PHYSICS

EDITORS

I. Prigogine

Faculté des Sciences, Université Libre de Bruxelles, Brussels, Belgium

S. Rice

Institute for the Study of Metals, University of Chicago, Chicago, Illinois

Vol. XV

Stochastic Processes
in
Chemical Physics

Edited by K. E. SHULER

Department of Chemistry, University of California
at San Diego, La Jolla, California

INTERSCIENCE PUBLISHERS

a division of John Wiley & Sons, New York – London – Sydney – Toronto

Library of Congress Catalog Card Number 58-9935

SBN 471   789674

PRINTED IN THE UNITED STATES OF AMERICA

PREFACE

There has been considerable work over the past decade on the application of the theory of stochastic processes to a variety of problems in the physical, biological, engineering, and social sciences. Several monographs on stochastic processes which have been published have stressed applications in a number of diverse fields (genetics, epidemiology, biology, operations research, demography, information processing, traffic control, physical sciences) and numerous research papers on both methodology and applications are spread throughout the literature. One of the areas of applications in which much interesting research has been carried out recently is that of chemical physics. In order to obtain a sampling and an overview of some of this work, a topical conference was organized in 1968 in which a number of the active workers in the field were asked to report on their work.

The papers on which the articles in this volume are based, were prepared at the invitation of the organizing committee, for presentation at the Conference on Stochastic Processes in Chemical Physics which was held at the University of California at San Diego, La Jolla, March 18–22, 1968. The purpose of this meeting was to bring together selected experts in the fields of probability theory, applied mathematics, transport processes, statistical mechanics, chemical kinetics, polymer chemistry, and molecular biochemistry for an exchange of ideas and to stimulate interest and activity in the application of the theory of stochastic processes to problems in chemical physics.

The articles in this volume are representative of some of the current work on the application of stochastic theory to a variety of problems in chemical physics. Their very diversity is an indication of the power and wide utility of stochastic concepts in attacking and solving problems in broad areas of chemistry and physics. In the sense that essentially all time-dependent processes in chemistry and physics which involve a sufficiently large number of particles can be treated by probabilistic (i.e., stochastic) methods, the particular topics discussed in this volume, even though of great diversity, are still only a small subset of a much larger set.

The arrangement of the articles in this book is from the general to the particular. The first four papers (I. Oppenheim, I. Prigogine, N. van Kampen, B. Koopman) deal with some of the broad fundamentals relating stochastic processes to classical and quantum mechanics. The next four

v

papers (R. Gordon, R. Kubo, R. C. Desai and S. Yip, P. Verdier) are concerned with the application of the time-dependent correlation function formalism to various stochastic problems in chemical physics. The third set of papers (D. McQuarrie, J. Gibbs, G. Weiss, T. Bak) discuss the application of stochastic theory to rate and relaxation processes. The fourth group (C. Domb, P. Mazur, Rabinowitz et al., R. A. Orwoll and W. H. Stockmayer, R. Zwanzig) deals with the application of stochastic theory to a number of problems in polymer chemistry and physics. The last three papers (M. Fisher, R. Burke and A. Siegel, E. Guth) are concerned with some special techniques and results of interest and importance in the application of stochastic theory.

It is the hope of the Editor that this volume will serve as a selective status report anno 1968 and that it will stimulate additional work and new approaches in this interesting field.

Grateful acknowledgment is made to the Advanced Research Project Agency of the Department of Defense, The National Bureau of Standards, Washington, D.C., and the University of California, San Diego at La Jolla, California for their support in the organization of this conference.

KURT E. SHULER

January 1969

AUTHORS

THOR BAK, Chemical Laboratory III, H. C. Ørsted Institute, Copenhagen, Denmark

TERENCE BURKE, Department of Physics, Boston University, Boston, Massachusetts

RASHMI C. DESAI, Department of Nuclear Engineering, Massachusetts Institute of Technology, Cambridge, Massachusetts

CYRIL DOMB, Belfer Graduate School of Science, Yeshiva University, New York, New York

MICHAEL E. FISHER, Baker Laboratory, Department of Chemistry, Cornell University, Ithaca, New York

JULIAN H. GIBBS, Metcalf Research Laboratory, Brown University, Providence, Rhode Island

ROY G. GORDON, Department of Chemistry, Harvard University, Cambridge, Massachusetts

EUGENE GUTH, Oak Ridge National Laboratory, Oak Ridge, Tennessee

ROBERT E. HARTWIG, Baker Laboratory, Cornell Laboratory, Ithaca, New York

BERNARD O. KOOPMAN, Arthur D. Little, Inc., Acorn Park, Cambridge, Massachusetts

RYOGO KUBO, Department of Physics, University of Tokyo, Tokyo, Japan

ELIZABETH LOFTUS, Case Western Reserve University, Cleveland, Ohio

DONALD A. MCQUARRIE, Science Center, Aerospace and Systems Group, North American Rockwell Corporation, Thousand Oaks, California

JACOB MAZUR, Institute for Materials Reserach, National Bureau of Standards, Washington, D.C.

IRWIN OPPENHEIM, Department of Chemistry, Massachusetts Institute of Technology, Cambridge, Massachusetts

R. A. ORWOLL, Department of Chemistry, Dartmouth College, Hanover, New Hampshire

I. PRIGOGINE, Faculté des Sciences de l'Université Libre de Bruxelles, Belgique, and Center for Statistical Mechanics and Thermodynamics, University of Texas, Austin, Texas

PH. RABINOWITZ, The Weizmann Institute of Science, Rehovoth, Israel

ARMAND SIEGEL, Service de Physique Théorique, Saclay, France, and Department of Physics, Boston University, Boston, Massachusetts

A. SILBERBERG, Polymer Department, The Weizmann Institute of Science, Rehovoth, Israel

ROBERT SIMHA, Case Western Reserve University, Cleveland, Ohio

G. P. SØRENSEN, H. C. Ørsted Institute, Copenhagen, Denmark

W. H. STOCKMAYER, Department of Chemistry, Darthmouth College, Hanover, New Hampshire

NICO VAN KAMPEN, Institute for Theoretical Physics, University of Utrecht, Utrecht, Holland.

PETER H. VERDIER, Polymers Division, National Bureau of Standards, Washington, D.C.

GEORGE H. WEISS, Division of Computer Research and Technology, National Institutes of Health, Education, and Welfare, Bethesda, Maryland

SIDNEY YIP, Department of Nuclear Engineering, Masscachusetts Institute of Technology, Cambridge, Massachusetts

ROBERT ZWANZIG, Institute for Fluid Dynamics and Applied Mathematics, Institute for Molecular Physics, University of Maryland, College Park, Maryland

CONTENTS

PROBABILISTIC AND DYNAMIC APPROACHES TO THE THEORY OF STOCHASTIC PROCESSES

IRWIN OPPENHEIM

Department of Chemistry,
Massachusetts Institute of Technology,
Cambridge, Massachusetts

CONTENTS

I. INTRODUCTION

In this paper we present a brief discussion and comparison of the probabilistic and dynamic approaches to the treatment of nonequilibrium phenomena in physical systems. The discussion is not intended to be complete but only illustrative. Details of many of the derivations appear elsewhere and only the results will be discussed here. We shall focus our attention on the probabilistic approach and shall emphasize its advantages and drawbacks. The main body of the paper deals with the properties of the master equation and, more cursorily, with the properties of the Langevin equation.

II. PROBABILISTIC PRELIMINARIES

The probabilistic approach to time-dependent physical phenomena is useful because it is capable of yielding general results via a relatively simple formalism. On the other hand, it is just this generality which may be misleading and which requires a reference to a physical investigation of the details of the physical problem.

We consider a system whose state at time t is characterized by the value of the stochastic variable $X(t)$.[1,2] We define the joint probability

1

densities $p_r(x_1, t_1; x_2, t_2; \ldots; x_r, t_r)$, $t_1 \leqq t_2 \leqq \cdots \leqq t_r$, $r = 1, 2, 3 \cdots$, where $p_r \, dx_1 \cdots dx_r$ is the joint probability that $X(t)$ lies between x_1 and $x_1 + dx_1$ at time t_1, that $X(t)$ lies between x_2 and $x_2 + dx_2$ at $t_2, \ldots$, and that $X(t)$ lies between x_r and $x_r + dx_r$ at t_r. The conditional probability density $w_r(x_r, t_r/x_{r-1}, t_{r-1}; \ldots; x_1, t_1)$, $r = 2, 3, \ldots$, is defined by the property that $w_r \, dx_r$ is the probability that if $X(t_1) = x_1$, $X(t_2) = x_2, \ldots, X(t_{r-1}) = x_{r-1}$, then $X(t_r)$ will lie between x_r and $x_r + dx_r$. The joint probability densities have the properties that:

$$p_r \geqq 0 \tag{1a}$$

$$\int p_r \, dx_j = p_{r-1}(x_1, t_1; \ldots; x_{j-1}, t_{j-1}; x_{j+1}, t_{j+1}; \ldots; x_r, t_r)$$
$$j = 1, \ldots, r \tag{1b}$$

and

$$\int p_1(x_1, t_1) \, dx_1 = 1 \tag{1c}$$

The conditional probability densities are related to the joint probability densities by the relation

$$p_r(x_1, t_1; \ldots; x_r, t_r) = w_r(x_r, t_r/x_{r-1}, t_{r-1}; \ldots; x_1, t_1)$$
$$\times \, p_{r-1}(x_1, t_1; \ldots; x_{r-1}, t_{r-1}) \tag{2}$$

and have the properties:

$$w_r \geqq 0 \tag{3a}$$

$$w_r(x_r, t_r/x_{r-1}, t_r; \ldots; x_1, t_1) = \delta(x_r - x_{r-1}) \tag{3b}$$

$$\int w_r \, dx_r = 1 \tag{3c}$$

A complete probabilistic description of the system is obtained either by specifying all of the joint probability densities, p_r, $r = 1, 2, 3, \ldots$, or by specifying the singlet probability density p_1 and all of the conditional probability densities w_r, $r = 2, 3, 4, \ldots$.

We shall restrict our considerations here to physical systems in which the joint probabilities factorize if the times $t_1, \ldots, t_r$ are each widely separated from each other. Thus, e.g., $p_2(x_1, t_1; x_2, t_2) \xrightarrow[t_2 \to \infty]{} p_1(x_1, t_1) p_1(x_2, \infty)$; this implies that

$$w_2(x_2, t_2/x_1, t_1) \xrightarrow[t_2 \to \infty]{} p_1(x_2, \infty) \tag{3d}$$

One question of interest in setting up a probabilistic description of a physical phenomenon is whether we are free to choose any form for the conditional probabilities which satisfy the necessary conditions (3a–3d).

Unfortunately, there are additional restrictions on the conditional probabilities. This is readily seen by considering the form

$$w_2(x, t/y, s) = \delta(x - y) \exp\left[-\alpha(t - s)^2\right]$$
$$+ p_1(x, \infty)\{1 - \exp\left[-\alpha(t - s)^2\right]\} \quad (4)$$

for all x, y and $t \geqq s$, which satisfies Eqs. (3a–3d). The singlet probability can be computed either using the formula

$$p_1(x, t) = \int p_2(z, 0; x, t)\, dz \equiv \int w_2(x, t/z, 0)p_1(z, 0)\, dz$$
$$= p_1(x, 0) \exp\left[-\alpha t^2\right] + p_1(x, \infty)\{1 - \exp\left[-\alpha t^2\right]\} \quad (5)$$

or the formula

$$p_1(x, t) = \int w_2(x, t/y, s)w_2(y, s/z, 0)p_1(z, 0)\, dy\, dz$$
$$= p_1(x, 0) \exp\left[-\alpha\{(t - s)^2 + s^2\}\right]$$
$$+ p_1(x, \infty)\{1 - \exp\left[-\alpha\{(t - s)^2 + s^2\}\right]\} \quad (6)$$

for $t \geqq s \geqq 0$. In Eq. (6) we have used the facts that

$$p_1(x, t) = \int w_2(x, t/y, s)p_1(y, s)\, dy \quad (7a)$$

and

$$p_1(y, s) = \int w_2(y, s/z, 0)p_1(z, 0)\, dz. \quad (7b)$$

Clearly, Eqs. (5) and (6) yield different results for $p_1(x, t)$ and the form for w_2 in Eq. (4) is not suitable. This is a reflection of a general property of the conditional probabilities for non-Markovian processes that we shall prove below.

A Markovian stochastic process is defined by the relations

$$w_r(x_r, t_r/x_{r-1}, t_{r-1}; \ldots; x_1, t_1) = w_2(x_r, t_r/x_{r-1}, t_{r-1}) \quad (8)$$

for all $r \geqq 2$. From Eq. (8) and the recursion relations, Eq. (1b), it is easy to derive the Smoluchowski-Chapman-Kolmogorov (SCK) equation

$$w_2(x, t/z, r) = \int w_2(x, t/y, s)w_2(y, s/z, r)\, dy \quad (9)$$

Equation (9) is valid for all x and z and for all times such that $t \geqq s \geqq r$. Although there are some bizarre conditional probabilities, termed pseudo-Markovian, which obey the SCK equation for all x, z, $t \geqq s \geqq r$, which do not obey Eq. (8), these do not occur in physical situations and we may therefore take Eq. (9) as a definition of a Markov process.

With this in mind we equate Eqs. (5) and (6) to obtain

$$\int w_2(x, t/z, 0)p_1(z, 0)\, dz = \int w_2(x, t/y, s)w_2(y, s/z, 0)p_1(z, 0)\, dy\, dz \tag{10}$$

Equation (10) is valid for *all* stochastic processes for all values of $x, y, t \geqq s \geqq 0$. Now if we choose

$$p_1(z, 0) = \delta(z - \eta), \tag{11}$$

we obtain from Eq. (10)

$$w_2(x, t/\eta, 0) = \int w_2(x, t/y, s)w_2(y, s/\eta, 0)\, dy \tag{12}$$

which is identical to the SCK equation; it is valid for all stochastic processes for which the initial condition of Eq. (11) applies. It is therefore clear from our discussion above that, *the conditional probabilities for non-Markovian processes must depend on the initial conditions for the singlet probabilities.* Thus, since the conditional probability of Eq. (4) does not obey the SCK equation and does not depend on $p_1(y, s)$ it is not a possible conditional probability.

It would be pleasant if one could make the statement that the conditional probability for a Markov process could not depend on the initial condition for the singlet probability. That this statement is not correct is easily shown by considering the special case

$$w_2(x, t/y, s) = \delta(x - y)\frac{\bar{x}(\infty)}{\bar{x}(\infty) + \bar{x}(s)\{\exp[k(t - s)] - 1\}}$$
$$+ p_1(x, \infty)\frac{\bar{x}(s)\{\exp[k(t - s)] - 1\}}{\bar{x}(\infty) + \bar{x}(s)\{\exp[k(t - s)] - 1\}} \tag{13}$$

where $\bar{x}(s)$ is the first moment of the singlet probability, i.e.,

$$\bar{x}(s) = \int_0^\infty xp_1(x, s)\, dx \tag{14}$$

Equation (13) clearly depends on $p_1(x, s)$ through $\bar{x}(s)$; it also obeys the SCK equation for all pertinent values of the arguments and thus represents a Markov process. Therefore, the only statement we can make is that *the conditional probability densities for a Markov process may* (*but need not*) *depend on the initial values of the singlet probability.*

III. MASTER EQUATIONS

It is easy to obtain master equations which describe the time dependences of the singlet probability densities and the pair conditional probability densities.[2] The equation for the singlet probability is obtained by rewriting Eq. (7a) in the form

$$p_1(x, t + \Delta) = \int w_2(x, t + \Delta/y, t)p_1(y, t) \, dy, \tag{15}$$

by subtracting $p_1(x, t)$ from both sides of Eq. (15), by dividing by Δ, and taking the limit as $\Delta \to 0$, to obtain

$$\frac{\partial p_1(x, t)}{\partial t} = \int a(x, y, t)p_1(y, t) \, dy \tag{16}$$

where

$$a(x, y, t) = \lim_{\Delta \to 0} \frac{w_2(x, t + \Delta/y, t) - \delta(x - y)}{\Delta} \tag{17}$$

Equation (16) is the master equation for $p_1(x, t)$. If the transition rates a are supplied, together with $p_1(x, 0)$, Eq. (16) can be solved to yield $p_1(x, t)$. Equation (16) is valid for all stochastic processes for which the transition rates a exist.

Although Eq. (16) has a very simple form, the quantities $a(x, y, t)$ may be very complicated. This is why the probabilistic master equation, Eq. (16), appears much simpler than the physical master equation which will be discussed presently. The equations which describe the time development of the conditional probabilities w_2 are also obtained straightforwardly from Eqs. (1b) and (2). The results for a Markov process are

$$\frac{\partial w_2(x, t/z, r)}{\partial t} = \int a(x, y, t)w_2(y, t/z, r) \, dy \tag{18}$$

where a is again given by Eq. (17). For a non-Markovian process, we obtain

$$\frac{\partial w_2(x, t/z, r)}{\partial t} = \int a_3(x, y, t; z, r)w_2(y, t/z, r) \, dy \tag{19}$$

where a_3 is defined by

$$a_3(x, y, t; z, r) = \lim_{\Delta \to 0} \frac{w_3(x, t + \Delta/y, t; z, r) - \delta(x - y)}{\Delta} \tag{20}$$

It follows from Eq. (18) that, for a Markov process, w_2 is a functional of p_1 if and only if a is a functional of p_1. For the example of Eq. (13), $a(x, y, t)$

is given by

$$a(x, y, t) = k \frac{\bar{x}(t)}{\bar{x}(\infty)} \{ -\delta(x - y) + p_1(x, \infty) \} \tag{21}$$

and a is a functional of p_1. For a non-Markovian process, the transition rates, a, may also depend on p_1.

The physical master equation has been obtained by a number of investigators.[3] In notation similar to that of Eq. (16) it can be written

$$\dot{p}_1(x, t) = \int dy \int_0^t d\tau k(x, y, \tau) p_1(y, t - \tau) \tag{22}$$

where the kernel $k(x, y, \tau)$ depends on the Hamiltonian of the system but does not depend on any of the joint or conditional probabilities. In Eq. (22), $p_1(x, t)$ can be, for example, the diagonal part of the density matrix of the system or the N-particle momentum distribution. If we wish to cast Eq. (22) in the form of Eq. (16), the transition rates a can be written

$$a(x, y, t) = \frac{\int_0^t k(x, y, \tau) p_1(y, t - \tau) \, d\tau}{p_1(y, t)} \tag{23}$$

In the particular case of a Pauli equation,[1]

$$k(x, y, \tau) = 2k(x, y) \, \delta(\tau) \tag{24}$$

and Eq. (23) becomes

$$a(x, y, t) = k(x, y) \tag{25}$$

Equation (22) has a more complicated form than Eq. (16) because all dependence on the probabilities is made explicit.

We note that frequently the transition rates defined by Eq. (17) are zero if they are calculated using the exact dynamical equations (i.e., the classical or quantal Liouville equation) since the expansion of $w_2(x, t + \Delta/y, t)$ in powers of Δ contains only even powers. However, appropriate approximate calculations do yield nonzero transition rates.

In order to determine whether a given physical phenomenon can be described by a Markov process, it is not sufficient to study equations for the time dependence of $p_1(x, t)$, such as Eqs. (22) and (16). It is necessary to investigate the equation for $\partial w_2/\partial t$. We[4] have undertaken this investigation for $w_2(\mathbf{p}, t/\mathbf{p}_0, t_0)$, the conditional probability density for a particle to have momentum between $\mathbf{p}$ and $\mathbf{p} + d\mathbf{p}$ at time t if it had momentum $\mathbf{p}_0$ at time t_0, in the low density limit. We find that w_2 does obey the SCK equation, Eq. (19), though it does depend on $p_1(\mathbf{p}, t)$, and therefore the process is Markovian.

An interesting, but probably incorrect, application of the probabilistic master equation is the description of chemical kinetics in a dilute gas.[5] Instead of using the classical deterministic theory, several investigators have introduced single time functions of the form $P(n_1, n_2, t)$ where $P(n_1, n_2, t)$ is the probability that there are n_1 particles of type 1 and n_2 particles of type 2 in the system at time t. They use the transition rate $A(n_1, n_2; n_1', n_2', t)$ from the state with n_1' particles of type 1 and n_2' particles of type 2 to the state with n_1 and n_2 particles of types 1 and 2, respectively, at time t. The rates that are used are obtained by assuming that only uncorrelated binary collisions occur in the system. These rates, however, are only correct in the thermodynamic limit for a low density system. In this limit, the Boltzmann equation is valid from which the deterministic theory follows. Thus, there is no reason to attach any physical significance to the differences between the results of the stochastic theory and the deterministic theory.[6]

In closing this section, we note that the stochastic master equation, Eq. (16), can be used to study the effect of boundary conditions on transport equations. If $a(x, y, t)$ is sufficiently peaked as a function of $|x - y|$, that is if transitions occur from y to states in the near neighborhood of y, only, then the master equation can be approximated by a Fokker-Planck equation. The effects of the boundary on the master equation all appear in the properties of $a(x, y, t)$. However, in the transition to the Fokker-Planck differential equation, these boundary effects appear as boundary conditions on the differential equation.[7] These effects are prototypes for the study of how molecular boundary conditions imposed on the Liouville equation are reflected in the macroscopic boundary conditions imposed on the hydrodynamic equations.

IV. LANGEVIN EQUATION

In this section, we discuss briefly how the Langevin equation, which is a stochastic equation, can be derived from the molecular equations of motion. The stochastic model described by the Langevin equation has been of great use in interpreting a large number of experiments and physical systems. The stochastic model is extremely simple but, as always, its ultimate justification rests on the molecular dynamical laws.

We consider a system consisting of a heavy particle immersed in a bath of light particles. The Langevin equation is

$$\dot{\mathbf{P}}(t) = -\gamma \mathbf{P}(t) + \mathbf{E}(t) \tag{26}$$

where $\mathbf{P}(t)$ is the momentum of the heavy particle, γ is a constant, and $\mathbf{E}(t)$ is a fluctuating force whose properties are described by a Gaussian-Markov process. Thus, all of the pertinent properties of $\mathbf{E}(t)$ are described by its probability distribution or by its moments

$$\overline{\mathbf{E}(t)} = 0$$
$$\overline{\mathbf{E}(t)\mathbf{E}(0)} = \alpha I \delta(t) \tag{27}$$
$$\vdots$$

where the bar denotes a stochastic average, α is a constant which is related to γ, and I is the unit tensor. The stochastic properties of $\mathbf{E}(t)$ are supposed to reflect the effect of the fluctuating force on the heavy particle due to the light particles. Once the stochastic properties of $\mathbf{E}(t)$ have been postulated, the stochastic properties of $\mathbf{P}(t)$ follow directly from Eq. (26). Thus, for example

$$\overline{\dot{\mathbf{P}}(t)} = -\gamma \overline{\mathbf{P}(t)}; \qquad \overline{\mathbf{P}(t)} = \exp\left[-\gamma t\right]\mathbf{P}(0) \tag{28}$$

In order to derive Eq. (26) from molecular considerations it is necessary to specify the system more completely.[8] We consider a classical system of volume V consisting of one heavy particle of mass M, position $\mathbf{R}$, and momentum $\mathbf{P}$, and N light particles of mass m whose positions are denoted by r^N and whose momenta are denoted by p^N. The Hamiltonian for the system is given by

$$H = \frac{P^2}{2M} + \frac{p^N \cdot p^N}{2m} + U(r^N) + H_{int}(\mathbf{R}, r^N) = \frac{P^2}{2M} + H_b \tag{29}$$

where H_b is defined by Eq. (29), $U(r^N)$ is the short range interaction among the light particles and H_{int} is the short range interaction between the heavy particle and the light particles. The Liouville operator for the system is given by

$$iL = \frac{\mathbf{P}}{M} \cdot \nabla_R + \mathbf{F} \cdot \nabla_P + iL_b \tag{30}$$

where

$$\mathbf{F} = -\nabla_R H_{int} \tag{31}$$

and

$$iL_b = \frac{p^N}{m} \cdot \nabla_{r^N} - \nabla_{r^N}\{U + H_{int}\} \cdot \nabla_{p^N} \tag{32}$$

The average over the equilibrium distribution of the bath particles will be denoted by $\langle \ \rangle$, so that

$$\langle A \rangle \equiv \frac{\int \exp\left[-\beta H_b\right] A \, dr^N \, dp^N}{\int \exp\left[-\beta H_b\right] dr^N \, dp^N} \tag{33}$$

where $\beta = 1/kT$ and A is an arbitrary dynamical variable. We also define a projection operator $\mathscr{P}$ by the relation

$$\mathscr{P} A = \langle A \rangle \tag{34}$$

We define the following time dependent quantities:

$$A(t) = \exp\left[iLt\right] A \tag{35a}$$

$$A_0(t) = \exp\left[iL_b t\right] A \tag{35b}$$

$$A^+(t) = \exp\left[i(1 - \mathscr{P})Lt\right] A \tag{35c}$$

It is then straightforward to derive the exact equation

$$\dot{\mathbf{P}}(t) = \mathbf{F}^+(t) - \int_0^t \exp\left[iL(t - \tau)\right]\left\{\frac{\mathbf{P}}{MkT} - \nabla_P\right\} \cdot \langle \mathbf{F}\mathbf{F}^+(\tau) \rangle \, d\tau \tag{36}$$

In the limit in which $M \to \infty$, $t \to \infty$, t/M fixed, Eq. (36) becomes

$$\dot{\mathbf{P}}(t) = -\gamma \mathbf{P}(t) + \mathbf{E}(t) \tag{37}$$

where

$$\gamma = \frac{1}{3MkT} \int_0^\infty \langle \mathbf{F} \cdot \mathbf{F}_0(t) \rangle \, dt \tag{38}$$

and the averages defined by Eq. (33) of products of $\mathbf{E}(t)$ have the properties assigned to the stochastic averages of Eq. (27). Thus, the stochastic equation, Eq. (26), has been derived from the exact equations of motion.

This completes our summary of probabilistic and physical approaches to the theory of irreversible processes. As we have seen, probabilistic models are of great use in the description of irreversible processes but their ultimate justification rests on physical studies and approximations.

References

1. More details concerning the definitions in Section II and the master equation in Section III are given in: I. Oppenheim and K. E. Shuler, *Phys. Rev.*, **138**, B 1007 (1965) and in Ref. 2.
2. I. Oppenheim, K. E. Shuler, and G. H. Weiss, *Advan. Mol. Relaxation Processes*, **1**, 13 (1967).
3. See, e.g., R. Zwanzig, *Physica*, **30**, 1109 (1964).

4. I. Oppenheim and R. C. Desai, to be published.
5. See the review article: D. A. McQuarrie, *J. Appl. Prob.*, **4**, 413 (1967) where a summary of these approaches is given.
6. I. Oppenheim, K. E. Shuler, and G. H. Weiss, *J. Chem. Phys.*, in press, (1968).
7. N. G. van Kampen, I. Oppenheim, and K. E. Shuler, to be published.
8. P. Mazur and I. Oppenheim, to be published.

QUANTUM STATES AND DISSIPATIVE PROCESSES

I. PRIGOGINE

*Faculté des Sciences de l'Université Libre de Bruxelles, Belgique,
and Center for Statistical Mechanics and Thermodynamics,
University of Texas, Austin, Texas*

CONTENTS

I. INTRODUCTION

In his interesting book, *The Conceptual Development of Quantum Mechanics*, Jammer[15] reports that in 1908, A. Haas submitted his dissertation on quantum theory to the University of Vienna. It was probably the first application of *quantum theory to the calculation of energy levels.* However, his contribution was rejected since the application of the quantum theory, then considered a part of the theory of heat, to spectroscopy was considered ridiculous.

Today, the situation is just the opposite and it seems at first strange to try to improve our understanding of quantum theory by using methods and techniques developed in statistical mechanics and in thermodynamics. That is, however, what I shall try to do. I shall not go into any technical details which may be found elsewhere.[19, 21] But I would like to emphasize here the physical ideas behind the formalism. It seems to me that this new development may lead to a clarification of concepts used in widely different fields such as thermodynamics and statistical mechanics of irreversible processes, atomic spectroscopy, and theory of elementary particles. In all these fields one finds again and again the same questions: *What is the meaning of a quantum state corresponding to a finite lifetime? Can we associate an energy to such a state? How can we incorporate decay processes and dissipation into quantum theory?*

These are the questions we want to discuss. But before doing so I would like to introduce the problem by a few general remarks.

II. EINSTEIN'S THEORY OF SPONTANEOUS EMISSION IN UNSTABLE PARTICLES

An early (perhaps the first) example of a quantum treatment of a dissipative process is Einstein's theory of spontaneous emission.[6] To describe the interaction between matter and light, Einstein assumed the Boltzmann type of kinetic equations

$$\frac{dN_n}{dt} = \sum_m (P_{m \to n} N_m - P_{n \to m} N_n) \tag{1}$$

The first term on the right-hand side is a "gain" term due to transitions between level m and n, the second a loss term; N_n is the number of atoms in level n. The important new element introduced by Einstein was the discovery of spontaneous emission. The transition probability is the sum of two contributions:

$$P_{m \to n} = B_{m \to n} \rho + A_{m \to n} \tag{2}$$

where ρ is the spectral density of the photons corresponding to frequency $(\varepsilon_m - \varepsilon_n)/\hbar$, and $B_{m \to n}$ the coefficient of induced emission. The transition probability $A_{m \to n}$ which is independent of the photon density represents the spontaneous emission.

The importance of spontaneous emission is that we can now understand the *evolution of the system matter + radiation in thermodynamic terms* as the evolution toward a state of maximum entropy which is realized when the matter reaches the Boltzmann distribution and the photons the Planck distribution.

Such a system is then as "ergodic" as, for example, a classical gas, only the mechanisms of ergodicity are different (in one case elastic collisions, in the other decay of excited states through induced and spontaneous emission).

In Einstein's theory we deal with atomic states. But quite similar considerations apply to unstable elementary particles. Most of the elementary particles we know today are unstable. The stable ones appear as a special case which is realized when selection rules prevent a further disintegration. The tendency for particles with larger rest-mass to transform into particles of lower rest-mass is of course not a new thermodynamic principle. It corresponds simply to the fact that we study the physical world usually under conditions "near zero temperature." The existence of selection rules preventing further transformation is here of essential importance exactly as in the atomic problems where the Pauli principle prevents the outer electrons from falling into the $1s$ state.

It seems essential to include unstable particles in any coherent schema. Even the simplest isotopic doublet, neutron–proton, contains one stable and one unstable particle, and the more refined group theoretical classifications introduce both stable and unstable particles on the same footing.[17] This is especially true since the discovery of resonances which are not only produced by strong interactions but also decay through strong interactions.

The spontaneous emission in atomic problems and the decay of unstable particles are irreversible processes which manifest the ergodicity of these systems. It is therefore interesting to compare the mechanism of irreversibility which is involved to that in the usual many-body systems such as a classical gas.

III. MECHANISMS OF DISSIPATION

In a classical dilute gas the mechanism of dissipation (or of "irreversibility") is well understood: it is the repetition of a binary scattering process. (See Figure 1.)

Each scattering process randomizes the velocities. In a time-dependent formalism the contribution of a single scattering process is

$$\sim t/L^3 \tag{3}$$

where t is a time long with respect to the duration of the interaction and L^3 is the volume of the system. Each collision introduces the small factor

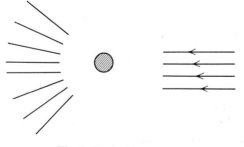

Fig. 1. Scattering process.

L^{-3}, and therefore in the case of a system with a few degrees of freedom in a macroscopic volume recollisions may be neglected.[18] However, in the "thermodynamic limit" (N = number of particles)

$$N \to \infty, \qquad L^3 \to \infty$$
$$N/L^3 = \text{constant} \tag{4}$$

the small factors L^{-3} are compensated by factors of N and recollisions have to be taken into account. The addition of sequences of collisions gives the typical irreversible time evolution characterized by the exponential

$$\exp\left[-t/t_{rel}\right] \tag{5}$$

where t_{rel} is some characteristic relaxation time. In the case of problems involving excited atomic levels or unstable particles we also have, of course, similar scattering processes; however, in addition we have the processes of spontaneous emission and decay of unstable particles. The distinction of these two types of processes has been most clearly indicated by Heitler[11]:

(*a*) In the second class there exists a finite transition probability per unit time which cannot be made to vanish taking the limit $L^3 \to \infty$ as in Eq. (3).

(*b*) The description of the processes of class 2 involves an initial time problem. We have to start from some finite time $t = 0$. However, in scattering processes, we may give the asymptotic conditions for $t \to -\infty$. As a consequence of such differences we cannot, as in the case of scattering, first study the "reversible" process (Eq. (3)), then by "repetition" obtain the irreversible result (Eq. (5)) but we obtain directly a decay law of the form (5). (In reality the decay law is more complicated because of the occurrence of branch points, but this is not important here. For more details, see the excellent book by Goldberger and Watson.[10]) We cannot consider the reversible situation separately, but we have to face directly the dissipative situation.

This can be made more explicit by considering the Hamiltonian responsible for the interaction. In the first case we have

$$H = \sum_{i=1}^{N} \frac{p_i^2}{2m} + \sum_{i,j=1}^{N} V_{ij} \tag{6}$$

and we may consider either the case N finite or the thermodynamic limit (Eq. (4)). The situation is quite different for the matter–radiation interaction responsible for the spontaneous emission. We may write

$$H = \text{atom} + \text{electromagnetic field} + \text{interaction} \tag{7}$$

The two last terms introduce the vector field

$$\mathbf{A} = \sum_{\mathbf{k}} \mathbf{a_k} \exp\left[i\mathbf{k} \cdot \mathbf{x}\right] \tag{8}$$

For all problems of interest, the sum in Eq. (8) may be considered as an integral and the field as a collection of an infinite number of field oscillators.

We can no longer deal "at our will" with problems of finite or infinite number of degrees of freedom. The physical problem requires an infinite number of degrees of freedom.

Now, mechanics of systems with an infinite number of degrees of freedom is probably something basically different in structure from mechanics of a system with a finite number of degrees of freedom (I am thinking, of course, of situations where these degrees of freedom are not separable into finite groups of independent degrees of freedom).

In the finite case we may specify the state of the system at some time $t = 0$ (through the canonical variables $q_1 \cdots q_r, p_1 \cdots p_r$ or through the wavefunction $\psi(q_1 \cdots q_r, t = 0)$) and then calculate the evolution to time t. But when the number of degrees of freedom goes to ∞, this specification is in fact impossible. The main point is then to obtain results independent of such an exact specification and depending only on some general qualitative features.

That this is at all possible is of course the main result of thermodynamics which indicates that the evolution proceeds in the direction of increasing entropy independently of the details of the initial correlations (as long as some general requirements are satisfied).[1,18]

One has the impression that the familiar examples of classical mechanics and nonrelativistic quantum theory have given us an exaggerated impression of simplicity. In situations with an infinite number of degrees of freedom, one probably always has to extract some "contracted description." The extreme case is again the thermodynamic description where only "macroscopic variables" such as pressure and temperature are introduced (see also Section X).

We have unfortunately only very little experience in dealing with mechanics of an infinite number of degrees of freedom. It is precisely here that our experience in statistical nonequilibrium mechanics may serve us as a guide. Before going into more detail let us first discuss the role of probability amplitudes in quantum mechanics.

IV. PROBABILITY AMPLITUDES AND QUANTUM TIME

Einstein's treatment of spontaneous emission uses occupation numbers and transition probabilities. On the other hand, quantum mechanics is based on probability amplitudes. The difference between these two points of view has been discussed in an illuminating way by Feynman.[7] (See also Schwinger.[28]) The transition amplitude from state c to state a may be written

$$\varphi_{ac} = \sum_{bde \cdots} \varphi_{ab} \varphi_{bd} \varphi_{de} \cdots \varphi_{mc} \tag{9}$$

This involves a sum of all possible paths leading from state c to state a. The transition probability P_{ac} is related to φ_{ac} through

$$P_{ac} = |\varphi_{ac}|^2 \tag{10}$$

It is clear that no simple result of the form of Eq. (9) can be expected for P_{ac} because if we take the square of Eq. (9) we obtain products of amplitudes which cannot all be expressed in terms of transition probabilities. This result indicates the interference of transition probabilities.

The equations which we shall discuss later (see Section IX) take this interference of probabilities into account in an explicit way.

It is interesting to notice that a simple formula for the addition of transition probabilities exists only in extremely simple models of stochastic processes. An example is the Chapman-Smoluchowski-Kolmogoroff equation.[30]

$$P(at \mid c\tau) = \sum_b P(at \mid bs)P(bs \mid c\tau) \tag{11}$$

for all times s; $t \geqq s \geqq \tau$. Similarly an equation of this form cannot generally be expected to be valid in classical mechanics. If we start at τ with a well-defined classical state, all subsequent states are fixed (the transition probabilities are δ-functions, that is, highly singular distributions) and no summation over intermediate states b is left at all in Eq. (11).

It is true that there exist situations (corresponding to statistical ensembles) where Eq. (11) would be true in classical mechanics. Examples are given in the Feynman lectures.[8] However, in general Eq. (11) is incorrect in both quantum and classical mechanics. Indeed, the type of interference of probabilities which we derive in our theory (see Section IX) is qualitatively similar for classical and quantum processes.

Still there exists a large gap between the quantum-mechanical description, Eq. (9), in terms of amplitudes and the classical or stochastic description. It seems to me that the basic reason is that the ordering in Eq. (9) does not proceed according to the macroscopic time but according to microscopic, specifically quantum time. Indeed the time evolution of an observable is given in the Heisenberg representation by

$$A(t) = U(t)AU^+(t) \tag{12}$$

with

$$U(t) = \exp[-iHt] \tag{12'}$$

It is very important to notice that time enters twice, once in $U(t)$ and once in $U^+(t)$. In contrast, the time ordering involved in Eq. (9) refers to a single factor U or U^+. We may say that to describe the evolution of $A(t)$ we use, in Eq. (12) a "two-dimensional" time representation corresponding to separate ordering of the events in U and in U^+. This is only possible in quantum mechanics. To make contact with classical mechanics or stochastic theory we have to reorder these two sequences into a single sequence describing, so to speak, the history of $A(t)$. How this can be done is described elsewhere.[20, 25, 26] We do not want to go into details here. Let us only mention that it is in this way that concepts such as collision operators take a simple physical meaning (see papers quoted above). Also the difficulties met in the S-matrix theory in expressing causality[5] may well be due to the difficulties in matching the macroscopic time involved in causality with the microscopic time of quantum-mechanical probability amplitudes.

V. QUANTUM STATES OF FINITE LIFETIME

What are the difficulties in the usual quantum-mechanical treatment of dissipative processes, such as spontaneous emission or the lifetime of unstable particles?

Let us consider the problem of excited atomic levels and write the Hamiltonian (Eq. (7)) in the form

$$H = H_0 + \lambda V \tag{13}$$

where H_0 is the unperturbed Hamiltonian and λV the perturbation responsible for spontaneous emission. There is, of course, no difficulty as long as λV is neglected. The atomic states (as well as the states of the electromagnetic field) are the eigenfunctions $u_n{}^0$ of the unperturbed Hamiltonian

$$H_0 u_n{}^0 = E_n{}^0 u_n{}^0 \tag{14}$$

But surely the physical states corresponding to the problem of the atom interacting with the field cannot be solutions of the "exact" Schrödinger equation

$$H u_n = E_n u_n \tag{15}$$

If this would be so, each state u_n would be an invariant of motion (the probability of the configuration $|u_n|^2$ would be independent of time) and the system would not be ergodic. The very existence of spontaneous emission shows that this is not so. The system evolves toward thermodynamic equilibrium.

This difficulty is somewhat hidden in the usual presentation of the subject.[10] One starts at $t = 0$ with a solution $u_n{}^0$ of the unperturbed equation (Eq. (14)) and one " switches in " the interaction λV. The solution is then represented for $t \geqq 0$ by a Laplace integral

$$\Psi(t) = \frac{1}{2\pi i} \int_C dE \exp [-iEt]G(E)u_n{}^0 \qquad (16)$$

The resolvent

$$G(E) = 1/(E - H) \qquad (17)$$

is an analytic function of the complex variable E in the cut plane from $E_{\min} \leqq E < \infty$ where $E_{\min}$ is the lowest eigenvalue of (Eq. 15) (see Fig. 2).

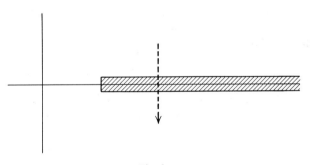

Fig. 2

The resolvent can be continued analytically from above through the cut into a second Riemann sheet. The decaying state is now associated with a pole on the second sheet. Let us write the coordinates of the pole as

$$E_{\text{pole}} = (\varepsilon_n{}^0 + \varepsilon') + i\varepsilon'' \qquad (18)$$

Then ε' is associated with a level shift (or mass renormalization) of the unperturbed level $\varepsilon_n{}^0$ while ε'' gives us the decay time.

This method replaces the older Wigner-Weisskopf method for the decay of atomic states.[11]

While this is an elegant and basically correct description of the decay process, there are still important questions which are not answered:

(a) Why do we start at $t = 0$ with the "bare" state u_n^0 of the unperturbed equations? Should we not start with some dressed state already containing some part of the perturbation? But then which one? Modern developments in perturbation theory make an essential distinction between real and virtual processes. What happens to this distinction here?

(b) We identify the level shift with the shift of the real part ε' in Eq. (18). Is this justified? Instead of the decay of an atomic state we could imagine the decay of a resonance, say

$$\rho \rightarrow \pi + \pi \qquad (19)$$

then the energy shift corresponds to a mass renormalization. Now the mass should be compatible with energy conservation in reaction (19). Is this the same mass?

These questions are irrelevant for scattering which may be described in terms of asymptotic states corresponding to $t \rightarrow \pm \infty$.

These asymptotic states are, by definition, stable-state solutions of some Schrödinger equation. No spontaneous emission or decay process is permitted to go on asymptotically. This situation is then conveniently handled by the S-matrix. Difficulties arise only when the region of interaction is analyzed in terms of some interpolating field.[2] As is well known, such difficulties (existence of divergences, strong coupling which makes perturbation theory inapplicable, etc.) have led many physicists, notably Chew, Low, Mandelstam, and others (see Ref. 3), to give up the approach based on equations of motion and to try to found the theory on general features of the S-matrix.

Again the situation is much simpler when only asymptotic states containing stable particles are considered. Then unstable particles enter neither into the completeness relation nor into the unitary relations of the theory.[5] However, in the intermediate states unstable particles may appear. They manifest themselves as poles exactly as in Eq. (16). We may then describe such poles by various approximate formulas of the Breit-Wigner type. But again this approach is severely limited. By definition we have to exclude the production or destruction processes involving unstable particles. It is even not easily seen how this can be done in a consistent manner.

Let us consider the physical scattering process

$$A_1 + A_2 \rightarrow A_3 + A_4 \qquad (20)$$

and suppose that

$$m_1 > m_2 + m_3 + m_4 \qquad (21)$$

Then using the usual postulates of S-matrix theory the amplitude which describes process (20) should also, after a suitable analytic continuation describe the physical process

$$A_1 \rightarrow A_2 + A_3 + A_4 \tag{22}$$

in which now the unstable particle A appears in the initial state.

Also it is not clear in what way the parameters, which appear in the pole corresponding to an unstable particle, are related to quantities, such as mass, which characterize the formation or destruction process in Eqs. (19) or (22).

Of course, one may try an even more phenomenological approach in which unstable particles are introduced as well in the asymptotic states. In his recent book Barut[3] goes so far as to write: "There is one S-matrix for the whole universe; we shall look at individual elements and sub-matrices of this one continuously infinite matrix." For a human being that seems quite an assertion as our average lifetime does not permit us to take an asymptotic point of view in respect to the whole history of the universe.

But on an even less cosmological scale there is a deep difficulty involved with such an approach and that is to make a distinction between what is truly asymptotic (stable particles) and only approximately asymptotic (unstable particles).

Such a theory needs at least an independent check and this is one of the aims of the approach I shall describe in the next paragraphs.

We may now make the direction in which we intend to go more precise. All problems related to decaying atomic states or unstable particles involve interacting fields (or atoms and fields). Two extreme attitudes are possible: (a) Fields are treated as mechanical objects; the difference due to the existence of an infinite number of degrees of freedom are hoped to play a minor role. (b) The mechanical equations of motion are completely eliminated and replaced by the study of the S-matrix. It is amazing how much has been achieved in this way (see especially the beautiful monograph by Eden et al.[5]).

The approach we shall now outline corresponds to an intermediate viewpoint. We take the limit $N \rightarrow \infty$ very seriously and obtain in this way a statistical mechanical description. This immediately takes into account the ergodicity of such systems.

The basic difference between free fields and interacting fields would be of the same order as between a small (reversible) mechanical system and ergodic dissipative systems. But this means that physical states can no longer be associated with invariants of motion which no longer exist. This leads to deep changes in the structure of the theory.

VI. KINETIC EQUATIONS: FEYNMAN DIAGRAMS AND CORRELATION DIAGRAMS

Let us start the statistical theory with the von Neumann equation for the density matrix

$$i \frac{\partial \rho}{\partial t} = [H, \rho] \qquad (23)$$

In terms of ρ the average value of an observable O can be written (in occupation number representation)

$$\langle O \rangle = \sum_{nn'} \langle n | \rho | n' \rangle \langle n' | O | n \rangle \qquad (24)$$

The time t as it appears in Eqs. (23) or (24) is directly the time of "observables," as in the left-hand side of Eq. (11), and not the microscopic time of probability amplitudes. Also it should be noticed that as the density matrix satisfies the linear equation (23) and is also linearly related to observables through Eq. (24), asymptotic procedures become especially simple to handle.

It is convenient to perform the change of variables

$$n - n' = \nu, \qquad n + n' = 2N \qquad (25)$$

and to use the notation

$$\langle n | O | n' \rangle \equiv O_{n-n'} \left(\frac{n + n'}{2} \right) \equiv O_\nu(N) \qquad (26)$$

In this way Eq. (24) now becomes

$$\langle O \rangle = \sum_N \left(O_0 \rho_0 + \sum_\nu O_\nu \rho_\nu \right) \qquad (27)$$

In a model in which a random phase approximation would be valid, all ρ_ν would vanish. It is therefore appropriate to consider ρ_ν as expressing the correlations in the system while ρ_0 refers to the "vacuum of correlations." We shall illustrate the theory with the example of an atom in interaction with a radiation field. (For more details, see Henin.[12]) Then the quantum-mechanical version of Eq. (7) is

$$H = H_0{}^a + H_0{}^f + \lambda V \qquad (28)$$

with

$$H_0{}^a = \sum_\mu n_\mu \omega_\mu, \qquad H_0{}^f = \sum_k n_k \omega_k \qquad (29)$$

$$V = \sum_{\mu\nu k} \sum_{\varepsilon = \pm 1} V_{\mu|\nu k}^{(\varepsilon)} a_\mu{}^\varepsilon a_\nu{}^{-\varepsilon} a_k{}^{-\varepsilon} \qquad (30)$$

where ω_μ are the (unperturbed) atomic levels, ω_k the photon levels, and V the usual perturbation energy corresponding to products of three creation—destruction operators. The typical Feynman diagram corresponding to Eq. (30) is one in which the atomic state μ is created, while ν and the photon k are destroyed.

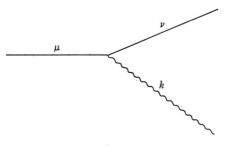

Fig. 3.

Using notations (25)–(27), Eq. (23) after a few elementary manipulations takes the form

$$-i\frac{\partial\rho_\nu}{\partial t} = \sum_{\nu'} \langle \nu | L_0 + \lambda\,\delta L | \nu' \rangle \rho_{\nu'} \qquad (31)$$

with

$$\langle \nu | L_0 | \nu' \rangle = \exp\left[-\frac{\nu'}{2}\frac{\partial}{\partial N}\right](H_0)_{\nu-\nu'}\exp\left[\frac{\nu}{2}\frac{\partial}{\partial N}\right]$$

$$- \exp\left[\frac{\nu'}{2}\frac{\partial}{\partial N}\right](H_0)_{\nu-\nu'}\exp\left[-\frac{\nu}{2}\frac{\partial}{\partial N}\right]$$

$$= \left(\sum_\mu \nu_\mu\omega_\mu + \sum_k \nu_k\omega_k\right)\delta_{\nu\nu'} \qquad (32)$$

Similarly

$$\langle \nu | \delta L | \nu' \rangle = \exp\left[-\frac{\nu'}{2}\frac{\partial}{\partial N}\right]V_{\nu-\nu'}\exp\left[\frac{\nu}{2}\frac{\partial}{\partial N}\right]$$

$$- \exp\left[\frac{\nu'}{2}\frac{\partial}{\partial N}\right]V_{\nu-\nu'}\exp\left[-\frac{\nu}{2}\frac{\partial}{\partial N}\right] \qquad (33)$$

The two terms in Eqs. (32) and (33) correspond to the two terms in the original commutator (Eq. (23)).

The interest of Eq. (26) is in its striking analogy with the Liouville equation of classical statistical mechanics. The variables ν play the role of the classical angle variables while the N play the role of the action variables. For this reason I have called Eq. (26) the "Liouville-von Neumann" equation. We shall not write the explicit form of Eq. (33). We want only to notice that because of the form, Eq. (30), of the potential energy the only nonvanishing elements are

$$\langle v\,|\delta L|\,v_\mu + \varepsilon,\, v_\nu - \varepsilon,\, v_k - \varepsilon\rangle \qquad \varepsilon = \pm 1 \tag{34}$$

This may be represented by a vertex at which two electron lines and one photon line meet. Examples are given in Figure 4. While the graphical

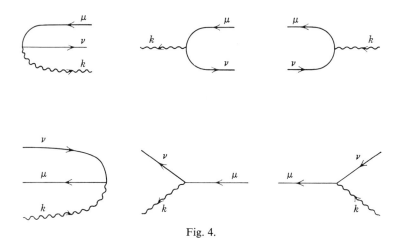

Fig. 4.

expression is very similar to the Feynman graph Figure 3 the physical meaning is quite different. For example, as shown by Eq. (31), the matrix element

$$\langle 0\,|\delta L|\, 1_\mu,\, -1_{\mu'},\, -1_k\rangle \rho_{1_\mu,\, -1_{\mu'},\, -1_k} \tag{35}$$

gives a contribution to ρ_0. In other words the matrix elements of δL correspond to transitions between different correlations or between correlations and the vacuum of correlations ρ_0. Also as indicated by Eq. (33), the matrix elements $\langle v\,|\delta L|\,v'\rangle$ are still operators acting on the occupation numbers N. Therefore, $\langle v\,|\delta L|\,v'\rangle$ has a double function corresponding to a change in correlation and a change in occupation number.

Let us compare what can be achieved by the explicit evaluation of the Feynman diagrams (Fig. 3) and of the correlation diagrams (Fig. 4).

The most direct application of the Feynman diagrams is, of course, the evaluation of cross sections (the difficulties which may in fact arise in more complicated situations will not be discussed here[25]). This gives us, at least in principle, the opportunity to study the time evolution of ρ_0 in Eq. (27) which depends only on occupation numbers.

On the other hand the correlation diagrams express the evolution both of ρ_v and of ρ_0. Collisions are represented then by a succession of vertices corresponding to transitions from the vacuum of correlation to the vacuum of correlation. The simplest collision (two vertices) is represented on

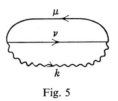

Fig. 5

Figure 5. From the point of view of correlations it corresponds to the formation of a correlation involving one photon k and two atomic states which has a finite lifetime (this is by definition the "duration" of the collision). From the point of view of occupation numbers it corresponds to a change of ± 1 for two atomic states and of ± 1 for a photon state.

The important point is that dynamics has a double aspect: the Feynman diagrams emphasize one of them, the correlation diagrams the other.

Let us now briefly mention some results which can be obtained from Eq. (31). For ρ_0 we obtain the evolution equation valid in both the classical and the quantum cases.[18, 19, 21]

$$\frac{\partial \rho_0}{\partial t} = \int_0^t d\tau G(t - \tau)\rho_0(\tau) + \mathscr{D}(t; \rho_v(0)) \qquad (36)$$

In this equation, $G(t)$ is a generalized collision operator defined formally in terms of all irreducible transitions from vacuum of correlations to vacuum of correlations. A fundamental role is played by the Laplace transform $\psi(z)$ of $G(t)$.

The finite duration of the collision is expressed through the noninstantaneous character of Eq. (36). The second term in the right-hand side of Eq. (36) expresses the influence of initial correlations.

The fundamental asymptotic property which makes this formulation important can be summarized by the following assumption:

$$\mathscr{D}(t; \rho_v(0)) \to 0 \qquad (37)$$

For simple cases this property may be verified by direct calculation. It should be stressed that it can only be satisfied for very large systems and for well-defined classes of initial distributions corresponding to correlations of a finite range. We shall assume this property here (see also the discussion in Section X). Moreover, we may rewrite Eq. (36) in the form

$$i\frac{\partial\rho_0}{\partial t} = \psi\left(i\frac{\partial}{\partial t}\right)\rho_0(t) \tag{38}$$

The lowest approximation to Eq. (38) is obtained by neglecting the time dependence in the operator ψ. One then obtains

$$i\frac{\partial\rho_0}{\partial t} = \psi(0)\rho_0(t) \tag{39}$$

This is possible when one has widely separated time scales such that the relaxation time is by far the longest characteristic time involved in the time evolution of the system.

Equation (39) corresponds to the Boltzmann approximation of statistical physics (or the so-called Pauli equation). We shall discuss it in more detail in Section VII.

A more general equation is obtained when $\psi(i\partial/\partial t)$ is formally developed in a power series of $(i\partial/\partial t)$. After reordering of the series, Eq. (38) becomes

$$i\frac{\partial\rho_0}{\partial t} = \Omega\psi(0)\rho_0(t) \tag{40}$$

where Ω is a functional of $\psi(z)$ and its derivatives with respect to z, for $z \rightarrow +i0$; its explicit form is given elsewhere.

The transition from Eq. (38) to Eq. (40) is only possible if the relaxation process still corresponds to the longest relevant time scale in the system.

To conclude this survey let us consider briefly correlations. Any given correlation may be split into two parts:

$$\rho_v(t) = \rho_v'(t) + \rho_v''(t) \tag{41}$$

The evolution of the first part is given by an equation similar to the kinetic equation for ρ_0 which describes the scattering of the free correlations. This part vanishes for $t \rightarrow \infty$ exactly as in Eq. (37). The second part corresponds for long times to the creation of correlations from $\rho_0(t)$. It is given by an expression of the form

$$\rho_v''(t) = \int_0^t d\tau \mathscr{C}_v(\tau)\rho_0(t-\tau) \tag{42}$$

Expanding $\rho_0(t-\tau)$ around $\rho_0(t)$ we may obtain $\rho_v''(t)$ in terms of the distribution function $\rho_0(t)$ at the same time. We then obtain an expression of the form

$$\rho_v''(t) = C_v \rho_0(t) \tag{43}$$

This corresponds exactly to the "post-Boltzmannian" approximation, Eq. (40), in which we also have expressed $\partial\rho_0/\partial t$ in terms of ρ_0 taken at the same time.

After this brief survey of the general theory let us discuss in a little more detail the Boltzmann approximation (Eq. (39)) and the equation (Eq. (40)) retaining higher order effects.

VII. BOLTZMANN APPROXIMATION

To make the discussion easier let us write explicitly the kinetic equation, Eq. (39), for the interaction between radiation and matter [see Eq. (28)]. One obtains[12]

$$
\begin{aligned}
\frac{\partial\rho_0(N, t)}{\partial t} &= -2\pi \sum_{\mu\mu'} \sum_k \delta(\omega_\mu - \omega_{\mu'} - \omega_k)|V_{\mu|\mu'k}|^2 \sum_{\varepsilon = \pm 1} \delta_{N\mu,(1+\varepsilon)/2} \, \delta_{N\mu',(1-\varepsilon)/2} \\
&\quad \times \left(N_k + \frac{1+\varepsilon}{2}\right)\left[1 - \exp\left\{-\varepsilon\left(\frac{\partial}{\partial N_\mu} - \frac{\partial}{\partial N_{\mu'}} - \frac{\partial}{\partial N_k}\right)\right\}\right]\rho_0(N, t) \\
&= -2\pi \sum_{\mu\mu'} \sum_k \delta(\omega_\mu - \omega_{\mu'} - \omega_k)|V_{\mu|\mu'k}|^2\{\delta_{N_\mu, 1}\,\delta_{N_{\mu'}, 0}(N_k + 1) \\
&\quad \times [\rho_0(N) - \rho_0(\{N\}', N_\mu - 1, N_{\mu'} + 1, N_k + 1)] \\
&\quad + \delta_{N_\mu, 0}\,\delta_{N_{\mu'}, 1}\, N_k \\
&\quad \times [\rho_0(N) - \rho_0(\{N\}', N_\mu + 1, N_{\mu'} - 1, N_k - 1)]\} \tag{44}
\end{aligned}
$$

This equation is, of course, well known and often called the "Pauli equation." We recognize on the right-hand side the familiar gain and loss terms. The transition probabilities which appear in the Pauli equation correspond to the Born approximation for one-photon processes. For further reference let us summarize the main properties of this weakly coupled approximation.

(a) There is an obvious energy conservation expressed by

$$\delta(\omega_\mu - \omega_{\mu'} - \omega_k) \tag{45}$$

(b) For long times we have[18]

$$\rho_0 \to \sim\exp\left[-\frac{H_0}{kT}\right] \tag{46}$$

We obtain the unperturbed canonical distribution. This is a special case of a general rule: if in the kinetic equation, terms up to order λ^{2n} are retained, the macroscopic properties are correct up to order λ^{2n-2}. As we retain here only terms of order λ^2 we cannot obtain any effect related to correlations (which are at least of order λ^2). In our specific case the asymptotic equilibrium distribution corresponds (for a finite temperature) to a Boltzmann distribution of matter and a Planck distribution of radiation.

(c) As all correlations are neglected the general formula for averages, Eq. (27), reduces to the sum taken over the diagonal

$$\langle O \rangle = \sum_{v} O_0(N)\rho_0(N) \tag{47}$$

(d) The entropy (or the $\mathcal{H}$ quantity) is given for both equilibrium and nonequilibrium by the Boltzmann functional

$$\mathcal{H} = \sum_{N} \rho_0(N) \log \rho_0(N) \tag{48}$$

The situation becomes much less clear when we use the higher order kinetic equation, Eq. (40). There is no more energy conservation in the sense that a given δ-function such as in Eq. (45) is no longer associated with the "correct" change in occupation numbers.

What is the reason of this increased complexity? The theory is still correct, as it may be shown that for long times we again [see Eq. (46)] recover the correct canonical distribution (now including correlations). We can no longer interpret the kinetic equation in terms of energy-conserving collision processes. This is perhaps not so unexpected. As we have seen in Section VI, the same physical processes modify both the occupation numbers and the correlations; we may therefore say that part of the energy available in collisions is now used to build up correlations. This prevents us from a simple particle interpretation of the time evolution. But this gives us also a clue as to how to try to obtain a consistent particle description: we have to derive a transformation theory of the density matrix such that in the new representation the contribution of correlations to the physical quantities may be neglected exactly as in the weakly coupled case. After we have constructed a theory in which the role of correlations is stated as clearly as possible, we want to eliminate them to obtain a description based entirely on real energy-conserving collisions.

VIII. PHYSICAL PARTICLES AND ENTROPY

As we have just emphasized, our main problem is the elimination of correlations to obtain a simple particle description of the time evolution. This presents no problem as long as we deal with averages of the form in

Eq. (27). Indeed, using Eq. (43) we may write

$$\langle O \rangle = \sum_N \left(O_0 + \sum_v O_v C_v \right) \rho_0$$
$$= \sum_N \left(O_0 + \sum_v D_v O_v \right) \rho_0 \qquad (49)$$

where D_v is the hermitian adjoint operator of C_v. Moreover, if we introduce the new distribution function

$$\tilde{\rho} = \chi^{-1} \rho_0 . \qquad (50)$$

where χ^{-1} is a time-independent operator acting on occupation numbers, we may write (χ^+ is the adjoint of χ)

$$\langle O \rangle = \sum_N \chi^+ \left(O_0 + \sum_v D_v O_v \right) \tilde{\rho}$$
$$= \sum_N O_R \tilde{\rho} \qquad (51)$$

Therefore we may eliminate the correlations in many ways. A different definition of the physical quantity O_R corresponds to each χ. Equation (51) already looks like the average, Eq. (47), taken in a weakly coupled system with ρ_0 replaced by $\tilde{\rho}$ and O by O_R. There still remains a difference. We have as yet no relation between $\tilde{\rho}$ and the entropy. If we could find a $\tilde{\rho}$ such that the $\mathcal{H}$ quantity of Boltzmann would be given by

$$\mathcal{H} = \sum_N \tilde{\rho}(N) \log \tilde{\rho}(N) \qquad (52)$$

we would have a theory of strongly coupled systems where in all averages correlations are eliminated and which therefore in all essential aspects would be formally identical to the theory of weakly coupled systems.

This is what we have done by an appropriate choice of the operator χ (see Ref. 21). This theory may be conveniently called an "entropy transformation" theory in contrast with the classical or quantum transformation theory whose aim is to provide us with a representation in which the Hamiltonian takes an especially simple form (i.e., is diagonal). On the other hand, the aim of our theory is to provide us with a representation in which both at non-equilibrium and at equilibrium we may represent the entropy in the form of Eq. (52). In the conventional notations we have then

$$S = -k \sum_{\{N\}} p(N_1 \cdots) \log p(N_1 \cdots) \qquad (53)$$

The characteristic feature of Eq. (52) or (53) is that the entropy appears as a function of the occupation numberal alone and may be understood in terms of the usual combinatorial arguments. The correlations are entirely included in the "dressing" operator χ^{-1} (see Eq. 50) (see especially George[9]). How this "dressing" operator can be effectively constructed is discussed elsewhere.[4, 13, 21] Here we want to discuss how we go from our new representation to the definition of physical particles and quantum states with finite lifetime. For situations corresponding to separable Hamiltonians or for free fields there is no difficulty. We know what we mean by particles: they are essentially invariants (such as the action variables in classical mechanics). But here we deal with dissipative systems and there are no such invariants. Still there is at least one example where the particle concept does not conflict with ergodicity and that is the case of weakly coupled systems. We have a consistent particle description of the evolution as provided by the Boltzmann approximation discussed in Section VII. We now invert this argument, using our transformation theory to bring the description into a form similar to that of weakly coupled systems and concluding that in this representation we deal with physical particles.

This is of course a postulate. Before discussing some of its consequences in Section IX, let us add a few general remarks.

(a) It is not so unexpected as it first seems, that entropy plays an important role in the identification of physical particles. It is one of the few physical quantities (perhaps it is not exaggerated to say the only one) which has a simple arithmetic meaning. It depends only on the distribution of the units over the physical states.

(b) The elimination of correlations means also the elimination of virtual states. In the initial representation the evolution of the situation may be described graphically as in Figure 6. Particles are "colliding" and "interacting" at the same time. No clear distinction between a "real" collision

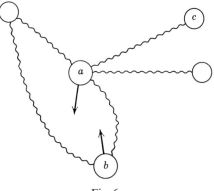

Fig. 6

process between particles a and b and a "virtual" process leading to the interaction between a and c can be made.

On the contrary in our new representation we have a description such as indicated in Figure 7.

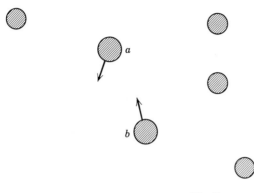

Fig. 7

We can no longer speak about forces or correlations. Only "real" collision processes are going on. We see that our approach, while starting from quite a different point of view, has essentially the same goal as the analytic S-matrix theory: the complete elimination of virtual processes.

In equilibrium statistical mechanics there is, of course, no reason to eliminate correlations. It may only be a matter of practical convenience (see our remarks in Section X). But the situation is quite different in non-equilibrium statistical mechanics where we need to isolate the "real" processes to obtain the $\mathscr{H}$ theorem which can be expected to deal only with real transitions and not with the forces transmitted through virtual particles.

In elementary particle physics the need to eliminate virtual processes is emphasized in many excellent texts.[5,17] For quite different reasons we come to a conclusion rather near to that derived from the S-matrix theory. There is a consistent particle picture. But at this point we have lost mechanics in the usual sense. We no longer deal with forces, correlations, and virtual particles, but with scattering cross sections and lifetimes.

IX. KINETIC EQUATIONS AND QUANTUM STATES

Let us illustrate the general considerations of the preceding paragraphs by some examples. As in previous sections, we shall not give any calculation (see Refs. 12, 13, and 19 for more details). Let us again consider the interaction between radiation and matter. The quasi-particle distribution $\tilde{\rho}$ [see Eq. (50)] then satisfies the kinetic equation (written up to order λ^4)

$$i \frac{\partial \tilde{\rho}}{\partial t} = (\lambda^2 \varphi_2 + \lambda^4 \varphi_4) \tilde{\rho} \tag{54}$$

Contrary to what happens with the higher order kinetic equation (Eq. (40)) each term now has a simple physical meaning. The operator φ_2 has exactly the same structure as the Boltzmann operator, (Eq. (44)); it contains the δ-function

$$\delta(\omega_\mu - \omega_{\mu'} - \omega_k) \tag{55}$$

and involves one-photon collisions (the energies are renormalized, but that is not important here). On the contrary, φ_4 contains all two-photon effects. For example, it contains a term with the δ-function

$$\delta(\omega_{k_1} - \omega_{k_2}) \tag{56}$$

in which one photon is created and the other destroyed. This leads to a remarkably simple time description of the interaction between matter and radiation. As an example, let us consider a beam experiment in which photons are directed toward a two-level atom. We may then have two mechanisms: either we form (through absorption of the initial photon ω_{k_1}) the excited state, say b, which is then deactivated through emission of ω_{k_2}, or level b enters only "virtually" into the process. The first process is described by a succession of two operators φ_2 applied on the initial state while the second is described by operator φ_4. Moreover, in the first case the duration of the process involves the lifetime of the excited state b; it may be expected to be much larger than in the second case.

We have in this way obtained a generalization of Einstein's theory of the interaction between matter and radiation including multiple photon processes and involving transition probabilities. But there is a basic difference. The operator φ_4 in Eq. (54), is *not definite positive*. We no longer have a simple addition of transition probabilities. This corresponds exactly to the interference of probabilities discussed in Section IV. The process is not of the simple Chapman-Smoluchowski-Kolmogoroff type (Eq. (11)); the operator φ_4 now corresponds to an "excess" transition probability. As the result, the second of the two sequences discussed above may decrease the effect of the first one. It is very interesting that even in the limit of classical mechanics (which may be performed easily in the case of anharmonic oscillators) this interference of probabilities persists. This is in agreement with our conclusion in Section IV.

Let us now consider more closely the meaning of an excited state. The state in which one electron at time $t = 0$ is on the excited level $|\mu\rangle$ would now be described in terms of $\tilde{\rho}$:

$$\tilde{\rho}(1_\mu, t = 0) = 1 \qquad (57)$$

This specification corresponds in terms of the initial distribution function to the diagonal elements (see Eq. (50))

$$\rho_0 = \chi\tilde{\rho}(1_\mu, t = 0) \qquad (58)$$

and to off diagonal elements (see Eq. (43)).

$$\rho_v = C_v[\chi\tilde{\rho}(1_\mu, t = 0)] \qquad (59)$$

In the initial representation this state corresponds to a statistical mixture. Now two cases are possible. If we deal with the ground state, the statistical mixture Eqs. (58) and (59) may be reduced to the canonical representation

$$\begin{vmatrix} 0 & & & & & & \\ & 0 & & & & & \\ & & \cdot & & 0 & & \\ & & & \cdot & & & \\ & & & & 1 & & \\ & 0 & & & & \cdot & \\ & & & & & 0 & \\ & & & & & & 0 \end{vmatrix} \qquad (60)$$

However, if we deal with an excited state (of finite lifetime) then we can at most bring it to the form[12, 21]

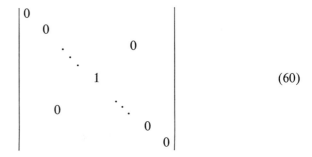

$$\begin{vmatrix} \alpha_1 & & & \\ & \cdot & & 0 \\ & & \alpha_i & \\ & & & \cdot \\ 0 & & & \cdot \end{vmatrix} \qquad \sum_i \alpha_i = 1 \qquad (61)$$

In other words, an excited state is not reducible to a pure state, it is no longer the eigenfunction of any Hamiltonian.

We would like to emphasize a third aspect. Each term in the collision operator now contains the correct δ-function expressing conservation of energy. It is, therefore, in terms of these equations that we may describe in a simple way the production and destruction processes involving unstable particles or excited states. It is interesting to note that while in the usual dynamical picture excited states are broad ("uncertainty principle"

$\Delta E \Delta t \sim \hbar$) we have here well-defined excited levels in the quasi-particle picture. There is no contradiction as the superposition of both processes, Eqs. (55) and (56), gives to the total cross section a finite line width which is in agreement with the uncertainty principle.

X. CONCLUSIONS AND PERSPECTIVES

There are, at the moment of writing, severe limitations in this theory. The calculations are still based on perturbation theory and have been performed up to the order λ^6 in the coupling parameter. Serious possibilities exist, however, to extend it to arbitrary orders in λ (see Ref. 4) as well as to be able to give up perturbation techniques completely.[27] However, even in the present state of the theory, there are many problems which seem to be worthy of consideration.

From the point of view of thermodynamics we have now a microscopic model of entropy (see Eq. (52)). Therefore, we can verify that it leads to the basic expressions of thermodynamics of irreversible processes in the neighborhood of equilibrium.[29] These expressions were derived until recently in the weakly coupled limit, or for dilute gases.

From the point of view of statistical mechanics there are many problems, such as strongly anharmonic lattices, to which the theory can be applied.[14] It appears as a natural generalization of Landau's theory of quasi-particles in the case when dissipation can no longer be neglected. The most interesting feature is that equilibrium and nonequilibrium properties appear linked. The very definition of the strongly coupled anharmonic phonons depends on their lifetime.

In atomic physics, it gives a simple new approach to problems such as sequential emission and many photon transitions.[12,13] In particle physics it leads to a clear separation of dressing and dynamic effects and permits, therefore, a unified treatment of both stable and unstable states.

Many problems appear to be ripe for a more quantitative discussion. What is the error involved in the introduction of unstable states as asymptotic states in the frame of the S-matrix theory?[16] What is the role of dissipation in mass symmetry breaking? What is the consequence of the new definition of physical states for conservation theorems and invariance properties? We hope to report soon about these problems. We would like, however, to conclude this report with some general remarks about the relation between field description and particles. The full dynamical description, as given by the density matrix, involves both ρ_0 and the correlations ρ_ν. However, the particle description is expressed in terms of $\tilde{\rho}$ (see Eq. (50)). Now $\tilde{\rho}$ has only as many elements as ρ_0. Therefore the particle description appears as a "contracted" description as compared with the initial description in terms of the complete density matrix ρ. It is clear that an arbitrary initial value problem involving ρ cannot be expressed in terms of ρ̃ alone.

There is a close analogy with the problem of the validity of the kinetic description of many-body systems. The role of the initial correlations is represented in Eq. (36) by $\mathscr{D}$. Once the initial state is chosen such as to satisfy Eq. (37) for times longer than some characteristic time, t_c, then we have

$$\frac{\partial \rho_0}{\partial t} = \int_0^t d\tau G(t - \tau)\rho_0(\tau) \qquad \text{for all times} \quad t > t_c \qquad (62)$$

Initial correlations of this type are "self-propagating." Similarly if at some initial time (which may be taken in the remote past) the particle description ρ̃ was valid, it will be valid for all times later. To insure the validity at the initial time it would be sufficient to assume that then the system was formed by stable particles only. It is interesting that two widely different questions such as the validity of the kinetic (or thermodynamic) description of many-body systems and the particle description may be related to self-propagating initial correlations.

Such problems are characteristic for large systems. It is only for such systems that we can make a clear distinction between initial conditions which are "accepted" by the system and propagated, and conditions which are "forgotten." This again illustrates the basic difference between small and large systems we emphasized in Section III. This difference appears to me to be one of the most basic in physics. It accounts for the possibility of the thermodynamic description and probably as well for the relation between fields and physical particles.

Note added in proof: since the presentation of this paper great progress has been realized. The interested reader may consult the papers published by our group in Physica as well as in the Proc. Nat. Ac. Sc. U.S.A.

References

1. R. Balescu, *Physica*, **36**, 433 (1967).
2. G. Barton, *Introduction to Advanced Field Theory*, Interscience, New York, 1963.
3. A. Barut, *The Theory of the Scattering Matrix*, Macmillan, New York, 1967.
4. C. de Dominicis, *Compt. Rend.* 265, 1273 (1967).
5. R. J. Eden, P. V. Landshoff, D. I. Olive, and J. C. Polkinghorne. *The Analytic S-Matrix*, Cambridge Univ. Press, London, 1960, Chap. IV.
6. A. Einstein, *Verhandl. Deut. Physik. Ges.*, **18**, 318 (1916); *Physik Z.*, **18**, 121 (1917).
7. R. Feynman, *Rev. Mod. Phys.*, **20**, 267 (1948).
8. R. Feynman, *Lectures on Physics*, Addison-Wesley, London, 1964.

9. C. George, *Physica*, **37**, 182 (1967).
10. M. Goldberger and K. Watson, *Collision Theory*, Wiley, New York, 1964.
11. W. Heitler, *Quantum Theory of Radiation*, Oxford University Press, London, 1954.
12. F. Henin, *Physica*, **39**, 599 (1968).
13. F. Henin and de Haan, *Physica*, **40**, 399 (1968).
14. F. Henin, I. Prigogine, C. George, and F. Mayné, *Physica*, **32**, 1828 (1966).
15. M. Jammer, *The Conceptual Development of Quantum Mechanics*, McGraw-Hill, New York, 1966.
16. F. Mayné, to appear 1969.
17. D. Park, *Introduction to Strong Interactions*, Benjamin, New York, 1966.
18. I. Prigogine, *Non-Equilibrium Statistical Mechanics*, Interscience, New York, 1963.
19. I. Prigogine, Solvay: 14th Physics Conference—*Fundamental Problems in Elementary Particle Physics*, Interscience, London–New York, 1968.
20. I. Prigogine and P. Résibois, *Physica*, **27**, 629 (1961).
21. I. Prigogine, F. Henin, and C. George, *Proc. Natl. Acad. Sci. U.S.*, **59**, 7 (1968).
22. I. Prigogine, *Introduction to Non-Equilibrium Statistical Mechanics*, Springer, Berlin, 1968.
23. I. Prigogine, in *Fast Reactions and Primary Processes in Kinetics*, (Nobel Symposium 5), S. Claesson, Ed., Interscience, London–New York, 1968.
24. I. Prigogine, *Introduction to Thermodynamics of Irreversible Processes*, 3rd ed., Interscience, New York, 1968.
25. P. Résibois, *Physica*, **31**, 645 (1965).
26. P. Résibois, *Phys. Rev.*, **138**, B281 (1965).
27. P. Résibois and M. De Leener, *Phys. Rev.*, **152**, 305 (1966).
28. J. Schwinger, *Quantum Electrodynamics*, Dover Press, New York, 1958.
29. M. G. Velarde and J. Wallenborn, *Phys. Lett.*, **26A**, 584 (1968).
30. N. Wax, *Noise and Stochastic Processes*, Dover Press, New York, 1954.

RELAXED MOTION IN IRREVERSIBLE MOLECULAR STATISTICS

B. O. KOOPMAN

Department of Mathematics, Columbia University,
New York, New York

CONTENTS

I. THE BASIC ENIGMA

As has long been known, every derivation of the bulk properties of matter from its atomic properties by statistical methods encounters essential difficulties of principle. Their effect is that in all but the simplest cases (i.e., equilibrium) the development does not take the form of a *deductive* science. This contrasts with the usual situation in physics; e.g., Newtonian or relativistic mechanics, electromagnetism, quantum theory, etc. The present paper, after focusing on this difficulty, seeks a way out by exploring the properties of a special class of statistical kinetics to be called "relaxed motion" and to be defined by methods of generalized information theory.

This work has been partially supported by the Air Force Office of Scientific Research under contracts AF 18(600)562 and AF 49(638)231 and by the Office of Naval Research under contract N00014-67-A-0108.

The basic issue is at a higher level of generality than that of the particular mechanical assumptions (Newtonian, quantum-theoretical, etc.) concerning the system. For simplicity of exposition, we deal with the classical model of N similar molecules in a closed vessel $\mathscr{V}$, intermolecular forces being conservative, and container forces having a force-function usually involving the time. Such a system is Hamiltonian, and we assume that the potentials are such that its Hamiltonian function $\mathfrak{H}$ is bounded below. The statistics of the system are conveyed by a probability density function $\mathscr{F}$ defined over the phase space Ω^N of our Hamiltonian system. Its time evolution is completely determined by Liouville's equation

$$\frac{\partial \mathscr{F}}{\partial t} + [\mathscr{F}, \mathfrak{H}] = 0$$

whose characteristics are, of course, the canonical equations of motion.

For over a century it has been known that two classes of variables have to be distinguished: the *microscopic* variables, which are functions of the points of Ω^N and thus pertain to the detailed positions and motions of the molecules; and the *macroscopic* variables, observable by operating on matter in bulk, exemplified by the temperature, pressure, density, hydrodynamic velocity, thermal and viscous coefficients, etc. And it has been known for an equally long time that the latter quantities, which form the subject of phenomenological thermo- and hydrodynamics, are definable either in terms of *expected values* based on the probability density $\mathscr{F}$, or as gross parameters in the Hamiltonian. But at once three difficulties of principle have been encountered.

The first difficulty derives from the fact that given *any* values of the macroscopic expected values (restricted only by broad moment inequality conditions), a probability density always exists (mathematically) giving rise to these expected values. This means that as far as the mathematical framework of dynamics and probability goes, the macroscopic variables could have values violating the laws of phenomenological physics (e.g., the equation of state, Newton's law of heat conduction, Stokes' law of viscosity, etc.). In other words, there is a *macroscopic dependence* of macroscopic variables which reflects nothing in the microscopic model. *Clearly, there must exist a principle whereby nature restricts the class of probability density functions, $\mathscr{F}$, so as to ensure the observed phenomenological dependences.*

In the case of equilibrium, such a principle was formulated by Gibbs[1] as the maximizing of the integral $- \int_{\Omega^N} \mathscr{F} \log \mathscr{F} \, d\omega^N$, regarded as the transcription into statistical mechanics of the classical notion of entropy.

The corresponding formulation was made by von Neumann[2] for quantum mechanics. This entropy-maximizing (or information-minimizing) principle is the most direct path to the canonical distribution and thus to the whole equilibrium theory. It is understood that the extremalizing is conditional, i.e., certain expected values, such as that of the Hamiltonian, are fixed.

No such simple solution has been given in the general case, that of non-uniformity and nonequilibrium. It is here, moreover, that the two further difficulties of principle present themselves. The first is the contrast between macroscopic determinateness of the time-evolution of a system, with the ambiguity of its microscopic counterpart. The second difficulty is the old problem of irreversibility.

The question of determinateness presents itself as follows: Let the initial ($t = 0$) values of all the macroscopically independent macroscopic variables be given; the equations of macroscopic physics (thermal and hydrodynamic equations, etc.) show that these variables evolve deterministically with $t \geqq 0$. Yet there are infinitely many different probability densities $(\mathscr{F})_{t=0}$ which have the moments, etc., coinciding with the set of given initial macroscopic values. Each evolves (by Liouville's equation) differently, and hence may induce a different set of macroscopic expected values at $t > 0$. *By what principle of natural selection is the class of probability densities so restricted as to restore macroscopic determinacy?*

The problem of irreversibility lies in the contrast between the irreversible nature of the above equations of macroscopic evolution, with the reversibility of Liouville's equation governing the evolution of every probability density $\mathscr{F}$.

The traditional method of dealing with irreversible processes is, of course, the use of the Boltzmann integro-differential equation and its various extensions. But this method leads to two serious difficulties. The first is that Boltzmann's equation is neither provable nor even meaningful except in the context of molecular *encounters*, i.e., under the assumption that the intermolecular forces are of such short range in comparison with molecular distances that a molecule spends only a negligible fraction of its time within the influence of others. This drastically restricts the field of applicability, confining the treatment to gases close to the ideal state. But even then the equation can only be established on the basis of an essential assumption of molecular probabilistic independence ("micromolecular chaos").[3]

This assumption cannot be exactly true in the Hamiltonian context, since it leads to setting the probability density $\mathscr{F}$ equal to a product of N factors, each containing the coordinates and momenta of a single molecule.

It is an elementary exercise in substitution to show that such an $\mathscr{F}$ cannot in general satisfy Liouville's equation.

It might be possible to save the assumption in this context, by regarding it as an approximation. But this would introduce a major question of principle, since the motions which, without this approximate assumption are reversible, become, after it is made, irreversible: One of the earliest applications Boltzmann made of his equation was to prove that the entropy integral *increases*, whereas Liouville's equation proves that it must remain strictly constant. In addition, the macroscopic determinacy appears to be established. This means that the assumption goes beyond the modest role of quantitative approximation, and assumes that of a new principle of physics—entering in a vague way through the back door.

II. THE BASIC MACROSCOPIC FUNCTIONS

Of all the macroscopic quantities in our model, the hydrodynamic density ρ, flow velocity vector $\mathbf{u} = (u_\alpha)$, and thermodynamic energy E, have the unique property of being produced by *additive invariants* of the microscopic motion. The latter, also called sum functions[4] and summation invariants,[5] occur at an early stage in most treatments. The precise formulation follows.

Let $\mathscr{A}$ be any subregion of $\mathscr{V}$. At each epoch t in any given motion, the mass $M(\mathscr{A})$, vector momentum $P(\mathscr{A})$, and internal energy $E(\mathscr{A})$ of the matter which happens to be in $\mathscr{A}$ at that time are random variables whose statistics is induced by $\mathscr{F}$. They have the three following properties.

(*a*) They are *invariant* in the sense that, if the forces due to all the matter in the universe outside $\mathscr{A}$ were annihilated, their values would be unchanged in the subsequent motion: they would be integrals of the reduced equations of motion.

(*b*) They are *additive*: if $\mathscr{A}$ and $\mathscr{B}$ are two nonoverlapping subregions of $\mathscr{V}$ (contiguous or not), and if $\mathscr{A} + \mathscr{B}$ is their union,

$$M(\mathscr{A} + \mathscr{B}) = M(\mathscr{A}) + M(\mathscr{B})$$

$$P(\mathscr{A} + \mathscr{B}) = P(\mathscr{A}) + P(\mathscr{B})$$

$$E(\mathscr{A} + \mathscr{B}) \doteq E(\mathscr{A}) + E(\mathscr{B})$$

It is noted that the third relation is written as an approximate equation. This is because a term has been omitted: the mutual potential energy of the matter in $\mathscr{A}$ and $\mathscr{B}$. But in the prospective applications, this is negligible in comparison with the rest, once $\mathscr{A}$ and $\mathscr{B}$ become "macroscopic," assuming short-range forces.

(c) In the model considered, no other additive invariants except linear combinations with momentum-free coefficients of the above exist.[6]

The passage from these to (ρ, u_α, E), which are functions of (x) on $\mathscr{V}$ (as well as of t) is as follows: From the additivity of the random variables $M(\mathscr{A})$, $P(\mathscr{A})$, $E(\mathscr{A})$ follows that of their expected values (with respect to $\mathscr{F}$). The latter set-functions can be assumed on physical grounds to be absolutely continuous (and σ-additive). Hence, by the Radon-Nikodym theorem,[7] they possess densities with respect to the volume (Borel measure) in $\mathscr{V}$. These densities are precisely the functions $\rho(x)$, $\rho(x)u_\alpha(x)$, $\rho(x)E(x)$. This identification is the mathematically exact rendering of the conventional physical-pictorial reasoning.

An identical line of reasoning leads from our additive invariants to certain important macroscopic *fluxes*. Here, instead of considering a fixed epoch t and a three-dimensional spacial region in $\mathscr{V}$, we consider a surface $\mathscr{S}$ in, or on the boundary of, $\mathscr{V}$, and interval of time $\mathscr{T}$. If $\mathscr{R}$ is a three-dimensional region in this three-dimensional variety $\mathscr{S} \times \mathscr{T}$, e.g., if it is a subarea $\mathscr{S}_1$ of $\mathscr{S}$ considered during a subinterval $\mathscr{T}_1$ of $\mathscr{T}$, then the flux of mass, momentum, or energy across it ($\mathscr{S}_1$ during $\mathscr{T}_1$) due both to passage of matter and also to the action of intermolecular forces, is a random set-function in $\mathscr{S} \times \mathscr{T}$. Again there is additivity (but not invariance), so that a flux density at t and the point x on $\mathscr{S}$ is defined (intermediating the expected values).

In the case of the flux of mass, the result is the normal component of ρu_α. But for the flux of momentum and energy, in general the flux density is not the normal component of a vector or tensor function of (t, x), since it will depend on the extended shapes of $\mathscr{S}$ and $\mathscr{V}$. But in the case of short-range forces and slowly varying ρ, u_α, E, it can be shown to have this form with sufficient approximation. Thus one is led to the familiar pressure tensor $P_{\alpha\beta}$ and heat flow vector Q_α, both as functions of (t, x). It is to be emphasized that the general expression of these quantities involves not only expected values of products of momenta (or velocities), but the effect of intermolecular forces.

The time evolution of ρ, u_α, E obeys the *equations of transport*. These are obtained as logical deductions from Liouville's equation, by multiplying it through by appropriate microscopic expressions for mass, momentum, and energy, and then integrating over appropriate subregions of Ω^N and taking appropriate sums. At an intermediate stage, bimolecular joint probability densities appear under integral signs. These are reduced to the force contribution to the flux, by using the assumptions and methods referred to at the end of the last paragraph.[8]

The five resulting transport equations involve not only the five basic macroscopic functions ρ, u_α, E, but the $6 + 3 = 9$ flux quantities $P_{\alpha\beta}$, Q_α. Let us call *basic boundary conditions* the assignment over the boundary of $\mathscr{V}$ of the basic fluxes (of expected mass, momentum, and energy) across its different points and for the interval of time considered. Then the transport equations are insufficient to determine the solution of the initial value problem—even with these boundary conditions.

At the phenomenological level, there are enough further relations between the 14 variables to reduce the number to 5 and make the problem determinate. These further relations are the thermodynamic ones and Stokes' and Newton's laws of viscosity and heat flow. These lead from the transport equations to the Navier-Stokes equations. It is noted that these are irreversible.

On the basis of these considerations, the issues of Section I can be put quite precisely:

To find a principle which so narrows down the statistics (e.g., to a subclass of probability densities $\mathscr{F}$) that 9 relations in addition to the 5 transport equations will hold between our macroscopic quantities, so that the initial value problem for (ρ, u_α, E), with the basic boundary conditions, will become determinate. In actuality, this will amount to finding a principle from which the various phenomenological relations of two paragraphs back are (approximate) deductions.

We shall be led to a deeper examination of the forces at the boundary of $\mathscr{V}$ and their stochastic nature.

III. THE BOUNDARY FORCES

From the strict physical point of view, the forces at the boundary of $\mathscr{V}$ acting on the material system it contains are due to a second system: the material boundary. Let H be the Hamiltonian of the system within $\mathscr{V}$, not including boundary forces, and H' that of the material boundary, with a similar exclusion. Together they form a joint system with a Hamiltonian $H + H' + W$ where W is the mutual interaction potential between the two component systems. We may write $W = W(X, X', t)$, where X represents the totality of spacial coordinates of the first system, and X', that of the second. Clearly W is the instrumentality of the action of the boundary on our system within $\mathscr{V}$.

On any particular occasion, O, the microscopic motion gives the variables X, X', and the corresponding momenta, as functions of the time t; for example we may have $X' = G(t)$. This function $G(t)$ describes part of the history of what occurred on the occasion O. We could reconstruct more of this history by studying the system within $\mathscr{V}$ on the basis of the

Hamiltonian

$$\mathfrak{H} = H + W(X, G(t), t) = H + w(X, t)$$

In fact, with the same initial data, the same solution will be obtained as in O.

On another occasion, O', a similar consideration would apply; but of course $G(t)$ would have to be replaced by a different function, $G'(t)$, since even if we started with microscopically identical initial conditions for the system within $\mathscr{V}$, we assume in the interests of physical realism that such knowledge of the boundary system (which could be the rest of the universe) is impossible.

We are thus led to the realization that the boundary component in our Hamiltonian $\mathfrak{H}$ is an unknown member of the class of functions

$$w(X, t) = W(X, G(t)), \qquad w'(t, X) = W(X, G'(t)), \text{ etc.}$$

Thus the boundary forces involve a random function (or random choice among an infinitude of functions): a *stochastic process*.

Within broad limits it is true that if basic macroscopic boundary conditions are imposed, as in Section II, the boundary system and motions can be such as to bring them into effect. But even with this restriction, the essentially stochastic element in $w(X, t)$ remains.

We are thus led to the fundamental question: How can general results regarding the macroscopic motion be obtained in spite of such a gulf in the knowledge of the boundary forces?

One indication is given in the case of a macroscopically isolated system, i.e., one in which all the basic macroscopic fluxes of Section II are zero across the boundary of $\mathscr{V}$. Then the total expected mass, momentum, and energy are constant. On the other hand, any initial probability density $\mathscr{F}$ in Ω^N consistent with these assumptions will evolve, during any time interval, in a manner which is deterministic for each given $w(X, t)$—and equally deterministic but different, for another $w'(x, t)$, etc. In each case we are led to the functions: $\mathscr{F}_t$, $\mathscr{F}_t'$, etc., each of which corresponds to the same total expected mass, momentum, and energy, and also has the same informational integral

$$I[\mathscr{F}] = \int_{\Omega^N} \mathscr{F} \log \mathscr{F} \, d\omega^N$$

$$I[\mathscr{F}] = I[\mathscr{F}_t] = I[\mathscr{F}_t'] = \cdots$$

Now if the boundary forces are thought of as drawn at random from a mixture of a proportion θ of $w(x, t)$, θ' of $w'(x, t)$, etc., simple probability reasoning shows that, *with regard to this body of knowledge*, the actual probability density at t will be the corresponding mixture

$$\theta \mathscr{F}_t + \theta' \mathscr{F}_t' + \cdots$$

and its informational integral will, by the strict convexity of the functional, be *less* than that of the original $\mathscr{F}$ (equal only in trivial cases).

If these ideas are combined with the concept of a stable distribution, i.e., one which is but minimally altered by any slight changes at the boundary, one is led to seek the $\mathscr{F}$ for which these effects have operated to their fullest extent, i.e., to the one which minimizes $I[\mathscr{F}]$ among all those that have the same total expected mass, momentum, and energy. This of course is the method of obtaining the canonical distribution noted in Section I.

It is in the direction of an extended theory of information that we shall seek the answer to our question.

We close this section with three remarks. First, as the boundary forces are supposed to have been acting for $t < 0$, the effects of their uncertainty must be thought of as having spread throughout $\mathscr{V}$, however large it is. Second, the uncertainty in boundary fields $v(x, t)$ does not need to be regarded as the only one which leads to a decrease of the informational integral: our reasoning can be applied to fields acting throughout $\mathscr{V}$. Third, the practice of Bogolubov and others[3] of allowing the boundary of $\mathscr{V}$ to go to infinity and using a limiting method to obtain results from those of the finite case differs only in technique from the method considered here: any portion of the matter studied is *bounded* by the (possibly infinitely extended) matter that surrounds it; and similar reasoning to the above can be given.

IV. THE INFORMATION CONTENT OF PROBABILITY STATEMENTS

In its simplest form, information theory concerns itself with the concrete verifiable statements (the "events") of the theory of probability. If α is such a statement and if all that is known initially concerning its truth is its probability $P(\alpha)$, then the *quantity of information* brought in by the subsequent knowledge that it is in fact true is $-c \log P(\alpha)$. Here the positive constant c depends on the unit of information; we take $c = 1$ henceforth.

Now consider a statement made, not about an event, but about the probabilities of a set of events; i.e., about a probability distribution. Consider, in other words, a *propositional function* $S = S(p)$ whose variable is a probability distribution $p = p(x)$. For example, S could state that $p(x)$ gives rise to some particular set of expected values. If the condition

S is not impossible, it is natural to define its information content as follows:

DEFINITION: *The information $I(S)$ of a statement S about probability distributions is the greatest lower bound of the set of informational integrals $\{I[P] = \int p(x) \log p(x)\, dx\}$ for the class of distributions p for which $S(p)$ is true.*

This $I(S)$ is always defined when there is at least one distribution for which S is true; but it need not be finite. Thus, if the domain of definition of S is the set of probability densities $p(x)$ on the whole x axis, a trivial S (i.e., true for every $p(x)$) and also an S which merely gives the value of the first moment, has $I(S) = -\infty$. On the other hand, if S states that the second moment is close to zero, $I(S)$ is very large, and $I(S) \to +\infty$ as this moment approaches zero. Of course there is no $p(x)$ having a zero second moment (only a point distribution, which is not a $p(x)$). Thus it might seem natural to define $I(S)$ as $+\infty$ when S defines an empty set. Then every S without exception has a unique $I(S)$.

Of course S could deal with probabilities defined on a discrete set (finite or countable), and corresponding modified formulas for information (sums instead of integrals) would be used.

To give perspective to $I(S)$ when S is defined for the continuous $p(x)$ considered before, we mention the following facts, provable by the elementary principles of convexity, calculus of variations, and moment theory.

(a) When S assigns the moments (μ_1, μ_2), with $\mu_2 > \mu_1{}^2$, the normal distribution having these moments is the one of minimum information for μ_1, μ_2, and $I(S)$ is calculated from it by elementary formulas.

(b) When S assigns the moments $(\mu_1, \ldots, \mu_{2k})$, $k > 1$, the point $(\mu_1, \ldots, \mu_{2k})$ will have to belong to a set M_{2k} satisfying the moment inequalities.[9] In the interior of M_{2k}, $I(S)$ will be finite. But only on a subset M_{2k}' of M_{2k} will there exist an actual information-minimizing $p(x)$. This M_{2k}' is easily obtained by the study of the orientation of the support hyperplane (of the Hahn-Banach Theorem)[10] to the $(2k + 1)$-dimensional convex set K_{2k+1} defined by the relations

$$K_{2k+1} = \{(\mu_1, \ldots, \mu_{2k}, \zeta) \mid \zeta \geq I(S);\ (\mu) \in M_{2k}\}$$

In M_{2k}' the information-minimizing $p(x)$ is given as the exponential of a polynomial in x, of even degree (in general $= 2k$) and negative highest coefficient.

(c) When S assigns a general point $(\mu_1, \ldots, \mu_{2k-1})$, no information-minimizing distribution $p(x)$ exists. But when a value of μ_{2k} can be found so that $(\mu_1, \ldots, \mu_{2k}) \in M_{2k}$, $I(S)$ lies between that for the latter and for $(\mu_1, \ldots, \mu_{2k-2})$; i.e., when $k > 1$, between finite limits. If, furthermore, $(\mu_1, \ldots, \mu_{2k-1})$ is such that $(\mu_1, \ldots, \mu_{2k}) \in M_{2k}'$, the value of $I(S)$ can be obtained as the limit of $I(S')$ (S' assigning $\mu_1, \ldots, \mu_{2k}$) as the moment point moves through M_{2k}' to a minimizing position.

When extended to distributions in 3-momentum space, the above considerations lead to first-order approximations to macroscopic expressions, based on theorems rather than on uncontrolled formalism.

Associated with each macroscopic "point" (ρ, u_α, E) is a quantity of information $I[\rho, u_\alpha, E] = I(S)$, defined as above, S being the statement that the probability density $\mathscr{F}$ corresponds (by the expected value formulas) to the macroscopic quantities ρ, u_α, E, for all $(x) \in \mathscr{V}$.

Actually, this $I(S)$ can be expressed explicitly in terms of an information-minimizing $\mathscr{F}$ which, as will be shown in Section VII, can be found as a "locally canonical" distribution (cf. the zero'th approximation in the Chapman-Enscog process). We will denote it by $\mathscr{F}^*$; it is a functional of ρ, u_α, E and a point function of (x) on Ω^N.

In closing, it is emphasized that we are basing this work upon the simplified single-density formula for information, as is permitted by Liouville's measure-preserving theorem, which gives unity for the second (basic) density.[11]

V. HEURISTIC INTRODUCTION TO RELAXED MOTION

As the next stage beyond the zero fluxes and stability underlying the canonical distribution, we consider more general initial $(t = 0)$ basic macroscopic data (ρ, u_α, E) and their basic macroscopic fluxes $(t \geq 0)$ on the boundary of $\mathscr{V}$, but under restrictions which may be described intuitively as follows: $\mathscr{V}$ is of "reasonable" shape and proportions—not much more irregular than a potato. The initial data (ρ, u_α, E) vary "slowly" (percentagewise) with (x). On the boundary of $\mathscr{V}$ the flux of ρ is zero; those of u_α and E are piecewise "slowly" varying (percentagewise) with position and time.

While to give absolute precision to these assumptions would lead to complications (e.g., turbulence and Reynolds number phenomena), they are taken here merely as an intuitive basis for the following more precise assumptions:

There exists a time inverval of length τ for which the following facts are true:

(a) The interval $(0 \leq t \leq \tau)$ is so *short* that the evolution of the basic macroscopic variables is well approximated (i.e., to $\{t^2\}$) by the linear equations

$$\rho(t) = \rho + t\left(\frac{\partial \rho}{\partial t}\right)_0, \qquad u_\alpha(t) = u_\alpha + t\left(\frac{\partial u_\alpha}{\partial t}\right)_0,$$

$$E(t) = E + t\left(\frac{\partial E}{\partial t}\right)_0 \tag{1}$$

Here ρ, u_α, E are the initial values, while the time derivatives formed at $t = 0$ are found from the transport equations, and hence involve $P_{\alpha\beta}$, Q_α, in addition to ρ, u_α, E—and also the random part of the forces. When the latter are replaced by their expected values, Eq. (1) shall be said to constitute a *tangential macroscopic path*.

(b) The interval $(0 \leq t \leq \tau)$ is so *long* that during it the stochastic element in the forces have a substantial information-diminishing effect on $\mathscr{F}_\tau$, in a sense now to be made precise.

Let S_t be the statement that $\mathscr{F}_t$ gives rise to the basic $\rho(t), u_\alpha(t), E(t)$ given (to terms of order higher than $\{t\}$) by the tangential macroscopic path (Eq. (1)); and let S_0' be the statement that $\mathscr{F}_0$ gives rise to (ρ, u_α, E, $P_{\alpha\beta}$, Q_α). Then the logical product $S_0 S_\tau$ ("both S_0 and S_τ") implies S_0'. But, except when the random element in the forces is strictly absent, S_0' does *not* imply S_t for any $t > 0$, even to terms of order $\{t^2\}$, since the transport equations exhibit a random term in the time derivatives in Eq. (1). However, we have the trivial but useful logical equivalence of $S_0 S_\tau$ with $S_0' S_\tau$.

In the computation of $I(S_0 S_\tau)$ according to Section IV, we must take the g.l.b. of $I[\mathscr{F}_{0,\tau}]$ (where $\mathscr{F}_{0,\tau}$ is the joint distribution on $\Omega_{t=0}^N \times \Omega_{t=\tau}^N$), over such $\mathscr{F}_{0,\tau}$ that both S_0 and S_τ are true, i.e., both S_0' and S_τ.

And now the precise effect that we are formulating of the randomness of the forces acting over the τ-interval is that they cause the *independence* property: $\mathscr{F}_{0,\tau} = \mathscr{F}_0 \mathscr{F}_\tau$, so that, according to information theory, $I[\mathscr{F}_{0,\tau}] = I[\mathscr{F}_0] + I[\mathscr{F}_\tau]$. And furthermore, that in taking the g.l.b., $\mathscr{F}_0$ (subject to S_0') and $\mathscr{F}_\tau$ (subject to S_τ) may be varied independently of each other, so that finally

$$I(S_0 S_\tau) = I[\rho, u_\alpha, E, P_{\alpha\beta}, Q_\alpha] + I[\rho(\tau), u_\alpha(\tau), E(\tau)] \tag{2}$$

This conception of time-relaxation is crucial to the present theory.[12] Without it, each $\mathscr{F}_0$ would determine $\mathscr{F}_\tau$ uniquely, S_0' would then imply S_τ, and the sum on the right in Eq. (2) would reduce to its first term.

On the basis of these ideas, we are led to the study of relaxed motion, according to the following:

DEFINITION: *Under the conditions set forth above regarding the existence of the relaxation time τ, a tangential macroscopic path* (Eq. (2)) *shall be said to constitute a mode of τ-relaxed motion initiating at* (ρ, u_α, E) *if* $P_{\alpha\beta}$, Q_α *of Eq.* (1) *minimize the* $I(S_0\,S_\tau)$ *given by Eq.* (1).

The value of τ is only determined within an interval of possible values ensuring the validity of (*a*) and (*b*). Except with very specialized models, it seems impossible to obtain it *a priori*: it has to remain a parameter in the theory, to be measured after its development. In the classical case of impacting molecules, it turns out to be half the usual relaxation time, regarded as the mean time between collisions. This could be obtained directly by replacing $I(S_0\,S_\tau)$ by its time average over the interval $(0 \leqq t \leqq \tau)$, obtaining the alternative to Eq. (2).

$$\frac{1}{\tau}\int_0^\tau I(S_0\,S_t)\,dt = I[\rho, u_\alpha, E, P_{\alpha\beta}, Q_\alpha] + \frac{1}{\tau}\int_0^\tau I[\rho(t), u_\alpha(t), E(t)]\,dt \qquad (3)$$

which will be used, to show the process, in Section VI.

It cannot be too strongly emphasized that from the point of view of the deductive logical structure of the present theory, the definition of τ-relaxed motion is the basic starting point: all the preceding qualitative discussion has been for motivation, and could in pure logic have been omitted.

Finally, it is seen that we have here a theory, not of "the true $\mathscr{F}_t$," but of classes of probability densities $\{\mathscr{F}_t\}$.

VI. PLAN OF EXPLICIT CALCULATION

The second term in Eq. (3) is, as stated at the end of Section IV, the relaxation mean of the integral $I[\mathscr{F}_t{}^*]$ for the information-minimizing (generalized canonical) $\mathscr{F}_t$ having the basic macroscopic functions $\rho + t(\partial\rho/\partial t)_0$, $u_\alpha + t(\partial u_\alpha/\partial t)_0$, $E + t(\partial E/\partial t)_0$. This $\mathscr{F}_t{}^*$ may be calculated directly, but with the involvement of Lagrange multiplier functions (see below), and the same will follow for $I[\mathscr{F}_t{}^*]$. Then, to the first order,

$$I[\mathscr{F}_t{}^*] = I[\mathscr{F}^*] + t\left(\frac{d}{dt}I[\mathscr{F}_t{}^*]\right)_0,$$

$$\frac{1}{\tau}\int_0^\tau I[\mathscr{F}_t{}^*]\,dt = I[\mathscr{F}^*] + \frac{\tau}{2}\left(\frac{d}{dt}I[\mathscr{F}_t{}^*]\right)_0 \qquad (4)$$

Here the first term is explicitly given in terms of the initial data (ρ, u_α, E), while the second term is an explicit expression in terms of these and, in addition, $P_{\alpha\beta}$, Q_α (calculated at $t = 0$)—introduced through the equations of transport. This may be indicated by writing, in functional notation,

$$\left(\frac{d}{dt} I[\mathscr{F}_t{}^*]\right)_0 = J[\rho, u_\alpha, E, P_{\alpha\beta}, Q_\alpha]$$

$$\mathscr{I} \frac{1}{\tau} \int_0^\tau I[\mathscr{F}_t{}^*] \, dt = I[\mathscr{F}^*] + \frac{\tau}{2} J[\rho, u_\alpha, E, P_{\alpha\beta}, Q_\alpha]$$

(5)

The calculation of the first term in Eq. (3) requires the artifice indicated in example (c) of Section IV, concerning the set of odd-order-ending moments $(\mu_1, \ldots, \mu_{2k-1})$. This is because the statement whose information is being evaluated is a requirement involving moments of $\mathscr{F}$ through those of *third* order in the momenta ($\sim Q_\alpha$). No information-minimizing $\mathscr{F}$ exists in the class $\{\mathscr{F}\}$ defined by such requirements. If, on the other hand, we add to these a "purely mathematical" further requirement so that the expected value of some positive definite quartic form in the momenta, e.g., $(\sum_{\alpha=1}^3 P_\alpha{}^2)^2$, is given ($= M$, say), the possibility of such an information-minimizing $\mathscr{F}$ is reopened. If M_0 is the expected value of this quartic as given by the information-minimizing $\mathscr{F}^*$ determined by the given (ρ, u_α, E) then we must show that for a set of values of M with $M \to M_0$, the information-minimizing $\mathscr{F}$ exists, and that then the corresponding $I[\mathscr{F}]$ approaches the greatest lower bound under consideration (the first right-hand term in Eq. (1)), we shall have our required expression. For, as will be seen below, the formal computation is reasonably simple and gives the needed explicit formula.

Naturally, the full proof of the above statements concerning M, the information-minimizing $\mathscr{F}$, and the limit properties, which take us into the general theory of convexity, the Hahn-Banach theorem, and delicate minimization methods, are beyond the scope of this paper, and are being dealt with elsewhere. But once their theoretical justification is established, it is quite striking to see how simple is the formal derivation of an explicit expression of the first right-hand term in Eq. (3). This will be seen later on.

Putting these facts together, our basic problem is to find the nine functions $P_{\alpha\beta}, Q_\alpha$, which minimize the expression for $\mathscr{I}$:

$$I[\rho, u_\alpha, E, P_{\alpha\beta}, Q_\alpha] + I[\rho, u_\alpha, E] + \frac{\tau}{2} J[\rho, u_\alpha, E, P_{\alpha\beta}, Q_\alpha]$$

where ρ, u_α, E, as well as the basic macroscopic conditions of flux at the boundary of $\mathscr{V}$ ($0 \le t \le \tau$) are given.

After manipulations systematically dropping higher order terms in τ, the problem is reduced to one in classical calculus of variations. In taking the variations of $P_{\alpha\beta}$, Q_α, certain dependencies exist. Thus $\sum_\alpha P_{\alpha\alpha}$ is proportional to the kinetic energy part of E. Our final end product will be explicit functional dependencies of $P_{\alpha\beta}$, Q_α, on ρ, u_α, E, whose approximations are the classical macroscopic relations and the Navier-Stokes equations.

VII. SOLUTION IN A SIMPLIFIED CASE: "VESTIGIAL FORCES"

In order to illustrate the principles with an example leading to concrete results with a minimum of mathematical complication, we shall specialize the system to be considered by assuming that the intermolecular forces are so small that their potentials add but a negligible amount to the energy, and that their contribution to the pressure tensor $P_{\alpha\beta}$ and thermal flux Q_α can be neglected. While these assumptions are also made in the Boltzmann theory, there are two notable differences: First, we are not restricting the intermolecular forces to being short-range; second, they never become infinite or increase markedly, as in the models of elastic spheres or of mutual potentials acting as the reciprocal of a high power of the intermolecular distances. We are in fact assuming that the sole effect of our forces is that of an agency of random exchange and a statistical tendency towards evening out energy, momentum, and similar quantities; put precisely, to assure the relaxed nature of the motion, as defined in Section V. We will call this the model of *vestigial forces*.

Obviously the motions of encounter and of mean free path do not necessarily have any meaning here; nor are they needed. On the other hand, the relaxation time τ is easy to define, e.g., as the time taken by sound to travel unit distance, as computed in the equivalent body in equilibrium (equivalent, in having the same total mass and energy in $\mathscr{V}$).

On the basis of this model, we shall derive Stokes' and Newton's laws of viscosity and heat conduction, with expressions for the coefficients of viscosity (η) and heat conduction (κ) which are proportional to τ and, for the above choice, have the usual range of values. Their ratio turns out to be

$$\kappa/\eta = \tfrac{5}{3}c_v$$

where c_v is the specific heat at constant volume. The numerical coefficient $\tfrac{5}{3}$ may be compared with those obtained by the Chapman-Enskog method, which is $\tfrac{5}{2}$ with the Maxwell inverse fifth power law of intermolecular force, and with the slightly larger value of 2.522 (to the fourth order of approximation) for the rigid spheres. (See Ref. 5, Chapter 10 for computed values, and Chapter 13 for experimental values.) In view of the profound differences between the vestigial force model and both the classical models, and the physical concept of monatomic rare gases, the figure represents a closeness that may have to be regarded as a coincidence. The value of the example is, we repeat, solely as an illustration of a method.

The computation in Sections VIII and IX will be based on the following notation and assumptions. The lower case Greek subscripts will represent components in three-space, either geometrical space or momentum space, and so range over the values 1, 2, 3. The Einstein summation convention will be always used for them. The lower case Latin indices (usually superscripts) identify the individual molecules. They range from 1 to N, and when their summation occurs, it is always indicated by $\sum$, never by the Einstein convention. Finally, we omit any exterior fields of force spread through $\mathscr{V}$ solely for simplicity. But the boundary forces will be large and short-range and have the effects discussed in Section III.

The state of each molecule is represented by its coordinates of position x_α in $\mathscr{V}$ and momentum $p_\alpha = mv_\alpha$ (v_α = velocity); i.e., by the point (x, p) in 6-dimensional phase space. The whole N-molecular system is a point in the product space Ω^N, within which the probability $\mathscr{F}$ is a function of $6N$ state variables and the time t

$$\mathscr{F} = \mathscr{F}(t; x^1, p^1; \ldots; x^N, p^N)$$

On successively replacing each pair (x^i, p^i) by $x, p)$, integrating out all the remaining variables over the corresponding Ω^{N-1}, and adding, we obtain the distribution function in Ω: $f(t, x, p)$, often defined by the property that it is the density in Ω of the additive set-function $\bar{N}(\omega)$, which is the expected value (at t) of the number of molecules centered at points in the subset ω of Ω. It has the property of being nonnegative and of integral

$$\iint_\Omega f(t, x, p)\, dx\, dp = \iint_\Omega f(t, x, p)\, d\omega = N \qquad (6)$$

More interesting are the results of taking integrals over the three-dimensional momentum space $\subset \Omega$, of $f(t, x, p)$, as well as of products of powers of momentum components with $f(t, x, p)$, leading to various moments of these quantities. The zeroth moment is the " number density"

$$n(t, x) = \int f(t, x, p)\, dp = \rho(t, x)/m \qquad (7)$$

where $\rho(t, x)$ is the hydrodynamic density. The first moments

$$n(t, x)\bar{p}_\alpha(t, x) = \int p_\alpha f(t, x, p)\, dp = \rho(t, x)u_\alpha(t, x) \qquad (8)$$

lead to the hydrodynamic flow velocity components $u_\alpha(t, x)$. There are six second-order moments forming a square matrix; and certain sums of third- and fourth-order moments will be needed.

But the tasks of computation and interpretation are greatly facilitated by a change of variables for the momenta, by referring them to their expected values as origin, or to a set of local axes "moving with the flow." The resulting "random parts" will be denoted by capitals; we write

$$P_\alpha = p_\alpha - \bar{p}_\alpha = p_\alpha - mu_\alpha(t, x) \tag{9}$$

In these variables the density function f is replaced by the density F

$$F(t, x, P) = f(t, x, p) \tag{10}$$

All moments of the reduced momenta P_α will be denoted with the letter $\mu = \mu(t, x)$

$$\mu_0 = \int F \, dP = \int f \, dp = n(t, x)$$

$$\mu_\alpha = \int F P_\alpha \, dP = 0$$

$$\mu_{\alpha\beta} = \int F P_\alpha P_\beta \, dP, \qquad \mu_{\alpha\beta\gamma} = \int F P_\alpha P_\beta P_\gamma \, dP, \text{ etc.} \tag{11}$$

On introducing the reduced, or random part of the velocity v_α, i.e., $V_\alpha = v_\alpha - u_\alpha$, we see that

$$\mu_{\alpha\beta} = n(t, x) \frac{\int F P_\alpha P_\beta \, dP}{\int F \, dP} = n(t, x)\overline{P_\alpha P_\beta}$$

$$= m\rho(t, x)\overline{V_\alpha V_\beta} = mP_{\alpha\beta} \tag{12}$$

where $P_{\alpha\alpha}$ is the pressure tensor. Further, summing,

$$\mu_{\alpha\alpha} = m\rho\overline{V_\alpha V_\alpha} = 2m\rho Q = 2m\rho E \tag{13}$$

where Q is the thermal energy per unit mass, which, in the case of vestigial forces, coincides with the energy E per unit mass. They are, of course, both functions of (t, x).

Further, we have

$$\mu_{\alpha\beta\beta} = n(t, x)\overline{P_\alpha P_\beta P_\beta} = 2m^2\rho(t, x)Q_\alpha \tag{14}$$

where Q_α is the usual heat conduction vector.

Finally, from the Liouville equation for $\mathscr{F}$ we derive the equations of transport

$$\frac{\partial \rho}{\partial t} + \frac{\partial \rho u_\alpha}{\partial x_\alpha} = 0 \tag{15}$$

$$\frac{\partial u_\alpha}{\partial t} + u_\beta \frac{\partial u_\alpha}{\partial x_\beta} = \frac{1}{\rho} \frac{\partial P_{\alpha\beta}}{\partial x_\beta} = 0 \tag{16}$$

$$\frac{\partial E}{\partial t} + u_\beta \frac{\partial E}{\partial x_\beta} + \frac{1}{\rho} \frac{\partial Q_\beta}{\partial x_\beta} + \frac{1}{\rho} w_{\alpha\beta} P_{\alpha\beta} \tag{17}$$

$$w_{\alpha\beta} = \frac{1}{2} \left(\frac{\partial u_\alpha}{\partial x_\beta} + \frac{\partial u_\beta}{\partial x_\alpha} \right)$$

VIII. COMPUTATION OF $J[\rho, u_\alpha, E, P_{\alpha\beta}, Q_\alpha]$

To find $I[\rho, u_\alpha, E]$ for any given ρ, u_α, E, (functions of (x) or of (t, x)) we must find the corresponding canonical-like $\mathscr{F}^*$. In the vestigial force case, ρ, u_α, E are related to $\mathscr{F}$ only through f (or F), since inter-molecular dependences due to intermolecular potentials are absent at this level of approximation. It is an easy exercise in information theory to show that of all $\mathscr{F}$ having the same f, the product

$$\mathscr{F} = \prod_{i=1}^{N} f(t, x^i, p^i) N^{-1}$$

has the least information integral. Accordingly we may confine our study to these factors; in fact, to $F(t, x, P)$, whose information integral minus $N \log N$ is that of $\mathscr{F}$. We are thus led to the problem of finding $F^*(t, x, P)$, the information-minimizing $F \sim \rho, u_\alpha, E$.

I say that the minimization is accomplished by the choice

$$F^* = F^*(t, x, P) = \frac{\rho}{m(2\pi\sigma^2)^{3/2}} \exp \left[-\frac{P_\alpha P_\alpha}{2\sigma^2} \right]$$

$$\sigma^2 = \tfrac{2}{3} m^2 E = mkT \tag{18}$$

where T (temperature Kelvin in mechanical units) is so defined that kT is the expected *vis viva* per degree of freedom. This corresponds, of course, to the following relations, c_v being the specific heat at constant volume:

$$E = c_v T, \qquad c_v = 3k/2m \tag{19}$$

For a fuller explanation of this usage, see Ref. 5, p. 39. The expression for F^* in Eq. (18), when multiplied by m^3 to convert it from a density in momentum space to one in velocity space, and when σ^2 is replaced by mkT, coincides in form with the Maxwell velocity distribution. It is, however, not in general a canonical distribution since the coefficients ρ, σ^2 (or n, T) are not restricted to being constants, but may vary with both (x) and t. (Contrast the f_0 of p. 109 with the f of p. 72 of Ref. 5.)

The proof of the minimal property responses on a basic inequality of information theory[11] according to which, if F and F^* are two distributions having the same zeroth order moment (here, N in space Ω),

$$\int_\Omega F \log \frac{F}{F^*} \, d\omega > 0$$

except when $F = F^*$ almost everywhere. Applying this to any other F having the same ρ, u_α, E, we find that

$$\int_\Omega F \log F \, d\omega > \int_\Omega F \log F^* \, d\omega = \int_\Omega F^* \log F^* \, d\omega$$

The last equality is shown by calculating both members by means of Eq. (18) and using the fact that the only expected values occurring in each member are the same for F and F^*.

By a familiar calculation we obtain

$$I[F^*] = \frac{1}{m} \int_{\mathcal{V}} \rho(\log \rho - \log \sigma^3) \, dx + \text{constant}$$

$$= \frac{1}{m} \int_{\mathcal{V}} \rho(\log \rho - \tfrac{3}{2} \log E) \, dx + \text{constant}$$

Leibnitz' rule may be applied, leading us to

$$\frac{d}{dt} I[\mathscr{F}^*] = \frac{1}{m} \int_{\mathcal{V}} \left\{ \frac{\partial \rho}{\partial t} (\log \rho - \tfrac{3}{2} \log E) - \frac{3}{2} \frac{\rho}{E} \frac{\partial E}{\partial t} \right\} d\omega \tag{20}$$

here we have dropped the term

$$\frac{1}{m} \int_{\mathcal{V}} \frac{\partial \rho}{\partial t} \, dx = \frac{1}{m} \frac{d}{dt} \int_{\mathcal{V}} \rho \, dx = \frac{dN}{dt} = 0$$

Now we use Eqs. (15), (16), and (17) to express the integrand in Eq. (20) in a form free from time derivatives. After regrouping terms, the result is

$$\frac{3}{2} \frac{\partial}{\partial x_\alpha} (\rho u_\alpha \log E) + \frac{3}{2E} \left(\frac{\partial Q_\alpha}{\partial x_\alpha} + w_{\alpha\beta} P_{\alpha\beta} \right) - \log \rho \frac{\partial \rho u_\alpha}{\partial x_\alpha}$$

At this point we introduce the symbols defined by

$$p = \tfrac{1}{3} P_{\alpha\alpha} = \tfrac{2}{3} \rho E, \qquad S_{\alpha\beta} = P_{\alpha\beta} - p \delta_{\alpha\beta} \tag{21}$$

$\delta_{\alpha\beta}$ being the Kronecker delta. Of course p is the "hydrostatic pressure" and $S_{\alpha\beta}$ the viscous deviation from perfect fluidity. After making this substitution and regrouping its terms, the integrand becomes

$$\frac{3}{2E}\left(w_{\alpha\beta}S_{\alpha\beta} + \frac{\partial Q_\alpha}{\partial x_\alpha}\right) + \frac{\partial}{\partial x_\alpha}[\rho u_\alpha(1 + \tfrac{3}{2}\log E - \log \rho)]$$

The second term is a divergence, so that its integral becomes, by the divergence theorem, a surface integral over the boundary of $\mathscr{V}$ of an integrand containing as a factor the normal component of the material flux vector ρu_α; and this vanishes, according to our boundary conditions. Hence, finally (setting $t = 0$ in the result),

$$J = \left(\frac{d}{dt}I[\mathscr{F}^*]\right)_{t=0} = \frac{3}{2m}\int_{\mathscr{V}}\frac{1}{E}\left(w_{\alpha\beta}S_{\alpha\beta} + \frac{\partial Q_\alpha}{\partial x_\alpha}\right)dx \qquad (22)$$

We shall need the variation δJ in which $S_{\alpha\beta}$ and Q_α alone are varied and boundary variations are zero. We have

$$\delta J = \frac{3}{2m}\int_{\mathscr{V}}\frac{1}{E}\left(w_{\alpha\beta}\delta S_{\alpha\beta} + \frac{\partial}{\partial x_\alpha}\delta Q_\alpha\right)dx$$

$$= \frac{3}{2m}\int_{\mathscr{V}}\left[\frac{w_{\alpha\beta}}{E}\delta S_{\alpha\beta} - \frac{\partial}{\partial x_\alpha}\left(\frac{1}{E}\right)\delta Q_\alpha\right]dx + \frac{3}{2m}\int_{\mathscr{V}}\frac{\partial}{\partial x_\alpha}\left(\frac{\delta Q_\alpha}{E}\right)dx$$

The last integral vanishes, by the divergence theorem and the boundary conditions. Thus we obtain

$$\delta J = \frac{3}{2m}\int_{\mathscr{V}}\left(\frac{w_{\alpha\beta}}{E}\delta S_{\alpha\beta} + \frac{1}{E^2}\frac{\partial E}{\partial x_\alpha}\delta Q_\alpha\right)dx \qquad (23)$$

IX. COMPUTATION OF $I[\rho, u_\alpha, E, P_{\alpha\beta}, Q_\alpha]$

Our task is to find the greatest lower bound of all the information integrals of all the distributions $\mathscr{F}$ on Ω^N corresponding, at $t = 0$, to $\rho, u_\alpha, E, P_{\alpha\beta}, Q_\alpha$ (regarded as given functions of (x) on $\mathscr{V}$), through the formulas of Section VII. As explained in Section VI, we shall restrict ourselves to the subclass of these distributions having the further property that the expected value of $(p_\alpha p_\alpha)^2$ is a given function of (x), whose choice will be specified later. Is there a distribution of least information among this subclass?

As explained in Section VIII, we may confine our attention to functions having the product form $\prod_{i=1}^{N}F(t, x^i, p^i)N^{-1}$; and we may change the form of our requirement to one concerning $(P_\alpha P_\alpha)^2$. Since the information of such functions equals the corresponding integral of F, minus $N\log N$, our problem is that of finding a function $F(x, P)$ which gives rise to the expected value quantities $\rho, u_\alpha, E, P_{\alpha\beta}, Q_\alpha$, through Eqs. (6)–(14), and furthermore gives

$$\int F(P_\alpha P_\alpha)^2 \, dP = M = M(x) \tag{24}$$

and is, among all such functions, the one giving $I[F] = \int_\Omega F \log F \, d\omega$ its minimum value.

By purely formal manipulations, e.g., by rewriting the integral side conditions as integrals over Ω of integrands containing the three-dimensional Dirac delta function as a factor, and then applying the Euler and Lagrange formalism, we are led to a function

$$F_M{}^{**} = \exp\left[-\{\lambda + \lambda_\alpha P_\alpha + \lambda_{\alpha\beta} P_\alpha P_\beta + \gamma_\alpha P_\alpha P_\beta P_\beta + \Lambda(P_\alpha P_\alpha)^2\}\right] \tag{25}$$

where $\lambda, \lambda_\alpha, \lambda_{\alpha\beta}, \gamma_\alpha, \Lambda$ are functions of (x) defined throughout $\mathscr{V}$. The following theorem is easy to prove rigorously:

THEOREM. *If there exist functions* $\lambda, \lambda_\alpha, \lambda_{\alpha\beta}, \gamma_\alpha, \Lambda$, *for which the* $F_M{}^{**}$ *defined by Eq. (25) satisfies the conditions giving the functions* $\rho, u_\alpha, E, P_{\alpha\beta}$, Q_α, M, *then* $F_M{}^{**}$ *gives the least* $I[F_M]$ *among all functions* F_M *satisfying these requirements.*

Again one uses the basic inequality[11]

$$0 < \int_\Omega F_M \log \frac{F_M}{F_M{}^{**}} \, d\omega = \int_\Omega F_M \log F_M \, d\omega - \int_\Omega F_M \log F_M{}^{**} \, d\omega$$

and shows that

$$\int_\Omega F_M \log F_M{}^{**} \, d\omega = \int_\Omega F_M{}^{**} \log F_M{}^{**} \, d\omega$$

by simple direct calculation.

It is equally simple to find, using Eq. (25) and the moment relations of Section VII that

$$I[F_M{}^{**}] = -\int_{\mathscr{V}} (\lambda\mu_0 + \lambda_{\alpha\beta}\mu_{\alpha\beta} + \gamma_\alpha\mu_{\alpha\beta\beta} + \Lambda M) \, dx \tag{26}$$

On writing this in terms of $\rho, u_\alpha, E, P_{\alpha\beta}, Q_\alpha$ with the use of the equations in Section VII and Eq. (21) we obtain

$$I[F_M{}^{**}] = -\int_{\mathscr{V}} \left(\frac{1}{m}\lambda\rho + m\lambda_{\alpha\beta}P_{\alpha\beta} + 2m^2\gamma_\alpha Q_\alpha + \Lambda M\right) dx \tag{27}$$

It is useful at this point to calculate the *variation* of $I[F_M{}^{**}]$ where the only varied functions are, of course, $P_{\alpha\beta}$ and Q_α (or $\mu_{\alpha\beta}$ and $\mu_{\alpha\beta\beta}$), together with all quantities that may vary with them (λ, $\lambda_{\alpha\beta}$, etc.). We have, using Eq. (26)

$$\delta I[F_M{}^{**}] = - \int_{\mathscr{V}} (\lambda_{\alpha\beta} \; \mu_{\alpha\beta} + \gamma_\alpha \, \delta\mu_{\alpha\beta\beta}) \, dx$$

$$- \int_{\mathscr{V}} (\delta\lambda \cdot \mu_0 + \delta\lambda_{\alpha\beta} \cdot \mu_{\alpha\beta} + \delta\gamma_\alpha \cdot \mu_{\alpha\beta\beta} + \delta\Lambda \cdot M) \, dx$$

Now the second line on the right vanishes. To see this, take the variation of both sides of the identity (cf. Eq. (6))

$$\int_{\mathscr{V}} dx \int F_M{}^{**} \, dP = N$$

On the right we get $\delta N = 0$. On the left, using Eq. (25) we obtain

$$\delta \int_{\mathscr{V}} dx \int F_M{}^{**} \, dP = \int_{\mathscr{V}} dx \int \delta F_M{}^{**} \, dP$$

$$= - \int_{\mathscr{V}} dx \int F_M{}^{**}(\delta\lambda + \delta\lambda_\alpha \cdot P_\alpha + \delta\lambda_{\alpha\beta} P_\alpha P_\beta$$

$$+ \delta\gamma_\alpha P_\alpha P_\beta P_\beta + \delta\Lambda (P_\alpha P_\alpha)^2) \, dP$$

$$= - \int dx (\delta\lambda \cdot \mu_0 + \delta\lambda_{\alpha\beta} \cdot \mu_{\alpha\beta} + \delta\gamma_\alpha \cdot \mu_{\alpha\beta\beta} + \delta\Lambda \cdot M) \, dx,$$

the vanishing of which is thus established. Therefore,

$$\delta I[F_M{}^{**}] = - \int_{\mathscr{V}} (\lambda_{\alpha\beta} \, \delta\mu_{\alpha\beta} + \gamma_\alpha \, \delta\mu_{\alpha\beta\beta}) \, dx.$$

We return to the given set of functions, and observe that on account of Eq. (21) and the fact that ρE is not varied, $\delta P_{\alpha\beta} = \delta S_{\alpha\beta}$. The result is

$$\delta I[F_M{}^{**}] = - \int_{\mathscr{V}} (m\lambda_{\alpha\beta} \, \delta S_{\alpha\beta} + 2m^2\gamma_\alpha \, \delta Q_\alpha) \, dx \qquad (28)$$

X. THE VARIATIONAL PRINCIPLE

As explained in Section VI, we must find functions $S_{\alpha\beta}$, Q_α which minimize $\mathscr{I}$ Eq. (5). What we shall do is solve the modified problem containing the fourth moment condition M, and only at the end of the work allow M to approach its "canonical value" M^*. Furthermore, we shall use the formalism of the calculus of variations.

Starting with Eqs. (23) and (28), and using the fact that $I[\rho, u_\alpha, E]$

in $\mathscr{I}$, Eq. (5) is not varied, we are to investigate the consequences of the equation

$$\delta \mathscr{I} = \delta I[F_M{}^{**}] + \frac{\tau}{2} \delta J = 0$$

that is, of

$$\int_{\mathscr{V}} \left[\left(\frac{3\tau}{4m} \frac{w_{\alpha\beta}}{E} - m\lambda_{\alpha\beta} \right) \delta S_{\alpha\beta} + \left(\frac{3\tau}{4m} \frac{1}{E^2} \frac{\partial E}{\partial x_\alpha} - 2m^2\gamma_\alpha \right) \delta Q_\alpha \right] dx = 0 \quad (29)$$

There is no constraint among the three functions Q_α except on the boundary. Hence inside $\mathscr{V}$, δQ_α is an independent vector function, and Eq. (29) leads to the vector equation

$$\gamma_\alpha = \frac{3\tau}{8m^3} \frac{1}{E} \frac{\partial E}{\partial x_\alpha} \tag{30}$$

On the other hand, we have the identity $S_{\alpha\alpha} = 0$ throughout $\mathscr{V}$ so that $\delta S_{\alpha\alpha} = 0$ also. This can be written in terms of the Kronecker delta as $\delta_{\alpha\beta} \delta S_{\alpha\beta} = 0$. It introduces, according to the classical theory, a Lagrange multiplier function of (x), $\psi(x)$; so the deduction from Eq. (29) is

$$\lambda_{\alpha\beta} = \frac{3\tau}{4m^2} \frac{w_{\alpha\beta}}{E} + \psi(x) \delta_{\alpha\beta} \tag{31}$$

In these two equations, the value of the artificially introduced M is implicit in the quantities γ_α, $\lambda_{\alpha\beta}$, ψ. Moreover, the basis of the work in this and the preceding section is that the hypothesis of the theorem of Section IX is correct for needed values of M, and that the quantitative relations we are obtaining become exact in the limit as $M \to M^*$. To gain insight into these assumptions, and to be able to derive explicit expressions, we have to eliminate the multipliers γ_α, $\lambda_{\alpha\beta}$, ψ. This cannot be done by explicit formulas, but it is easy to do at the level of linear approximations in which higher powers than the first in quantities representing deviation from the mere (ρ, u_α, E) requirement are neglected in comparison with their first powers.

XI. THE LINEAR APPROXIMATION

The scheme is to write Eq. (25) in the form it takes when the conditions involving $P_{\alpha\beta}$, Q_α, M are discarded, only those regarding ρ, u_α, E being retained: then $F_M{}^{**}$ reduces to the function F^* of Eq. (18) (with $t = 0$), which may be written in the form of Eq. (25).

$$F^* = \exp - [\lambda^* + \lambda_{\alpha\beta}{}^* P_\alpha P_\beta]$$

$$\lambda^* = \log \frac{\rho}{m(2n\sigma^2)^{3/2}}, \qquad \lambda_{\alpha\beta}{}^* = \frac{\delta_{\alpha\beta}}{2\sigma^2} \qquad (32)$$

Further, the moments for F^* will be denoted by an asterisk. Because of the conditions both F^* and $F_M{}^{**}$ satisfy, those of order zero and unity are the same. On the other hand, using formulas for the normal law, we have

$$\mu_{\alpha\beta}{}^* = \mu_0\sigma^2\,\delta_{\alpha\beta}, \qquad \mu_{\alpha\beta\beta}^* = 0 \qquad M^* = 15\mu_0\sigma^2 \qquad (33)$$

We shall denote a quantity for $F_M{}^{**}$ minus the corresponding one for F^* as a Δ increment. Then $F_M{}^{**}$ itself may be written as

$$\begin{aligned}
F_M{}^{**} &= F^* \exp\left[-\{\Delta\}\right] \\
&= F^* \exp - \{\Delta\lambda + \Delta\lambda_\alpha P_\alpha + \Delta\lambda_{\alpha\beta} P_\alpha P_\beta \\
&\qquad\qquad + \Delta\gamma_\alpha P_\alpha P_\beta P_\beta + \Delta\Lambda (P_\alpha P_\alpha)^2\}
\end{aligned} \quad (34)$$

The 14 quantities $\Delta\lambda$, $\Delta\lambda_\alpha$, $\Delta\lambda_{\alpha\beta}$, $\Delta\gamma_\alpha$, $\Delta\Lambda$ (i.e., $1 + 3 + 6 + 3 + 1$) have to be determined by the 14 moment conditions, e.g.,

$$\int F^* \exp - [\Delta]\,dP = \mu_0 \qquad \int F^* \exp - [\Delta] P_\alpha\,dP = 0, \ldots,$$

$$\int F^* \exp - [\Delta](P_\alpha P_\alpha)^2\,dP = M^* + \Delta M$$

which reduce to 14 identities when all the Δ-quantities are annihilated. Their solubility for small $\Delta\lambda_0, \ldots, \Delta\Lambda$ when $\Delta\mu_0, \ldots, \Delta M$ are given and sufficiently small (the "infinitesimal" version of the hypothesis of the theorem in Section IX) is studied by applying convexity theory.

Without going into these questions here, we can linearize the problem by expanding the $\exp\left[-\{\Delta\}\right]$ in series and dropping all powers of the Δ-quantities higher than the first.

$$\begin{aligned}
\exp\left[-\{\Delta\}\right] &\doteq 1 - \{\Delta\lambda + \Delta\lambda_\alpha \cdot P_\alpha + \Delta\lambda_{\alpha\beta} \cdot P_\alpha P_\beta \\
&\qquad\qquad + \Delta\gamma_\alpha \cdot P_\alpha P_\beta P_\beta + \Delta\Lambda (P_\alpha P_\alpha)^2\}
\end{aligned}$$

and obtain the approximation to $F_M{}^{**}$

$$\begin{aligned}
F_M{}^{**} &\doteq F^*[1 - \{\Delta\lambda + \Delta\lambda_\alpha \cdot P_\alpha + \Delta\lambda_{\alpha\beta} \cdot P_\alpha P_\beta \\
&\qquad\qquad + \Delta\gamma_\alpha \cdot P_\alpha P_\beta P_\beta + \Delta\Lambda (P_\alpha P_\alpha)^2\}]
\end{aligned} \quad (35)$$

We then multiply this expression by the fourteen appropriate products of powers of P_α and integrate over momentum space. On setting the results—which are easily obtained explicitly by the formulas of the normal distribution—equal to the corresponding required moments, we obtain 14 linear equations in the unknowns $\Delta\lambda, \dots, \Delta\Lambda$. Before giving their solution, we must emphasize the nature of the approximation involved. In replacing $F_M{}^{**}$ by its linearized form, multiplying by a momentum monomial and integrating over all momentum space, we are dealing with a function having factors that become infinite, as fixed powers of the co-ordinates, over the region of integration. What makes the approximation a permissible one is, of course, the presence of the negative exponential factor, F^*, whose smallness dominates the power-infinites. This same phenomenon comes into play, of course, in the Chapman-Enskog approximation process.

The eight linear equations for the even degrees in the momentum are

$$\Delta\lambda + \sigma^2\,\Delta\lambda_{\varepsilon\varepsilon} + 3\cdot 5\sigma^4\,\Delta\Lambda = 0$$

$$\Delta\lambda + \sigma^2(2\Delta\lambda_{\alpha\beta} + \delta_{\alpha\beta}\,\Delta\lambda_{\varepsilon\varepsilon}) + 5\cdot 7\sigma^4\,\Delta\Lambda\,\delta_{\alpha\beta} = -mS_{\alpha\beta}/\mu_0\,\sigma^2 \qquad (36)$$

$$3\cdot 5\Delta\lambda + 5\cdot 7\sigma^2\,\Delta\lambda_{\varepsilon\varepsilon} + 3\cdot 5\cdot 7\cdot 9\sigma^4\,\Delta\Lambda = -m\,\Delta M/\mu_0\,\sigma^4$$

In the second, set $\alpha = \beta = \varepsilon$ and sum over this index. Since $S_{\varepsilon\varepsilon} = 0$ we obtain

$$3\,\Delta\lambda + 5\sigma^2\,\Delta\lambda_{\varepsilon\varepsilon} + 3\cdot 5\cdot 7\sigma^4\,\Delta\Lambda = 0 \qquad (37)$$

From this and the first equation in Eq. (36) we obtain

$$2\,\Delta\lambda + \sigma^2\,\Delta\lambda_{\alpha\alpha} = 0 \qquad (38)$$

Now divide Eq. (37) by 3 and subtract from the second equation in Eq. (36) written for $\alpha = \beta = 1$. Repeat for $\alpha = \beta = 2$, and for $\alpha = \beta = 3$. We obtain

$$\Delta\lambda_{\alpha\beta} - \frac{\delta_{\alpha\beta}}{3}\,\Delta\lambda_{\varepsilon\varepsilon} = -\frac{m}{2\mu_0\,\sigma^4}\,S_{\alpha\beta} \qquad (39)$$

for α and β equal. It is evident from Eq. (36) when they are unequal.

The linear equations for odd degrees in the moments are

$$\Delta\lambda_\alpha + 5\sigma^2\,\Delta\gamma_\alpha = 0$$

$$\Delta\lambda_\alpha + 7\sigma^2\,\Delta\gamma_\alpha = -2m^2 Q_\alpha/5\mu_0\sigma^4 \qquad (40)$$

from which we find

$$\Delta\gamma_\alpha = -\frac{m^2}{5\mu_0\,\sigma^6}\,Q_\alpha \qquad (41)$$

It is to be emphasized that the Eqs. (39) and (41) have a form independent of ΔM and $\Delta \Lambda$; therefore, they will be regarded to hold in the limit $\Delta M \to 0$ through appropriate values (cf. example in Section IV).

We turn now to Eq. (31). Write $\alpha = \beta = \varepsilon$ and sum over this index; then multiply the result by $\delta_{\alpha\beta}/3$ and subtract from the original Eq. (31); we obtain

$$\lambda_{\alpha\beta} - \frac{\delta_{\alpha\beta}}{3} \lambda_{\varepsilon\varepsilon} = \frac{3\tau}{4m^2E} \left(w_{\alpha\beta} - \frac{\delta_{\alpha\beta}}{3} w_{\varepsilon\varepsilon} \right).$$

Note that on account of Eq. (32), $\lambda_{\alpha\beta}$ may be replaced by $\Delta\lambda_{\alpha\beta}$ in the last equation. On combining this result with Eq. (39) we obtain *Stokes' law of viscosity*

$$S_{\alpha\beta} = - \eta 2 \left(w_{\alpha\beta} - \frac{\delta_{\alpha\beta}}{3} w_{\varepsilon\varepsilon} \right) \tag{42}$$

where the coefficient of viscosity η is given by

$$\eta = \frac{\tau}{3} \rho E = \frac{\tau}{2} p \tag{43}$$

Turning to Eqs. (30) and (41) and observing that $\Delta\gamma_\alpha = \gamma_\alpha$, we obtain Newton's law of thermal conduction,

$$Q_\alpha = - \kappa \frac{\partial T}{\partial x_\alpha}, \tag{44}$$

where the coefficient of thermal conductivity is

$$\kappa = \tfrac{5}{6}\tau p c_v \tag{45}$$

We have therefore

$$\frac{\kappa}{\eta} = \tfrac{5}{3} c_v \tag{46}$$

as stated in Section VII. On defining a mean free path L by the product $\tau\sqrt{2E/3}$, the expressions for η and κ can be related to the various familiar ones (e.g., Ref. 5, p. 101, Eq. 1).

XII. GENERALIZATION

In more general and realistic cases than that of vestigial forces, the same basic formulation applies, only the mathematical derivations are much more complicated, inasmuch as the full functions $\mathscr{F}$ on Ω^N which do not split into products of functions on Ω have to be used. The problem breaks into the two following:

(*a*) The qualitative problem of deriving laws of viscosity and thermal conduction, approximated by those of Stokes and Newton.

(*b*) The quantitative problem of the evaluation of the coefficients.

Problem (*a*) turns out to be reasonably easy to handle, but not by calculations as explicit as those used above, but by the application of group-theoretic properties of minima of information. To illustrate this type of reasoning, suppose given a distribution $f(x)$ having a prescribed set of moments, and transforming by a one-to-one measure-preserving point transformation T of (x) into another distribution $Tf(x)$ having the same moments. We must have $I[Tf] = I[f]$. Now if $0 < \theta < 1$, the weighted mean $(1 - \theta)f(x) + \theta Tf(x)$ will be a probability distribution having the same moments, and, if $Tf(x) \neq f(x)$, a *lower* information. Hence, $f(x)$ could not be the distribution of least information having the moments in question. In other words, the distribution of least information and given moments will have all the symmetries of the given set of moments—*and so will its further moments, etc.* This gives a basis for solving (*a*). It will be remarked that comparable symmetry reasoning has been used in the classical proof of Stokes' law of phenomenological physics.

Problem (*b*) is much harder and is under investigation by the use of various approximating devices.

References

1. J. W. Gibbs, *Collected Works*, Vol. II, Part I, Longmans, Green, London, 1928, Chapters XI and XIV.
2. J. von Neumann, *Mathematische Grundlagen der Quantenmechanick*, Springer, Berlin, 1932, Chap. V, Section 3, particularly pp. 208–209.
3. The assumption has been rephrased and set in a variety of forms. See *Fundamental Problems in Statistical Mechanics*, compiled by E. G. D. Cohen, North-Holland Publ. Co., Amsterdam, 1962, particularly pp. 110–153, where Bogolubov's method of hierarchies and assumption of functionals are set forth.
4. See, for example, A. I. Khinchin, *Statistical Mechanics*, Dover Press, New York, 1949, p. 97.
5. S. Chapman and T. G. Cowling, *The Mathematical Theory of Non-Uniform Gases*, Cambridge University Press, London, 1953, Chap. 4.
6. See Ref. 5 above, p. 70.
7. For these concepts and the Radon-Nikodym theorem, see P. R. Halmos, *Measure Theory*, Van Nostrand, Princeton, N.J., 1950; particularly Section 31. In the case of $E(\mathscr{A})$, which is not microscopically additive, the density $E(t, x)$ is written directly by an explicit formula.
8. In the cause of logical clarity, it is unfortunate that the equations of transport are so often derived from the Boltzmann integro-differential equation. Their derivation from the Liouville equation is a straightforward exercise in *n*-dimensional calculus,

and the result is more general and more accurate: R. M. Mazo, *Theories of Transport Processes*, Pergamon, London, 1967.

9. See, for example, D. V. Widder, *The Laplace Transform*, Princeton University Press, Princeton, N.J., 1941, p. 134.

10. See, for example, N. Bourbaki, *Espaces Vectorielles Topologiques*, Hermann, Paris, Chap. II.

11. Modern Information Theory is based on the invarientive double density functional $\int p(x) \log [p(x)/q(x)] \, dx$. In classical or quantum mechanics a basic time-independent $q(x)$ exists. In the case considered here, $q(x) = 1$ by Liouville's theorem. *Cf.* S. Kullback, *Information Theory and Statistics*, Wiley, New York, 1959.

12. Crucial, in fact, to any treatment ever given; e.g., as a possible rational basis for Boltzmann's micromolecular chaos. Bogolubov has set forth this situation clearly. See Ref. 3 above, p. 122.

THERMAL FLUCTUATIONS IN NONLINEAR SYSTEMS

N. G. VAN KAMPEN*

*School of Physics and Astronomy, University of Minnesota,
Minneapolis, Minnesota*

CONTENTS

I. INTRODUCTION: THE LINEAR CASE

Consider the simple electric circuit in Figure 1, where R is an ohmic resistance. The charge Q on the condenser obeys the *linear* equation

$$\frac{dQ}{dt} = + \frac{Q}{RC} = -\gamma Q, \qquad \gamma = \text{constant} \tag{1}$$

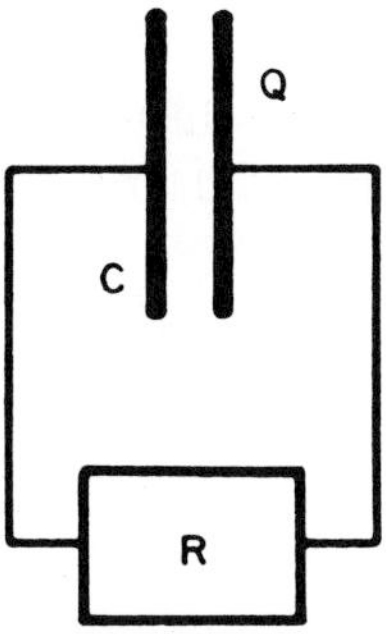

Fig. 1

*permanent address: Institute for Theoretical Physics,
University of Utrecht, Utrecht, Holland.

This is the macroscopic or "phenomenological" equation for the macroscopic observable Q.

In order to find the *thermal fluctuations* due to heat motion in R, one replaces Q by a fluctuating quantity q and adds a rapidly fluctuating Langevin force $K(t)$,

$$\frac{dq}{dt} + \gamma q = K(t), \qquad \langle K(t) \rangle = 0, \tag{2}$$

$$\langle K(t)K(t') \rangle = \Gamma \, \delta(t - t')$$

On averaging the equation for q one finds that $\langle q \rangle$ obeys Eq. (1), so it is natural to identify $\langle q \rangle$ with the macroscopic Q. The constant Γ can be found from the condition

$$\lim_{t \to \infty} \langle q^2 \rangle = \langle q^2 \rangle^{\mathrm{eq}} \tag{3}$$

where $\langle q^2 \rangle^{\mathrm{eq}}$ is known from equilibrium statistical mechanics to be kTC. The result is the Einstein relation

$$\Gamma = 2\gamma kTC = 2kT/R$$

It is now possible to compute the *autocorrelation function*

$$\langle q(0)q(t) \rangle^{\mathrm{eq}} = \langle q(0) \langle q(t) \rangle_{q(0)} \rangle^{\mathrm{eq}} \tag{4}$$

where $\langle q(t) \rangle_{q(0)}$ is the average of $q(t)$ conditional on the given $q(0)$, and $\langle \ \rangle^{\mathrm{eq}}$ indicates an average overall value of $q(0)$ as they occur in equilibrium distribution. Experimentally useful is the *spectral density of the fluctuations*, which according to the Wiener-Khintchine theorem is the Fourier transform of Eq. (4)

$$S_q(\omega) = \frac{2}{\pi} \int_0^\infty \langle q(0)q(t) \rangle^{\mathrm{eq}} \cos \omega t \, dt = \frac{2}{\pi} \langle q^2 \rangle^{\mathrm{eq}} \frac{\gamma}{\gamma^2 + \omega^2} \tag{5}$$

An alternative treatment of the fluctuations is provided by the *Fokker-Planck equation* for the probability distribution of q

$$\frac{\partial P(q, t)}{\partial t} = \gamma \frac{\partial}{\partial q} qP + \lambda kTC \frac{\partial^2 P}{\partial q^2} \tag{6}$$

The coefficient of the first term on the right is determined by the requirement that $\langle q \rangle$ obeys Eq. (1). The coefficient of the second term is determined by the requirement of Eq. (3); alternatively one may require that Eq. (6) is satisfied by the known equilibrium distribution

$$P^{\mathrm{eq}}(q) = (2\pi kTC)^{-1/2} \exp\left[-\frac{q^2}{2kTC} \right] \tag{7}$$

This treatment is entirely equivalent with the Langevin equation (Eq. (2)).

II. THE NONLINEAR PROBLEM

Now suppose the resistance is not constant but has a nonlinear I–V relation, so that the macroscopic law is

$$\frac{dQ}{dt} + f(Q) = 0 \tag{8}$$

It is no longer possible to describe fluctuations by the simple device of adding a Langevin force

$$\frac{dq}{dt} + f(q) = K(t) \tag{9}$$

The reason is that, on averaging, (q) does not reduce to Eq. (8) for $\langle q \rangle$ since $\langle f(q) \rangle \neq f(\langle q \rangle)$. In fact it leads to an equation involving $\langle q^2 \rangle$, $\langle q^3 \rangle$, etc.,

$$\frac{d\langle q \rangle}{dt} = -\langle f(q) \rangle = -f(\langle q \rangle) - \tfrac{1}{2}(\langle q^2 \rangle - \langle q \rangle^2)f''(\langle q \rangle) - \cdots \tag{10}$$

An attempt[1] to rescue this approach was made by postulating that q is a stochastic process whose average $\langle q \rangle$ obeys Eq. (8), but Polder[2] showed that that is impossible.

The Fokker-Planck approach does not lead to a sensible extension for the nonlinear case either. Suppose one writes[3]

$$\frac{\partial P(q, t)}{\partial t} = -\frac{\partial}{\partial q} \alpha_1(q)P + \frac{1}{2}\frac{\partial^2}{\partial q^2} \alpha_2(q)P \tag{11}$$

It is again impossible to choose $\alpha_1(q)$ such that $\langle q \rangle$ obeys Eq. (8). In fact, different but equally plausible attempts to compute the fluctuation spectrum led to physically different results. [4]The conclusion is that the clever guess of Langevin does not work in the nonlinear case and that a more fundamental starting point is indispensable.

III. THE MASTER EQUATION

We only assume that q is a Markov process, so that its probability distribution obeys the Chapman-Kolmogorov equation

$$P(q, t + \tau) = \int P_\tau(q \mid q')P(q', t) \, dq' \tag{12}$$

where $P_\tau(q \mid q')$ is the transition probability in time τ. Of course $P_0(q \mid q') = \delta(q - q')$ and we suppose that for small τ one may expand

$$P_\tau(q \mid q') = (1 - \alpha_0 \tau)\, \delta(q - q') + \tau W(q \mid q') + 0(\tau^2) \tag{13}$$

where $W(q \mid q')$ is the transition probability per unit time, and α_0 follows from the normalization condition

$$\alpha_0(q') = \int W(q \mid q')\, dq \tag{14}$$

Then Eq. (12) may be written in the differential form

$$\frac{\partial P(q, t)}{\partial t} = \int \{ W(q \mid q')P(q', t) - W(q' \mid q)P(q, t) \}\, dq' \tag{15}$$

This, and only this, will be called the Master Equation.[5]

Let q represent an observable quantity of a macroscopic system such as the circuit in Figure 1. Assuming that there are no other macroscopic observables, one can derive Eq. (15) from the equation of motion of all particles at the expense of a regrettable, but indispensable, *repeated randomness assumption*, similar to Boltzmann's "Stosszahlansatz."[6] It then also follows that, provided q is an even variable, W has a symmetry property called "detailed balancing."[6, 7]

$$W(q \mid q')P^{eq}(q') = W(q' \mid q)P^{eq}(q) \tag{16}$$

We list some properties of the Master Equation.[4] Denote the right-hand side by $\mathbf{W}P$. Owing to Eq. (16) the linear operator $\mathbf{W}$ has a complete set of eigenfunctions with real eigenvalues. Clearly P^{eq} is an eigenfunction with eigenvalue zero. This eigenvalue may be taken to be nondegenerate because otherwise the matrix of $\mathbf{W}$ is reducible, i.e., the set of states of the system decomposes in two subsystems with no transitions between them. It can be shown that all other eigenvalues are negative.

Let the eigenvalues be $-\lambda$, and the corresponding eigenfunctions $P_\lambda(q)$. The completeness relation states

$$\sum_\lambda P_\lambda(q)P_\lambda(q') = P^{eq}(q) \qquad \delta(q - q') \tag{17}$$

Evidently that solution (15) that reduces at $t = 0$ to $\delta(q - q_0)$ is

$$P_t(q \mid q_0) = \sum_\lambda \exp\left[-\lambda t\right] P_\lambda(q)P_\lambda(q_0)/P^{eq}(q_0) \tag{18}$$

Substitution in Eq. (4) yields an expression for the autocorrelation function

$$\langle q(0)q(t) \rangle^{eq} = \sum_\lambda \exp\left[-\lambda t\right]\left[\int q P_\lambda(q)\, dq\right]^2 \tag{19}$$

and for the fluctuation spectrum

$$S_q(\omega) = \frac{2}{\pi} \sum_\lambda \frac{\lambda}{\lambda^2 + \omega^2} \left[\int q P_\lambda(q) \, dq \right] \qquad (20)$$

Although Eq. (15) is a linear equation for $P(q, t)$ it does not, in general, correspond to a linear behavior of $\langle q \rangle$. Multiplication of Eq. (15) with q and integration yields

$$\frac{d}{dt} \langle q \rangle = \left\langle \int q' \mathbf{W}(q' \mid q) \, dq' \right\rangle \qquad (21)$$

In order that the right-hand side can be written $-\gamma \langle q \rangle$ one must have

$$\int q' \mathbf{W}(q' \mid q) \, dq' = -\gamma q \qquad (22)$$

Thus, *the necessary and sufficient conditions are that $\langle q \rangle$ obeys a linear equation,* (Eq. (1)) *and q is a left eigenvector of $\mathbf{W}$* (i.e., $q P^{eq}(q)$ is a right eigenvector). If q is indeed a left eigenvector with eigenvalue $-\gamma$, it is orthogonal to all right eigenvectors $P_\lambda(q)$ with $\lambda \neq \gamma$, so that the fluctuation spectrum, Eq. (20), reduces to the single term, Eq. (5). An example of a linear process is the "homogeneous" case: $W(q \mid q') = w(q - q')$. This case is of some interest because it can be fully solved. Unfortunately, it does not exhibit the most interesting features, since it is linear and, moreover, has no P^{eq}.

Finally we note that the Master Equation, Eq. (15), may be formally expanded in the Kramers-Moyal series[8]

$$\frac{\partial P}{\partial t} = \sum_{n=1}^\infty \frac{(-1)^n}{n!} \frac{\partial^n}{\partial q^n} \alpha_n(q) P \qquad (23)$$

where the $\alpha_n(q)$ are the "derivate moments"

$$\alpha_n(q) = \int (q' - q)^n W(q' \mid q) \, dq' \qquad (24)$$

The first two terms of Eq. (23) constitute the Fokker-Planck equation (Eq. (11)). However, since Eq. (23) is not an expansion in powers of a small quantity, there is no *a priori* justification for breaking off after two terms. It has also been demonstrated by an example that there may be solutions of Eq. (15) which do not obey Eq. (23), but they hardly contribute to the fluctuation spectrum.[9]

IV. EXPANSION OF THE MASTER EQUATION

The Master Equation, Eq. (15), can only be solved in rare cases. Hence, it is desirable to have an approximation method for computing the thermal fluctuations and, in particular, their spectral density. Moreover, an approximate method is necessary to extract a macroscopic law from it, since the macroscopic law itself is only approximately valid (unless the process happens to be linear). In order to search for a sensible approximation method, we list the various magnitudes involved.

(a) The magnitude of individual jumps δq. In the example of Figure 1 the individual jumps of the charge equal the electron charge, $\delta q = e^-$.

(b) The width of the equilibrium distribution $\Delta^{eq}q = (\langle q^2 \rangle^{eq})^{1/2}$. In the above example, $\Delta^{eq}q = (kTC)^{1/2}$. In other cases one always finds that there is a parameter Ω, analogous to the capacity C and measuring some size of the system, such that $\Delta^{eq}q \sim \Omega^{1/2}$. We shall call $X = q/\Omega$ the intensive variable conjugate with q.

(c) A parameter l_q measuring roughly the range over which the macroscopic law is approximately linear. Since the probability for a jump δq to occur is naturally expressed in the extensive variable X, one has $l_q \sim \Omega$.

(d) The magnitude q_P of the values of q for which $P(q, t)$ differs materially from zero. When computing equilibrium fluctuations one obviously has $q_P \sim \Delta^{eq}q \sim \Omega^{1/2}$. However, when calculating the macroscopic law one is interested in the case that X has a certain value, so that $q_P \sim \Omega$.

(e) The width $\Delta_P q$ of the $P(q, t)$ in which one is interested. When calculating the macroscopic law it is reasonable to take $\Delta_P q \sim \Delta^{eq}q \sim \Omega^{1/2}$. However, for computing the autocorrelation function of equilibrium fluctuations, one needs narrower distributions P.

TABLE I

Quantity	Notation	Order of magnitude	
Individual jumps	δq	1	
Width of $P^{eq}(q)$	$\Delta^{eq}q$	$\Omega^{1/2}$	
Range of linearity	l_q	Ω	
		Equilibrium fluctuations	Macroscopic law
Location of $P(q, t)$	q_P	$\Omega^{1/2}$	Ω
Width of $P(q, t)$	$\Delta_P q$	$<\Omega^{1/2}$	$\Omega^{1/2}$

It appears that there is one parameter Ω. When Ω tends to infinity, δq becomes small relative to all other pertinent magnitudes, so that one approaches the Fokker-Planck limit. However, at the same time $\Delta^{eq}q$ becomes small compared to lq, so that one simultaneously approaches the limit in which the fluctuations may be treated as linear. Consequently, *when including nonlinear effects one must simultaneously improve on the Fokker-Planck approximation.*

To find a systematic expansion in negative powers of Ω one must express all quantities in such a way that their dependence on Ω is explicit. This can be achieved by putting [10]

$$t = \Omega\tau, \qquad q = \Omega\varphi(t) + \Omega^{1/2}x, \qquad P(q, t) = \Omega^{1/2}\Pi(x, \tau) \quad (25)$$

$\Omega\varphi(\tau)$ is the macroscopic value $Q(t)$, and $\Omega^2 x$ are the fluctuations. If one substitutes this in the Kramers-Moyal series (Eq. (23)), and expands in Ω taking into account that the derivate moments α_n are functions of $X = q/\Omega$ rather than of q itself,[11] one obtains the following result.[12]

The terms of order Ω can be made to vanish by choosing for $\varphi(\tau)$ a solution of

$$\frac{d\phi}{d\tau} = \alpha_1(\phi) \qquad (26)$$

which is, therefore, to be identified with the macroscopic equation, Eq. (8). The terms of order $\Omega^{1/2}$ yield the linear Fokker-Planck equation, analogous to Eq. (6),

$$\frac{\partial\Pi}{\partial t} = -\frac{\partial}{\partial x}\{\alpha_1'x\Pi\} + \frac{1}{2}\frac{\partial^2}{\partial x^2}\{\alpha_2\Pi\} \qquad (27)$$

Here the coefficients α_1' and α_2 are independent of x; they are respectively the derivative of α_1 and the value of α_2 taken at $X = \varphi(\tau)$. For equilibrium fluctuations one has to take them, of course, at $X = 0$.

The next order corrects these coefficients by adding terms $\alpha_1''x^2$ and $\alpha_2'x$, respectively, but at the same time the term

$$-\frac{1}{3!}\alpha_3\frac{\partial^3\Pi}{\partial x^3} \qquad (28)$$

is added to Eq. (27). Similarly each successive order adds more nonlinear terms to the coefficients, but simultaneously introduces higher derivatives of Π. Thus, *the nonlinear Fokker-Planck equation* (11) *is not a consistent approximation.*[13]

V. ADDITIONAL REMARKS

1. The expansion method described above enables one to compute the spectral density of fluctuations in successive orders of Ω^{-1}, provided the Master Equation is known.[14] In the linear case, however, it was sufficient to know the macroscopic equation and the equilibrium distribution, as

shown in Eq. (5). The question, therefore, arises whether this is also true for the nonlinear case. This question may be regarded as the generalization of the Einstein and Nyquist relations. According to Eq. (26) the the macroscopic equation determines $\alpha^1(X)$, and α_2, α_3, ... are related to it by Eq. (16). Yet it turns out that this does not uniquely determine all α's: *In the nonlinear case the fluctuation spectrum is not fully determined by the macroscopic law.*

2. The addition of higher order derivatives like Eq. (28) drastically alters the character of the differential equation with dire consequences. In the first place, in the Fokker-Planck approximation, just as for the Master Equation itself, all eigenvalues other than $\lambda = 0$ are negative. This need no longer be true when higher derivatives are added, but the positive or complex eigenvalues that appear in this higher approximation are, of course, spurious. However, they will do no harm provided that one solves the corrected Fokker-Planck equation by means of perturbation theory, treating the Fokker-Planck term as zeroth order, and the terms with higher derivatives as perturbation.

An alternative way to avoid these anomalous eigenvalues was given by Siegel.[15] Since $-\mathbf{W}$ is positive semidefinite, it has a square root $\mathbf{U} = (-\mathbf{W})^{1/2}$. The expansion of $\mathbf{W}$ to the nth order, $\mathbf{W} = \mathbf{W}^n + o(\Omega^{-n})$, determines a corresponding approximation $\mathbf{U}_n$ of $\mathbf{U}$,

$$\mathbf{U}_n = (-\mathbf{W}^n)^{1/2} + o(\Omega^{-n})$$

Then $\mathbf{W}_n' = -\mathbf{U}_n^2$ is negative semidefinite and correct to order n. It also contains higher order terms, which are not the correct ones, but serve to make $\mathbf{W}'$ negative semidefinite.

3. A second consequence of the approximation is the following. Both the Master Equation and the Fokker-Planck approximation have the property that $P(q, t) > 0$ for $t > 0$, provided that $P(q, 0) > 0$. This property is not necessarily maintained in the higher approximations. Yet this is not a serious flaw, since P is only used for computing averages, such as the successive moments of q. Such averages, of course, will be correct to the desired order in Ω. Alternatively, one may apply Siegel's device to P, so as to obtain a P' that is nonnegative and correct to the desired order.

4. So far it has been tacitly assured that q ranges from $-\infty$ to $+\infty$. If the range of q is bounded by one or two end points, one has to impose a boundary condition at each end point, which describes the physical nature of the boundary. The most important cases are the following: (1) Reflecting boundary—$\partial P/\partial q = 0$ at the boundary; (2) Absorbing boundary—$P = 0$ at the boundary; (3) Natural boundary—the transition

probabilities vanish at the boundary and one only needs to require that P remains finite at the boundary.

Special examples involving these boundary conditions have been worked out and it appeared that a systematic expansion in $\Omega^{-1/2}$ again led to the Fokker-Planck equation with higher order corrections.[16] However, a general theory has not yet been developed.

5. Systems with driving forces are, of course, of great practical interest, but have to be treated with care, because the source of the driving force will in general also be subject to fluctuations. In the case of photoconductors the driving force is the external light source; if the photons are assumed to arrive independently, the driving force is subject to shot noise and the fluctuations in the number of excited electrons can be computed by means of the above expansion method.[17]

VI. THE MICROSCOPIC DESCRIPTION

The theory described so far is based on the Master Equation, which is a sort of intermediate level between the macroscopic, phenomenological equations and the microscopic equations of motion of all particles in the system. In particular, the transition from reversible equations to an irreversible description has been taken for granted. Attempts have been made to derive the properties of fluctuations in nonlinear systems directly from the microscopic equations, either from the classical Liouville equation [18] or the quantum-mechanical equation for the density matrix.[19] We shall discuss the quantum-mechanical treatment, because the formalism used in that case is more familiar.

First, one has to decide what the quantum-mechanical translation is of the autocorrelation function, Eq. (4). Let Q be the operator corresponding to the physical quantity q, and let

$$Q(t) = \exp\,[itH]\,Q\,\exp\,[-itH] \qquad (29)$$

where H is the total Hamilton operator of the system. The *left-hand* side of Eq. (4) suggests that the autocorrelation function is something like $\langle QQ(t)\rangle^{\text{eq}}$, or rather, as it should be a real quantity,

$$\tfrac{1}{2}\langle QQ(t) + Q(t)Q\rangle^{\text{eq}} = \text{Re} \sum_{n,\,m} \exp\,[-\beta E_n]\,Q_{nm}\,Q_{mn}(t) \qquad (30)$$

where n, m, E^n refer to eigenfunctions and eigenvalues of H.

On the other hand, the *right-hand* side of Eq. (4) suggests the following quantum-mechanical translation, which corresponds more closely to the physical situation. Let χ_v, q_v be the eigenfunctions and the eigenvalues of Q. To construct the conditional average $\langle q(t)\rangle_{q(0)}$ one has to take for the state of the system at $t = 0$ an eigenfunction χ_ν corresponding to a definite value $q(0) = q_\nu$. Then the state at $t > 0$ is $\exp[-itH]\chi_\nu$ and, therefore,

$$\langle q(t)\rangle_{q(0)} = \sum_\mu q_\mu |\langle \chi_\mu | \exp[-itH]\chi_\nu\rangle|^2 = \langle \chi_\nu | Q(t)| \chi_\nu\rangle \qquad (31)$$

The equilibrium probability for finding the system at $t = 0$ in the state χ_ν with eigenvalue q_ν is $\langle \chi_\nu | \exp[-\beta H] | \chi_\nu\rangle$. Hence, one finds[20]

$$\langle q(0)\langle q(t)\rangle_{q(0)}\rangle^{eq} = \sum_\nu \langle \chi_\nu | \exp[-\beta H]| \chi_\nu\rangle\langle \chi_\nu | QQ(t)| \chi_\nu\rangle \qquad (32)$$

This is different from Eq. (30), as appears from the following alternative form of Eq. (30)

$$\text{Re} \sum_{\nu,\lambda} \langle \chi_\nu | \exp[-\beta H]| \chi_\lambda\rangle\langle \chi_\lambda | QQ(t)| \chi_\nu\rangle \qquad (33)$$

Yet it can be argued that Eqs. (30) and (32) are practically the same, *provided that Q is a macroscopically observable variable.* Such observables are characterized by the fact that they are slowly varying and, therefore, almost commute with H, in the sense that their matrix elements in the energy representation are concentrated in a narrow strip along the diagonal.[6] Hence, the elements $\langle \chi_\nu | n\rangle$ of the transformation matrix connecting the H-representation with the Q-representation extend only over a small range of energy values E_n. Consequently, the rigorous relation

$$\sum_n \langle \chi_\nu | n\rangle\langle n | \chi_\lambda\rangle = \delta_{\nu\lambda} \qquad (34)$$

remains approximately true if one inserts a function of n which is practically constant in this range.

$$\sum_n \langle \chi_\nu | n\rangle \exp[-\beta E_n]\langle n | \chi_\lambda\rangle = \delta_{\nu\lambda} A \qquad (35)$$

A is some average of $\exp[-\beta E_n]$ in the range in which $\langle \chi_\nu | n\rangle$ differs appreciably from zero, and may appropriately be taken

$$A = \langle \chi_\nu | \exp[-\beta H] | \chi_\nu \qquad (36)$$

Inserting Eq. (35) with Eq. (36) reduces Eq. (33) to Eq. (32).[21]

Our conclusion is that Eqs. (30) *and* (32) *are equivalent in those cases in which the formula makes sense at all.* For it is clear that it only makes physical sense to speak about the autocorrelation function of a certain quantity, if this quantity can be measured at successive times without disturbing the system, that is, if it is a macroscopically observable quantity.

VII. THE MICROSCOPIC EQUATIONS OF MOTION

All that remains to be done for determining the fluctuation spectrum is to compute the conditional average, Eq. (31). However, this involves the full equations of motion of the many-body system and one can at best hope for a suitable approximate method. There are two such methods available. The first method is the Master Equation approach described above. Relying on the fact that the operator Q represents a macroscopic observable quantity, one assumes that on a coarse-grained level it constitutes a Markov process. The microscopic equations are then only required for computing the transition probabilities per unit time, $W(q|q')$, for example by means of Dirac's time-dependent perturbation theory. Subsequently, one has to solve the Master Equation, as described in Section IV, to find both the spectral density of equilibrium fluctuations and the macroscopic phenomenological equation.

The second approximate method for computing Eq. (31) consists in expanding the equations of motion themselves in successive powers of of $Q - \langle Q \rangle^{eq}$. This expansion also serves to find the macroscopic phenomenological equation, whose linear term is called the Kubo formula. However, this leads to a paradoxical result. According to this formula the coefficient of the linear term in the macroscopic equation is the Fourier transform of the autocorrelation function, and therefore, proportional to the fluctuation spectrum.[22] Hence, one is led to the conclusion that the fluctuation spectrum is uniquely determined by the linear term alone, regardless of the presence of nonlinearity.[19] It seems to me hard to believe that, in contrast to Eq. (20), the fluctuation spectrum in a highly nonlinear circuit should be fully determined by the slope of the I–V characteristic at the origin, no matter how strongly the characteristic is curved (Fig. 2). But there is also a basic difficulty in the derivation.

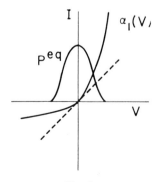

Fig. 2

The basic remark is that linearity of the macroscopic law is not at all the same as linearity of the microscopic equations of motion. In most substances Ohm's law is valid up to a fairly strong field; but if one visualizes the motion of an individual electron and the effect of an external field E on it, it becomes clear that microscopic linearity is restricted to only extremely small field strengths.[23] *Macroscopic linearity, therefore, is not due to microscopic linearity, but to a cancellation of nonlinear terms when averaging over all particles.* It follows that the nonlinear terms proportional to E^2, E^3, ... in the macroscopic equation do not correspond respectively to the terms proportional to E^2, E^3, ... in the microscopic equations, but rather constitute a net effect after averaging all terms in the microscopic motion. This is exactly what the Master Equation approach purports to do. For this reason, I have more faith in the results obtained by means of the Master Equation than in the paradoxical result of the microscopic approach.

References

1. D. K. C. MacDonald, *Phil. Mag.*, **45**, 63 (1954); W. Bernard and H. B. Callen, *Phys. Rev.*, **118**, 1466 (1960).
2. D. Polder, *Phil. Mag.*, **45**, 69 (1954).
3. D. K. C. MacDonald, *Phys. Rev.*, **108**, 541 (1957); N. G. van Kampen, *ibid.*, **110**, 319 (1957); R. O. Davies, *Physica*, **24**, 1055 (1958).
4. For a review, see N. G. van Kampen, in *Fluctuations in Solids*, R. E. Burgess, Ed., Academic, New York, 1965.
5. The name has been used so indiscriminately that it almost lost its meaning. We use it exclusively for the linear differential equation obeyed by the probability distribution of a Markov process.
6. N. G. van Kampen, *Physica*, **20**, 603 (1954); *Fortschr. Physik.*, **4**, 405 (1956). See also, *Fundamental Processes in Statistical Mechanics*, E. G. D. Cohen, Ed., North-Holland Publ. Co., Amsterdam, 1961.
7. E. P. Wigner, *J. Chem. Phys.*, **22**, 1912 (1954).
8. H. A. Kramers, *Physica*, **7**, 284 (1940); J. E. Moyal, *J. Roy. Statist. Soc.*, (*London*), **B11**, 150 (1949).
9. N. G. van Kampen, *J. Math. Phys.*, **2**, 592 (1961).
10. The scaling of time corresponds to the fact that a large system takes a longer time to approach equilibrium, as exhibited by the C in the denominator of (1). However, in other cases, such as fluctuations in semiconductors, a different scaling is sometimes required.
11. This has been verified for a number of examples and appears to be generally true. Actually it may happen that α_n involve higher powers of Ω^{-1} as well, but that is an innocuous complication, which does not upset the general method.
12. N. G. van Kampen, *Can. J. Phys.*, **39**, 551 (1961).
13. In special cases, such as the quantized oscillator, it may happen that $\alpha_3 = 0$, so that at least to one higher order a slightly nonlinear Fokker-Planck equation is consistent.
14. The fluctuation spectrum contains no terms of order $\Omega^{-1/2}$, $\Omega^{-3/2}$, etc.
15. A. Siegel, *J. Math. Phys.*, **7**, 378 (1960).

16. I. Oppenheim, K. E. Shuler, and N. G. van Kampen, to be published.
17. J. G. Cook, J. Blok, and N. G. van Kampen, *Physica*, **35**, 241 (1967).
18. V. B. Magalinskii and I. P. Terletskii, *Soviet Phys. JETP*, **7**, 501 (1958); **9**, 1234 (1959); *Ann. Physik*, **5**, 296 (1960).
19. W. Bernard and H. B. Callen, *Rev. Mod. Phys.*, **31**, 1017 (1959).
20. The same expression was found by J. L. Jackson (private communication).
21. Alternatively, one may argue that Eq. (32) does not really correspond to the physical situation, because a measurement of Q only determines its value with a certain margin and, therefore, does not force the system in one single eigenfunction χ_ν. This argument leads again to an equivalent expression, provided that Q is a macroscopic observable.
22. This is of course the fluctuation–dissipation theorem.
23. Of the order of 10^{-16} V/cm according to an estimate of J. L. Jackson.

ERROR BOUNDS
AND SPECTRAL DENSITIES

ROY G. GORDON*

*Department of Chemistry, Harvard University,
Cambridge, Massachusetts*

CONTENTS

I. INTRODUCTION

Time-dependent correlation functions are now widely used to provide concise statements of the miscroscopic meaning of a variety of experimental results. These connections between microscopically defined time-dependent correlation functions and macroscopic experiments are usually expressed through spectral densities, which are the Fourier transforms of correlation functions. For example, transport coefficients[1] of electrical conductivity, diffusion, viscosity, and heat conductivity can be written as spectral densities of appropriate correlation functions. Likewise, spectral line shapes in absorption, Raman light scattering, neutron scattering, and nuclear|magnetic resonance are related to appropriate microscopic spectral densities.[2]

These relations between spectral densities and experiments furnish only the formal framework for a comparison of theory and experiment. The most difficult step still remains: How can one evaluate the relevant correlation functions and spectral densities from a theoretical microscopic

* Alfred P. Sloan Foundation Fellow.

79

description of a system? Two basic types of approach have been applied to the theoretical evaluation of correlation functions; namely, *dynamical* and *stochastic*.

In the dynamical approach, one attempts to solve directly the quantum-mechanical or classical equations of motion for a system. Such a direct approach is practicable, for example, for treating the binary collisions between molecules in a gas, by either classical or quantum-mechanical methods.[3] However, in a dense system such as a liquid, only the classical equations are tractable,[4] even with high-speed computers.

In a stochastic approach, one replaces the difficult mechanical equations by stochastic equations, such as a diffusion equation, Langevin equation, master equation, or Fokker-Planck equations.[5] These stochastic equations have fewer variables and are generally much easier to solve than the mechanical equations. One then hopes that the stochastic equations include the significant aspects of the physical equations of motion, so that their solutions will display the relevant features of the physical motion.

The approach to calculating spectral densities which we shall describe in the present work is based on the rigorous equations of motion, and should therefore be classed as dynamical, rather than stochastic. However, we do not attempt a direct solution to the equations of motion. Rather we take the point of view that a spectral density is some function of unknown form, about which we can calculate certain features directly from the equations of motion. These simple features of the spectral density are its moments, averages of powers of the frequency, over the spectral density, which are discussed further in Section II.

Having calculated a certain number of moments of a spectral density from the equations of motion, we can then ask to what degree we have determined or restricted other features or averages over the spectral density. Such error bounds are constructed in Section III for the possible range of a number of physically significant weighted averages of the spectral density. In each case it is shown that these error bounds are the most precise possible, on the basis of the known moments of the spectral density. Section IV explores a new technique for estimating the spectral density itself, from its moments.

A number of typical applications of these techniques are illustrated in magnetic resonance, lattice dynamics, diffusion, optical properties, and intermolecular forces.

II. PROPERTIES OF SPECTRAL DENSITIES

The basic definition of a time correlation function is the equilibrium ensemble average (at $t = 0$)

$$C(t) = \langle A(0)A(t) \rangle_{\text{equil}} \tag{1}$$

The quantity of interest, $A(t)$, is a function of the variables of the system of interest, and the indicated time dependence in $A(t)$ is that due to the normal unperturbed motion of the system. The observable properties are ordinarily related to the Fourier transform of the correlation function

$$I(\omega) = \frac{1}{2\pi} \int_{-\infty}^{\infty} \exp\left[-i\omega t\right] C(t) \, dt \qquad (2)$$

in which $I(\omega)$ is called the spectral density of the correlation function. For example in a spectroscopic absorption experiment, A may represent the interaction of the dipole moment of the system with an electric field and $I(\omega)$ is proportional to the transition probability induced by radiation at frequency ω. For complete discussions of the relevant properties $A(t)$ for various experiments, and the connection between the spectral densities and observable properties, we refer to relevant reviews.[1,2]

The spectral density can equally well be written directly in terms of quantum-mechanical transition probabilities in the "golden rule" form.

$$I(\omega) = \sum_{if} \rho_i |\langle i| A |f\rangle|^2 \, \delta(\omega - (E_f - E_i)/\hbar) \qquad (3)$$

Here ρ_i is the probability of finding the ith state $|i\rangle$ in the equilibrium ensemble, ordinarily

$$\rho_i = \exp\left[-E_i/kT\right] \bigg/ \sum_i \exp\left[-E_i/kT\right] \qquad (4)$$

The spectral density, Eq. (3), is mathematically equivalent to Eqs. (1) and (2), when the time development in Eq. (1) is considered quantum mechanically.

A number of general features of spectral densities follow just from the form of these definitions, without solving any equations of motion. In this ection we summarize these known general properties, which will be exploited in the following sections.

Spectral densities are positive, or at least nonnegative, functions of frequency. This follows from their physical interpretations as transition probabilities, and is clear analytically from the "golden rule" formula, (Eq. (3)). The positive nature of spectral densities is essential to the methods of analysis we will use in the next two sections.

Some features of the frequency distribution of $I(\omega)$ follow directly from the form of Eq. (3). As a temperature goes to zero, only the quantum-mechanical ground state is occupied. Then all the excitation frequencies $(E_f - E_i)/\hbar$ are positive, and $I(\omega)$ vanishes for negative ω. When classical mechanics is applicable, as is ordinarily the case at high temperatures, $I(\omega)$

becomes an even function of ω. In general, $I(\omega)$ is an unsymmetrical function of ω, but its corresponding values at $\pm\omega$ are simply related by

$$I(-\omega) = I(\omega) \exp(-\hbar\omega/kT) \tag{5}$$

which follows directly from Eq. (3) by interchanging the summation indices i and f in the corresponding expression for $I(-\omega)$. This relation shows explicitly how rapidly $I(-\omega)$ vanishes as the temperature tends to zero, and how nearly symmetric $I(\omega)$ becomes as the temperature becomes large.

The above properties of $I(\omega)$ are quite general and do not depend on either the nature of the system or the perturbation. To obtain more specific information, one must of course make use of the specific Hamiltonian H for a system, and the specific perturbation A in which one is interested. The simplest specific properties which one can calculate are the moments μ_n of the spectral density

$$\mu_n \equiv \int_{-\infty}^{\infty} \omega^n I(\omega)\, d\omega \tag{6}$$

These moments can be evaluated in the following manner. For μ_0 we simply integrate Eq. (3) over all frequencies

$$
\begin{aligned}
\mu_0 &\equiv \int_{-\infty}^{\infty} I(\omega)\, d\omega \\
&= \sum_{if} \rho_i \langle i| A |f\rangle\langle f| A |i\rangle \\
&= \sum_i \rho_i \langle i| A^2 |i\rangle \\
&\equiv \langle A^2 \rangle_{\text{equil}}
\end{aligned} \tag{7}
$$

The summation over final states $|f\rangle$ has been carried out by the completeness relation, or equivalently, by matrix multiplication. Thus, the zeroth moment is just an *equilibrium average* of the square of the perturbation amplitude. The first moment can likewise be expressed as an equilibrium property.

$$
\begin{aligned}
\mu_1 &\equiv \int_{-\infty}^{\infty} \omega I(\omega)\, d\omega \\
&= \sum_{if} \rho_i \langle i| A |f\rangle\langle f| A |i\rangle (E_f - E_i)/\hbar \\
&= \sum_{if} \rho_i \langle i| A |f\rangle\langle f| HA - AH |i\rangle/\hbar \\
&= \sum_i \rho_i \langle i| A |(HA - AH)|i\rangle/\hbar \\
&\equiv \hbar^{-1} \langle A[H, A]\rangle_{\text{equil}}
\end{aligned} \tag{8}
$$

Here the Hamiltonian H has been used to replace the energies E_f and E_i, using

$$H|f\rangle = E_f|f\rangle \tag{9}$$

so that the sum over final states $|f\rangle$ involves coefficients independent of f, and can be carried out again using completeness.

Higher moments of a spectral density may likewise be evaluated as equilibrium properties, by introducing higher commutators of H to reproduce the higher powers of $E_f - E_i$, giving

$$\mu_k = \hbar^{-k}\langle A[H, [H, \ldots [H, A] \ldots]]\rangle_{\text{equil}} \tag{10}$$

in which the commutators contain H k times. Many equivalent expressions for these higher moments can be given by introducing some of the Hamiltonian factors into the first matrix element $\langle i|\,A\,|f\rangle$ rather than the second.

These expressions for the moments can be evaluated as equilibrium averages, without actually solving for all the quantum states of the system, or without solving the classical equations of motion for the classical trajectories. In the quantum-mechanical case, these equilibrium averages, Eq. (10), can be rewritten as traces, which can then be evaluated in any convenient basis. Thus the difficult step of solving for all the quantum states can be avoided in evaluating moments.

Moments of the relevant spectral densities have been evaluated for the absorption of light by atoms[6] and molecules,[7] Raman scattering of light by molecules,[8] nuclear magnetic resonance of solids,[9] neutron scattering,[10] and diffusion[11] and viscosity[12] of atomic fluids.

The moments can be given an alternative interpretation by considering the inverse Fourier transform to Eq. (2)

$$C(t) = \int_{-\infty}^{\infty} \exp\left[i\omega t\right]I(\omega)\,d\omega \tag{11}$$

which gives the correlation function, Eq. (1), as an integral over the spectral density. Expanding the exponential factor in Eq. (11) in a power series, and interchanging the order of summation and integration gives

$$C(t) = \sum_{k=0}^{\infty} \frac{(it)^k}{k!} \int_{-\infty}^{\infty} \omega^k I(\omega)\,d\omega$$

$$\equiv \sum_{k=0}^{\infty} \frac{\mu_k}{k!}(it)^k \tag{12}$$

Thus, the moments are the coefficients for a power series expansion in time for the correlation function, and hence, are time derivatives of $C(t)$

evaluated at $t = 0$.

$$\mu_k = (-i)^k \left. \frac{d^k C(t)}{dt^k} \right|_{t=0}$$

$$= (-i)^k \left\langle A(0) \frac{d^k}{dt^k} A(t) \right\rangle \Big|_{t=0} \qquad (13)$$

The commutators in Eq. (10) are just an explicit quantum-mechanical formula for evaluating the time derivatives.

Ordinarily the power series, Eq. (12), converges slowly except at short times,[13,14] so that it is not directly useful for evaluating spectral densities. Supposing that one could in fact evaluate all of the moments of the spectral density, there remains the question of whether they give sufficient information to determine $I(\omega)$ uniquely. Considerable attention has been given to this mathematical question, but no necessary *and* sufficient conditions are known. However, a number of sufficient conditions are known.[15,16] It is clear that if $I(\omega)$ falls off too slowly at large ω, the higher moments will diverge, and thus yield no more information about $I(\omega)$. But even having all moments finite is not enough to guarantee uniqueness and counterexamples, such as $I(\omega) \sim \exp[-|\omega|^{1/2}]$, are known not to be uniquely determined by their moments.[17] Perhaps the most useful uniqueness condition[18] is that $I(\omega)$ decrease exponentially or faster for large $|\omega|$, or, equivalently, that μ_k grow no faster than $k!$ at large k. It is interesting that the positive character of $I(\omega)$ is essential to this question of uniqueness, since it can be shown[19] that when the positive condition is relaxed, a function is never uniquely determined by its moments.

In practice one can hardly ever evaluate all of the moments of a spectral density, but rather one evaluates only the first few, until the calculations become too difficult or lengthy. If only the first $2M$ moments are evaluated, then $I(\omega)$ is never known uniquely, except in the special case that $I(\omega)$ consists of discrete contributions at M or fewer frequencies. Nevertheless, one expects that the knowledge of even a few moments of a spectral density furnishes some useful constraints on the possible forms of $I(\omega)$. The problem is to translate these moment constraints, and the other general properties of $I(\omega)$, into useful forms. Several schemes for making use of this information are outlined in the next section.

III. ERROR BOUNDS FOR AVERAGES OF SPECTRAL DENSITIES

Often the physical quantities of interest are some kind of averages over the spectral density, rather than $I(\omega)$ at only a single point ω. For example, if a spectrometer measures with frequencies spread over a range about ω_0, weighted by some slit function $S(\omega - \omega_0)$, the observed spectrum is

$$\bar{I}(\omega_0) = \int S(\omega - \omega_0)I(\omega)\,d\omega \tag{14}$$

If the slit function S is taken as a Lorentzian

$$S(\omega - \omega_0) = \frac{\varepsilon/\pi}{(\omega - \omega_0)^2 + \varepsilon^2} \tag{15}$$

then this broadened response corresponds to the transitions produced by an exponentially damped harmonic perturbation

$$H_1(t) = A \exp\left[-\varepsilon\,|t|\,\right] \cos \omega_0 t \tag{16}$$

rather than the idealized perfectly harmonic perturbation ($\varepsilon \to 0$) used in defining $I(\omega)$.

Second-order perturbation sums are a second example in which one is interested in an average or integral over a spectral density. For example, the dynamic polarizability α of a system at a frequency ω_0 is related to the spectral density $I(\omega)$ of the electric dipole moment of the system by

$$\alpha(\omega_0) = \int \left(\frac{2\omega}{\omega^2 - \omega_0{}^2}\right) I(\omega)\,d\omega \tag{17}$$

A third example of an average over the spectral density is the cumulative distribution

$$D(\omega_0) \equiv \int_{-\infty}^{\omega_0} I(\omega)\,d\omega \tag{18}$$

up to a frequency ω_0.

The most remarkable feature of these average properties is that they are determined to within rigorous error bounds just by the knowledge of the general properties of the spectral densities discussed in Section II. That is, if we calculate a certain finite number of moments of a spectral density, then averages such as Eqs. (14)–(18) must lie between certain calculable limits, no matter what (positive) functional form $I(\omega)$ actually has, as long as $I(\omega)$ has the specified moments.

A. Error Bounds for the Response to a Damped Harmonic Perturbation

We will first consider the error bounds for a spectral density broadened by a Lorentzian slit function, Eq. (15), describing the response to an exponentially damped perturbation. In this case the broadened spectrum,

Eq. (14), may be written in the equivalent complex form

$$\bar{I}(\omega_0, \varepsilon) = -\frac{1}{\pi} \operatorname{Im} \int_{-\infty}^{\infty} \frac{I(\omega)\, d\omega}{-\omega_0 + i\varepsilon + \omega}$$

$$\equiv -\operatorname{Im} \{\mathscr{I}(-\omega_0 + i\varepsilon)\} \tag{19}$$

where $\mathscr{I}(z)$ is the complex integral

$$\mathscr{I}(z) \equiv \frac{1}{\pi} \int_{-\infty}^{\infty} \frac{I(\omega)\, d\omega}{z + \omega} \tag{20}$$

This integral is of just the form considered by Hamburger,[20] who relates this integral to the fraction

$$C_{M+1}(z, \tau) = \cfrac{\alpha_1}{z + \alpha_2 - \cfrac{\alpha_2 \alpha_3}{z + \alpha_3 + \alpha_4 - \cfrac{\alpha_4 \alpha_5}{\begin{matrix}\ddots\\ \cfrac{\alpha_{2M-2}\,\alpha_{2M-1}}{z + \alpha_{2M-1} + \alpha_{2M} - \tau}\end{matrix}}}} \tag{21}$$

The coefficients α_n are determined by the requirement that $\mathscr{I}(z)$ and $C_{M+1}(z, 0)$ have the same formal expansions in powers of $1/z$, through order $(1/z)^{2M+1}$. The α_n are most conveniently constructed to satisfy these conditions by a recursion relation[21] starting from the moments μ_n of $I(\omega)$.

The usefulness of constructing the function $C_{M+1}(z, \tau)$ arises from the theorem[20,22] that as τ varies over the real axis, $C_{M+1}(z, \tau)$ varies over a circle in the complex plane. For all possible nonnegative densities $I(\omega)$ having the specified moments, $\mathscr{I}(z)$ must fall within or on this circle.[20,22] Thus we may determine the minimum and maximum possible values of $\bar{I}(Z_0, \varepsilon)$ using Eq. (19), from the minimum and maximum imaginary parts of these circles.[23] The upper and lower bounds to $\bar{I}(\omega_0, t)$ may be evaluated recursively from α_n for any given values of frequency ω_0 and pulse width ε^{-1}.

These upper and lower bounds for the broadened response $\bar{I}(\omega_0, t)$ are the most precise possible, on the basis of the known moments.[23] We can show this by counter-example, by constructing distributions having the correct moments and actually attaining the upper or lower bounds to $\bar{I}(\omega_0, t)$. Consider, for example, the fraction $C_{M+1}(z, \tau_{max})$ in Eq. (21), where τ_{max} is the value of τ corresponding to the point on the circle for which $\bar{I}(\omega_0, \varepsilon)$ is a maximum. Then we can rewrite Eq. (21) as an equivalent sum of partial fractions

$$C_{M+1}(z, \tau_{max}) = \sum_{j=1}^{M} \frac{\rho_M(j)}{z + \xi_{jM}} \qquad (22)$$

The particular spectral density consisting of M δ functions at the points ξ_{jM}, each weighted by the appropriate factor $\rho_M(j)$

$$I_{max}(\omega) = \sum_{j=1}^{M} \rho_M(j) \, \delta(\omega - \xi_{jM}) \qquad (23)$$

is just the one which when substituted into

$$\mathscr{I}(z) = \frac{1}{\pi} \int \frac{I(\omega) \, d\omega}{z + \omega} \qquad (24)$$

will allow $\mathscr{I}(z)$ and hence $\bar{I}(\omega_0, \varepsilon)$ to attain their extreme values. This "extreme distribution" $I_{max}(\omega)$ can be seen to satisfy all the requirements we have imposed. By expanding Eq. (22) in $1/z$ it may be seen to have the correct first $2M$ moments. From the method of construction [20, 21] it may be shown that the $\rho_M(j)$ are positive and the ξ_{jM} are real, so that $I_{max}(\omega)$ is an acceptable non-negative distribution. Thus, we conclude that no more precise upper and lower bounds are possible using only the known moments and the non-negative nature of $I(\omega)$.

These upper and lower bounds determine the optimum extent to which one can predict the response of a system to any specific damped harmonic perturbation, using only a knowledge of certain *equilibrium* properties of the *unperturbed* system, the moments. Naturally, the shorter the duration of the perturbation pulse (i.e., the larger ε is) the more accurate the prediction from equilibrium properties becomes. Conversely, the *longer* the duration of the perturbation (ε becomes small), the less relevant the few equilibrium ("time zero") properties of the system become to the time development at long times, and the predictions become less accurate. In the limit $\varepsilon \to 0$ (an idealized perturbation of infinite duration), the lower bounds to the response tend to zero and the upper bounds tend to infinity, for any fixed finite number of moments. The only exceptions to this degeneration of the predictions at long times, arise if the systems reponse occurs at only M distinct frequencies. Then if $2M$ or more moments are known, the upper and lower bounds as constructed will coincide and be exact for any ε. Such a simple response would only occur for simple systems such as spins or oscillators, but it is interesting that the upper and lower bound technique would spot such simple resonance behavior right from the equilibrium moments of the response.

As an example of these error bounds, we may consider the response of a nuclear spin system in a crystal to a perturbing magnetic field. This corresponds to a broad-line nuclear resonance spectrum. Figure 1 gives a comparison between theory[23] and experiment,[24] using moments calculated by Van Vleck.[9] $\varepsilon = 1$ was chosen as large enough to obtain reasonable error bounds from the limited number of moments, and the experiments on CaF_2 were given suitable additional broadening by convolution with a Lorentzian, in order to allow direct comparison with the theory.

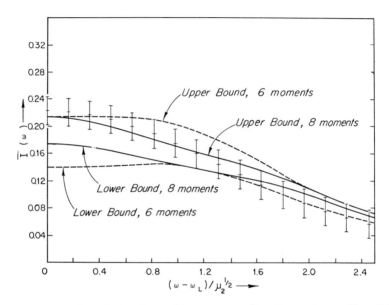

Fig. 1. Error bounds for the nuclear resonance line shape of crystalline CaF_2, broadened by a Lorentzian slit function (i.e., the energy absorption by the coupled nuclear spins, due to an exponentially damped harmonic perturbation by a radio-frequency magnetic field).

This calculation illustrates a point made in the introduction. We have been able to calculate a well-defined theoretical spectrum to a specified range of reliability. We used the rigorous mechanical equations of motion for a large spin system without actually undertaking the hopeless task of solving them, and without resorting to a phenomenological or stochastic equation of motion.

B. Error Bounds for the Cumulative Distribution

Another interesting average over a spectral density is its cumulative distribution $D(\omega_0)$, defined by

$$D(\omega_0) = \int_{-\infty}^{\omega_0} I(\omega)\, d\omega \tag{25}$$

whose derivative gives the spectral density itself

$$\frac{dD(\omega)}{d\omega} = I(\omega) \tag{26}$$

Since the cumulative distribution is obviously bounded

$$0 \le D(\omega) \le \mu_0 = \int_{-\infty}^{\infty} I(\omega)\, d\omega \tag{27}$$

it is reasonable to expect to find more precise bounds on $D(\omega)$ when one knows higher moments than μ_0. These bounds are supplied by the Chebycheff inequalities.[25] If we know $2M - 1$ moments, then we can construct a special extremal distribution

$$I_{\text{ext}}(\omega) = \sum_{j=1}^{M} \rho_M(j)\, \delta(\omega - \xi_{jM}) \tag{28}$$

which is a sum of M δ functions. The $2M$ constants $\rho_M(j)$ and ξ_{jM} are chosen to satisfy the $2M$ conditions

$$\xi_{1M} = \omega_0 \tag{29}$$

and

$$\mu_k = \int_{-\infty}^{\infty} \omega^k I_{\text{ext}}(\omega)\, d\omega$$

$$= \sum_{j=1}^{M} \xi_{jM}{}^k \rho_j(M) \qquad k = 0, 1, 2, \ldots, 2M - 2 \tag{30}$$

which is to say that one of the δ functions in $I_{\text{ext}}(\omega)$ lies at ω_0, the upper limit of the cumulative distribution, and that $I_{\text{ext}}(\omega)$ has the correct values of the $2M - 1$ known moments. These weights $\rho_M(j)$ and positions ξ_{jM} may be obtained conveniently by a recursion relation which reduces them to a linear eigenvalue problem.[21]

The lower bound to the cumulative distribution $D(\omega_0)$ is found by adding up all the weights $\rho_j(M)$ corresponding to points ξ_{jM} below ω_0, and the upper bound to $D(\omega_0)$ by including as well the weight $\rho_1(M)$ at ω_0[25]:

$$\sum_{\xi_{jM} < \omega_0} \rho_j(M) \le D(\omega_0) \le \sum_{\xi_{jM} \le \omega_0} \rho_j(M) \tag{31}$$

That these bounds are the most precise possible on the basis of the moment information, is again clear by counterexample. If we displace ξ_{1M} ever so slightly below ω_0, then the cumulative distribution one would calculate from $I_{ext}(\omega)$ will *attain* the upper bound. Similarly, moving ξ_{1M} just above ω_0 will remove its contribution to the cumulative distribution of $I_{ext}(\omega)$, thereby producing a distribution which *attains* the lower bound, and satisfies all the conditions imposed.

As an example, we consider these error bounds for the cumulative distribution of the spectral density of the *velocity* autocorrelation function,

$$I(\omega) = \frac{1}{2\pi} \int_{-\infty}^{\infty} \exp\,[-i\omega t]\langle \mathbf{v}(0) \cdot \mathbf{v}(t)\rangle\,dt \qquad (32)$$

which is important in studying diffusion and in neutron scattering.[26] For classical motion, the odd moments are zero, and the zeroth moment (normalization), the equilibrium mean squared velocity, is determined by the temperature. The second moment is determined by the equilibrium mean squared force on an atom, which may be determined from the isotope effect on the vapor pressure of atomic[27] or molecular[28] liquids. The fourth moment has been evaluated numerically for a model of liquid argon by Nijboer and Rahman.[29] Using their data, we evaluated upper and lower bounds to the cumulative distribution, which are plotted in Figure 2. Because of the small amount of input information, the bounds are fairly broad. For comparison, we have also plotted as x's in Figure 2 the cumulative frequency distribution calculated numerically for the same model of argon.[29] It is seen that the numerical points fall nearly half-way between

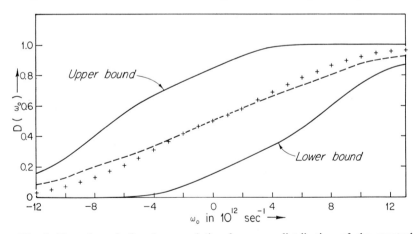

Fig. 2. Error bounds for the cumulative frequency distribution of the spectral density for the velocity autocorrelation function using μ_0, μ_2, and μ_4 evaluated for a classical model of liquid argon.[29]

the error bounds, never deviating by more than 0.05 from the mean of the upper and lower bounds. Somewhat improved bounds can be obtained in this case by taking advantage of the even character of a classical spectral density.

The diffusion constant D is determined by the zero-frequency component of this spectral density of the velocity correlation function, by the relation

$$D = \pi I(0)/3 \tag{33}$$

If we estimate $I(0)$ as the derivative of the *mean* of the upper and lower bounds to the cumulative distribution, we obtain a diffusion constant which agrees to within 20% with the numerical estimate given for the same system using molecular dynamics.[29] It is important to note that our estimate is derived entirely from equilibrium properties of the system. Unfortunately, we cannot give *a priori* estimates for the accuracy of the diffusion constant, since it is related to the spectral density at a single point (zero frequency), rather than to the cumulative distribution. However, in many other experiments such as in spectroscopy and neutron scattering, a whole range of frequencies is observable. Then cumulative distribution of intensity can be inferred directly from the experiments, and compared to the error range in the cumulative distribution which is allowed by calculated or observed equilibrium properties.

C. Error Bounds for Second-Order Perturbation Energies

Another important average over the spectral density of a perturbation is the second-order perturbation energy shift[30]

$$-E^{(2)} = \sum_{n \neq 0} \left\{ \frac{1}{\omega - \omega_0} + \frac{1}{\omega + \omega_0} \right\} |\langle 0| H_1 |n\rangle|^2 \tag{34}$$

$$\equiv \int_{\omega_1}^{\infty} \left\{ \frac{1}{\omega - \omega_0} + \frac{1}{\omega + \omega_0} \right\} I(\omega) \, d\omega$$

of a system in its ground state $|0\rangle$, due to a perturbation H_1 oscillating at frequency ω_0. ω_1 is the excitation frequency to the first excited state. For example, if the perturbation is the oscillating electric field in a light wave, then this second-order energy is essentially the dynamic polarizability of the system, and $I(\omega)$ is the spectral density for the fluctuations of the dipole moment of the system. For perturbations of the ground state, the equilibrium averages for the moments of the spectral density reduce to just expectation values over the ground state.

Error bounds for these perturbation energies can be constructed[31] from the moments with the help of the generalized theory of Gaussian integration,[16] in which integrals take the form

$$\int f(\omega)I(\omega)\,d\omega = \sum_{j=1}^{M} f(\xi_{jM})\rho_j(M) + R \tag{35}$$

Here $f(\omega)$ may be any known function which has at least $2M$ continuous derivatives, over the range of integration. The $2M$ constants ξ_{jM} and $\rho_j(M)$ are again chosen to have the $2M$ known moments

$$\sum_{j=1}^{M} \xi_{jM}{}^k \rho_j(M) = \mu_k \qquad k = 0, 1, \ldots, 2M-1 \tag{36}$$

Thus, if $f(\omega)$ were taken to be any polynomial of order $2M-1$ or less, Eq. (35) would correctly evaluate the integral, with zero remainder term R. Thus, it is not surprising that in the general case[32] the remainder R turns out to be proportional to the $2M$th derivative of $f(\omega)$ (which would vanish for $f(\omega)$ as a polynomial of order $2M-1$), evaluated at some (unknown) point in the range of integration. The proportionality constant multiplying $f^{(2M)}(\omega)$ in the remainder R is non-negative[32] as long as $I(\omega)$ is non-negative.

To apply Gaussian integration to the perturbation sum (Eq. (34)) we take

$$f(\omega) = \left\{ \frac{1}{\omega - \omega_0} + \frac{1}{\omega + \omega_0} \right\} \tag{37}$$

The $2M$th derivatives of this $f(\omega)$ are all positive in the region of integration, as long as the applied frequency ω_0 is smaller than the lowest allowed excitation frequency ω_1. Thus the remainder term R is positive, and we have a *lower bound*[31] to the magnitude of the energy shift

$$-E^{(2)} \geq \sum_{j=1}^{M} \left(\frac{1}{\xi_{jM} - \omega_0} + \frac{1}{\xi_{jM} + \omega_0} \right) \rho_j(M) \tag{38}$$

To evaluate the upper bound to the second-order energy, we construct another special distribution of M points, one of which is constrained to lie at ω_1, the excitation energy of the first excited state which contributes to the perturbation sum. The M weights $\rho_j(M)$ and the other $M-1$ positions ξ_{jM} are chosen to match $2M-1$ known moments. This gives an integration formula like Eq. (35), in which the remainder term[32] has the form of a positive constant times the $(2M-1)$th derivative of $f(\omega)$. Since the odd derivatives of $f(\omega)$ in Eq. (37), are negative in the range of integration, the formula analogous to Eq. (38) with the present constants gives an upper bound to the magnitude of the perturbation energy.[31]

As in the other cases, these bounds are the best ones possible on the basis of the known information. The special point distributions of spectral density, which are used to form the upper and lower bounds, are themselves counterexamples against better bounds without further information.

These methods have been applied to calculate the polarizabilities of atoms,[31] and the long-ranged forces between atoms,[33] with a typical calculated accuracy of 10% or less. Thus, we have been able to estimate successfully the significant features of zero-point fluctuations of atomic dipole moments, without actually solving the quantum equations of motion to obtain all the excited state energies and wave functions.

Similar methods have been used to integrate thermodynamic properties of harmonic lattice vibrations over the spectral density of lattice vibration frequencies.[21, 34] Very accurate error bounds are obtained for properties like the heat capacity,[34] using just the moments of the lattice vibrational frequency spectrum.[35] These moments are known[35] in terms of the force constants and masses and lattice type, so that one need not actually solve the lattice equations of motion to obtain thermodynamic properties of the lattice. In this way, one can avoid the usual stochastic method[36] in lattice dynamics, which solves a random sample of the (factored) secular determinants for the lattice vibration frequencies. Figure 3 gives a typical set of error bounds to the heat capacity of a lattice, derived from moments of the spectrum of lattice vibrations.[34] Useful error bounds are obtained

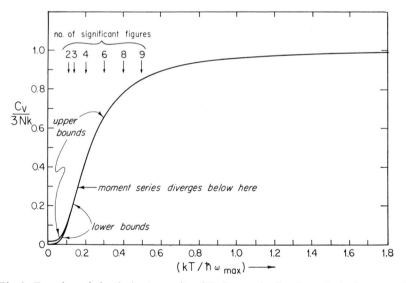

Fig. 3. Error bounds for the heat capacity of the harmonic vibrations of a body-centered cubic lattice with first- and second-nearest neighbor force constants.

even at such low temperatures that the usual high-temperature moment series[35] for the heat capacity diverges.*

IV. EXTRAPOLATION METHODS FOR SPECTRAL DENSITIES

Often one expects on physical grounds that the spectral density for a problem should be a smooth, or at least continuous, function of frequency. However, the special spectral densities constructed in the previous section were very singular functions, sums of δ functions (i.e., sharp lines). These special spectral densities were constructed uniquely to *minimize* or *maximize* various functionals of the spectral densities, subject to the constraints of having given values of a finite number of moments. One would like to be able to construct also some of the smoother spectral densities, which also have the correct moments, and thus will necessarily have functionals interpolating somewhere between the error limits. Of course such functions will not be unique unless other constraints are added.

The simplest, and most often used, method of estimating approximate spectral densities from their moments, is to choose a functional form with some parameters in it, and then choose the parameters so that the function has the correct moments. For example,[35] a systematic method of doing this is to expand the spectral density in a series of orthonormal functions, and choose the first M expansion coefficients to match the M known moments, and setting the higher expansion coefficients to zero. However, this procedure has the disadvantage that the approximate spectral density need not come out positive.

Another approach to estimating spectral densities, which has the advantage of guaranteeing that the approximate functions are positive, can be based on the error bounds constructed in Section III-A for the spectral density broadened by a Lorentzian slit function. If we had a sufficient number of moments to make the error bounds very precise, then we could reduce the broadening as much as we like, so that the broadened distribution of spectral density becomes as close as we like to the true distribution. In order to estimate these higher moments, we should need to take advantage of some special feature of the distribution. For example, in the case of the harmonic vibrations of a crystalline solid, the distribution of frequencies lies between limits $-\omega_{max}$ and $+\omega_{max}$, and is zero outside

---

* *Note added in proof:* Much more accurate bounds for the lattice vibration problem have now been obtained,[34] using the higher moments calculated by C. Isenberg, *Phys. Rev.*, **132**, 2427 (1963). We thank Professor C. Domb for bringing this work to our attention.

this interval. Then at large n, the moments approach the limiting ratio

$$\lim_{n \to \infty} \frac{\mu_{2n+2}}{\mu_{2n}} = \omega_{max}^2 \qquad (39)$$

If this limit is approached rather smoothly, then we might extrapolate the known moments to this limit in a form such as

$$\frac{\mu_{2n+2}}{\mu_{2n}} \sim \omega_{max}^2 \left(1 + \frac{a}{n} + \frac{b}{n^2} + \cdots \right) \qquad (40)$$

where the coefficients a, b, etc. are fit to the last few known moments. One immediate difficulty with such an extrapolation is that the extrapolated distribution will almost certainly not be positive. That is, as soon as one has specified the first M moments of a positive distribution over a finite range, the higher moments must certainly have values within very small ranges, or there will exist *no* positive distribution which has those moments. In fact, one can construct these bounds on the higher moments using the techniques of generalized Gaussian integration.[32] However, it is inconvenient to test whether the extrapolated moments will be consistent with some positive-definite distribution, and in practice one can carry out such a test only up to finite order. Therefore, we should like to perform such an extrapolation of the higher moments in such a way that we are guaranteed to always be consistent with a positive distribution. An easy way to guarantee a positive distribution is to extrapolate the continued fraction coefficients α_{2n}, α_{2n+1} in Eq. (21) associated[37] with the integral $\bar{I}(\varepsilon, \omega)$. For the case of a finite interval one can show that the limit of these coefficients is

$$\lim_{n \to \infty} (\alpha_{2n} \alpha_{2n+1}) = \tfrac{1}{4} \omega_{max}^2 \qquad (41)$$

Therefore, if this limit is approached asymptotically as

$$\alpha_{2n} \alpha_{2n+1} \sim \tfrac{1}{4} \omega_{max}^2 \left(1 + \frac{a}{n} + \frac{b}{n^2} + \cdots \right) \qquad (42)$$

a necessary and sufficient condition for this extrapolation to represent a positive distribution, is simply that these extrapolated coefficients themselves remain positive[37] for all n above the n for which the α_n have been calculated exactly. The expansion coefficients a, b, etc. can be fit to the last few of the exactly calculated α_n's. The evaluation of the approximate spectral density may then be completed by first summing the continued fraction to infinite order and then letting the resolution width ε tend to zero. Some care must be exercised in this procedure, since the order of these two limiting processes cannot be interchanged. It can be accomplished by direct evaluation of the continued fraction up to an order at which the α_n have substantially reached their limit (Eq. (41)), and then evaluating the remaining "tail" of the continued fraction to infinite order, by means of the result[38]

$$\lim_{\varepsilon \to 0} \left\{ \cfrac{1}{\varepsilon + i\omega + \omega_{max}^2/4 + \cfrac{\varepsilon + i\omega + \omega_{max}^2/4}{\varepsilon + i\omega + \omega_{max}^2/4 + \cfrac{}{\varepsilon + i\omega + \cdots}}} \right\}$$

$$= \frac{2}{\omega_{max}^2} (\omega_{max}^2 - \omega^2)^{1/2} - \frac{2i\omega}{\omega_{max}^2} \tag{43}$$

This approximate method has been generalized to cases other than a spectral density on a finite interval. For example, if a spectral density is known to exponentially fall off at large ω, then the continued fraction coefficients grow asymptotically as n^2 at large n. Then if enough moments are known so that one approaches this asymptotic behavior, a similar estimate of the spectral density can be made.

It should be clear that the extrapolation methods suggested in this section do *not* have rigorous error bounds like those developed in Section III. However, the extrapolation methods do furnish estimates of the spectral density itself, rather than only averages of the spectral density. Furthermore, these estimates satisfy all known conditions on the spectral density discussed in Section II. They are: (a) positive functions, (b) with correct moments, insofar as they are known, and (c) satisfy any known asymptotic behavior at the ends of the frequency intervals. In a number of test cases with known positive continuous functions with known asymptotic behavior, estimates generally were correct to within a few per cent, even when only a few (say 10) moments were given. A typical spectral density obtained in this way for a lattice vibration problem is plotted in Figure 4.[34] The results are similar to those obtained numerically for the same problem, by solving a random sample of secular equations for the lattice vibrations.[36]

It is interesting to note that the extrapolation method suggested in this section is essentially a method of analytic continuation of a function related to the one used by Dyson[39] in the study of lattice vibrations.

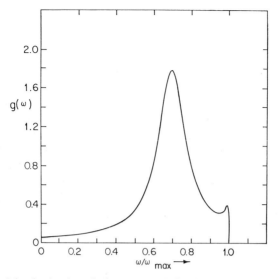

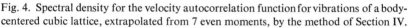

Fig. 4. Spectral density for the velocity autocorrelation function for vibrations of a body-centered cubic lattice, extrapolated from 7 even moments, by the method of Section IV.

V. SUMMARY AND DISCUSSION

The usefulness of spectral densities in nonequilibrium statistical mechanics, spectroscopy, and quantum mechanics is indicated in Section I. In Section II we discuss a number of known properties of spectral densities, which follow from only the form of their definitions, the equations of motion, and equilibrium properties of the system of interest. These properties, particularly the *moments* of spectral density, do not require an actual solution to the equations of motion, in order to be evaluated. Section III introduces methods which allow one to determine optimum error bounds for certain well-defined averages over spectral densities using only the equilibrium properties discussed in Section II. These averages have certain physical interpretations, such as the response to a damped harmonic perturbation, and the second-order perturbation energy. Finally, Section IV discusses extrapolation methods for estimating spectral densities themselves, from the equilibrium properties, combined with qualitative estimates of the way the spectral densities fall off at high frequencies.

It is of interest here to compare one of these methods with Mori's continued fraction representation for spectral densities.[40] Consider the case of Lorentzian broadening of the spectral density (which describes the response to a damped harmonic perturbation, Section III-A). If we set

$\tau = 0$ and let M tend to infinity in the finite fraction $C_{M+1}(z, \tau)$ in Eq. (21), we apparently obtain Mori's infinite continued fraction representation. However, to apply the infinite fraction, one needs to know all the moments, and this case is rarely realized in practice, except for very simple model systems. Simply truncating the infinite fraction in various ways[40] generally leads to an unknown error. Our approach effectively leads to rigorous error bounds for truncating the infinite fraction. We show also that these error bounds are the most precise possible limits obtainable from a given number of equilibrium moments of the spectral density. The present approach has the further advantage that it not restricted to the case of Lorentzian averages over the spectral density. We are able to give error bounds for other physically interesting averages over spectral densities, such as those discussed in Sections III-B and C: cumulative frequency distributions, thermodynamic properties, and second-order perturbation energies.

References

1. R. W. Zwanig, *Ann. Rev. Phys. Chem.* **16**, 67 (1965).
2. R. G. Gordon, *Advan. Magnetic Resonance*, **3**, 1 (1967).
3. R. G. Gordon, W. A. Klemperer, and J. I. Steinfeld, *Ann. Rev. Phys. Chem.*, **19**, 215 (1968).
4. B. J. Alder and T. E. Wainwright, *J. Chem. Phys.*, **27**, 1208 (1957); **33**, 1439 (1960); A. Rahman, *Phys. Rev.*, **136**, A405 (1964).
5. I. Oppenheim, K. E. Shuler, and G. H. Weiss, *Advan. Mol. Relaxation Processes*, **1**, 13 (1967).
6. J. P. Vinti, *Phys. Rev.*, **41**, 432 (1932).
7. R. G. Gordon, *J. Chem. Phys.*, **41**, 1819 (1964).
8. R. G. Gordon, *J. Chem. Phys.*, **40**, 1973 (1964).
9. J. H. Van Vleck, *Phys. Rev.*, **74**, 1168 (1948).
10. G. Placzek, *Phys. Rev.*, **86**, 377 (1952); P. G. DeGennes, *Physica*, **25**, 825 (1959).
11. S. A. Rice, *J. Chem. Phys.*, **33**, 1376 (1960); D. C. Douglas, *J. Chem. Phys.*, **35**, 81 (1961).
12. D. Forster, P. C. Martin, and S. Yip (to be published).
13. R. G. Gordon, *J. Chem. Phys.*, **43**, 1307 (1965).
14. B. R. A. Nijboer and A. Rahman, *Physica*, **32**, 415 (1966).
15. N. I. Akhiezer, *The Classical Moment Problem*, Oliver and Boyd, Edinburgh, 1965.
16. J. A. Shohat and J. D. Tamarkin, *The Problem of Moments*, Mathematical Surveys **1** 2nd ed., American Mathematical Society, Providence, R.I., 1950, Chap. 1.
17. D. V. Widder, *The Laplace Transform*, Princeton University Press, Princeton, N.J., 1946, p. 142.
18. Ref. 16, Corollary 1.2, p. 20.
19. Ref. 16, Theorem 3.11, p. 103.
20. H. Hamburger, *Math. Ann.*, **81**, 235 (1920); **82**, 120, 168 (1921); Ref. 16, Chaps. 2.
21. R. G. Gordon, *J. Math. Phys.*, **9**, 655 (1968).
22. Ref. 16, Theorem 2.7, p. 48.

23. R. G. Gordon, *J. Math. Phys.*, **9**, 1087 (1968).
24. C. R. Bruce, *Phys. Rev.*, **107**, 43 (1957).
25. P. Chebycheff, *J. Math. Pures Appl.*, (2) **19**, 157 (1874); Ref. 16, p. 43; p. 115.
26. A. Rahman, K. S. Singwi, and A. Sjölander, *Phys. Rev.*, **126**, 986 (1962).
27. K. F. Herzfeld and E. Teller, *Phys. Rev.*, **54**, 912 (1938).
28. R. G. Gordon, *J. Chem. Phys.*, **44**, 576 (1966).
29. B. R. A. Nijboer and A. Rahman, *Physica*, **32**, 415 (1966).
30. For recent reviews, see A. Dalgarno, *Advan. Phys.*, **11**, 281 (1962); J. O. Hirschfelder, W. Byers Brown, and S. T. Epstein, *Advan. Quantum Chem.*, **1**, 255 (1964).
31. R. G. Gordon, *Intern. J. Quantum Chem.*, (to be published).
32. Ref. 16, Chap. IV.
33. R. G. Gordon, *J. Chem. Phys.*, **48**, 3929 (1968).
34. J. C. Wheeler and R. G. Gordon (to be published).
35. E. W. Montroll, *J. Chem. Phys.*, **10**, 218 (1942); **11**, 481 (1943).
36. M. Blackman, in *Handbuch der Physik*, S. Flügge, Ed., Springer, Berlin, 1955, Vol. 71, p. 325; P. C. Fine, *Phys. Rev.*, **55**, 355 (1939).
37. Ref. 16, p. 31.
38. H. S. Wall, *Analytic Theory of Continued Fractions*, Van Nostrand, Princeton, N.J., 1948.
39. F. J. Dyson, *Phys. Rev.*, **92**, 1331 (1953).
40. H. Mori, *Progr. Theoret. Phys. Kyoto*, **34**, 399 (1965).

A STOCHASTIC THEORY OF LINE SHAPE

RYOGO KUBO

Department of Physics, University of Tokyo, Japan

CONTENTS

I. INTRODUCTION

Some years ago I gave a lecture on the present subject in the first Scottish Summer School.[1] In this article, we shall begin with a brief review of the basic concepts as treated in that lecture, then discuss a few examples of applications, with some generalizations, to physical and chemical problems, and finally comment on some points which are left for future studies.

Shapes or profiles of spectral lines are often very important for obtaining information about the physical system under observation. Thus a spectral profile can tell us the state of a stellar atmosphere, or it can be used as diagnostic for a plasma. The line shape of an NMR spectrum may disclose the internal motion of nuclei in a molecular system. The information thus obtained is admittedly not extremely detailed, but it may be very useful particularly when combined with other information, and often it is the only data available.

As is well known by now, a line shape function $I(\omega)$ is the Fourier transform of the correlation function of a physical variable, for example, a dipole moment of a molecule or an atom, or a magnetic moment of a spin. Thus,

$$I(\omega) = \frac{1}{2\pi} \int_{-\infty}^{\infty} \langle x^*(0)x(t) \rangle \exp\left[-i\omega t\right] dt / \langle x^* x \rangle \qquad (1)$$

where x^* is complex conjugate to x if, as is sometimes convenient, x is conveniently chosen to be complex. Here the motion of the moment x of the system is considered to be a stochastic process induced by the perturbations that arise from the interaction of the system with its environment. Generally the environment consists of a great number of atoms or molecules which move in a complicated fashion; the perturbations it causes can be regarded as stochastic. Thus, the stochastic motion of $x(t)$ is generated by a basic process which represents the interaction. The average denoted by $\langle \ \rangle$ in Eq. (1) means an average over the ensemble of this basic process. The simplest example is given by the equation

$$x(t) = i\Omega(t)x(t) \tag{2}$$

where $x(t)$, for instance, is the coordinate of an oscillator, with the frequency $\Omega(t)$ modulated by the random interaction with the environment. Throughout the present paper, the origin of the frequency ω is chosen at the center of the spectral distribution. This means that $\Omega(t)$ in Eq. (2) denotes the random part of the frequency, the constant part being subtracted; namely, we assume that

$$\langle \Omega(t) \rangle = 0$$

Equation (2) is a stochastic equation defining the process $x(t)$ in terms of a given process $\Omega(t)$. If complete knowledge of the derived process $x(t)$ could be obtained, one would be able to reconstruct the original process $\Omega(t)$. The line shape, however, only gives the correlation function of x, and so the information available about the process $\Omega(t)$ is necessarily limited. This means, at the same time, that there exist some general properties of the derived process of the type $x(t)$ of such generality that the details of the basic process are irrelevant. For example, we can generally say that the important elements in Eq. (2) are the amplitude or the variance of $\Omega(t)$ and its coherence. The variance may be characterized by

$$\Delta = \langle \Omega^2 \rangle^{1/2} \tag{3}$$

and the coherence by the correlation time τ_c defined by

$$\tau_c = \int_0^\infty \frac{\langle \Omega(0)\Omega(t) \rangle \, dt}{\Delta^2} \tag{4}$$

If the condition

$$\Delta\tau_c \gg 1 \tag{5}$$

is fulfilled, the modulation of the frequency is *slow*, and if

$$\Delta\tau_c \ll 1 \tag{6}$$

then the modulation is *fast*. In the fast modulation case, the spectrum shows the phenomena of *motional narrowing*. The line shape becomes sharp with a Lorentzian form. In the opposite limit of slow modulation, the line shape is a direct reflection of the random distribution of Ω.

The main purpose of this paper is to discuss similar problems which are generalizations of Eq. (2), in order to obtain an understanding of some of the general features of line shapes under various conditions; these conditions are characterized by the relative magnitudes of a few physical parameters relevant for the basic process.

II. RANDOM FREQUENCY MODULATION[2-4]

Here we will summarize some known results for the simplest example of random frequency modulation as defined by Eq. (2). Let us assume that the process $\Omega(t)$ in Eq. (2) is a *projection* of a Markovian process characterized by the evolution operator Γ. This is possible in principle, because the dynamical motion of the environment can be described in terms of a Liouville operator. The set of variables defining the Markovian process is designated by λ. If the variable Ω itself is Markovian, λ consists only of Ω, but in general it has to be supplemented by additional variables to complete the set. Let the function $W(x, \lambda, t)$ be the probability or the probability density for finding the random variables x and λ at the respective values at the time t. Then a systematic method of treating the problem, Eq. (2), is to rewrite it in the form

$$\frac{\partial}{\partial t} W(x, \lambda, t) = -i \frac{\partial}{\partial x} (\Omega x W) + \Gamma W \qquad (7)$$

which may be called the *stochastic Liouville equation.*[5] The simplification made in Eq. (7) is that this Liouville or evolution operator is independent of the motion of x; in other words, the reaction of x to the environment is ignored.

If the initial condition,

$$W(x, \lambda, 0) = \delta(x - x') \, \delta(\lambda, \lambda') \qquad (8)$$

is imposed, the solution of Eq. (7) is the transition probability from the initial state (x', λ') to the final state (x, λ) in the time interval $(0, t)$. It is convenient to write this probability as

$$(x, \lambda \,|\, W(t)| \, x', \lambda')$$

Assuming the process to be stationary, the evolution operator Γ is independent of the time. Furthermore, we assume that the process $\{\lambda\}$ has a unique equilibrium which is defined by the equation

$$\Gamma P_0(\lambda) = 0 \tag{9}$$

The normalized correlation function of $x(t)$,

$$\phi(t) = \langle x^*(0)x(t)\rangle/\langle x^*x\rangle$$

is now easily seen to be given by

$$\phi(t) = \int dx \sum_\lambda \sum_{\lambda'} x(x, \lambda \,|\, W(t)|\, x', \lambda')x'^* P_0(\lambda')/|x'|^2 \tag{10}$$

which may be written in a more symbolic form as

$$\phi(t) = (0|\,X(t)\,|0) = \sum_\lambda \sum_{\lambda'} (\lambda\,|X(t)|\lambda')P_0(\lambda') \tag{11}$$

Here we define, in analogy to Dirac's notation the zero (equilibrium) bra and ket vectors,

$$(0\,|\,\lambda') = 1, \qquad (\lambda'\,|\,0) = P_0(\lambda') \tag{12}$$

which satisfy the equations, $(0\,|\,\Gamma = 0, \qquad \Gamma\,|0) = 0$ and are normalized according to

$$(0\,|\,0) = \sum_{\lambda'} (0\,|\,\lambda')(\lambda'\,|\,0) = \sum_{\lambda'} P_0(\lambda') = 1$$

In Eq. (11), $X(t)$ is a kind of conditional expectation defined by the matrix

$$(\lambda\,|\,X(t)\,|\lambda') = \int dx \frac{x(x, \lambda\,|\,W(t)|\,x', \lambda')x'^*}{|x'|^2} \tag{13}$$

The equation for $X(t)$ is obtained from Eq. (7) by multiplying by x and then integrating over x. Thus we find the equation

$$\dot{X}(t) = i\Omega X + \Gamma X \tag{14}$$

with the initial condition,

$$X(0) = \delta(\lambda, \lambda') = \mathbf{1}$$

Note that Eq. (14) is a matrix equation for $(\lambda\,|X(t)|\,\lambda')$. By the Laplace transformation,

$$\int_0^\infty \exp\,[-st]X(t)\,dt \equiv X[s] \tag{15}$$

Eq. (14) becomes

$$(s - i\Omega - \Gamma)X[s] = \mathbf{1} \tag{16}$$

This has the obvious solution

$$X[s] = (s - i\Omega - \Gamma)^{-1} \tag{17}$$

The line shape function $I(\omega)$, Eq. (1), is then given by

$$I(\omega) = \frac{1}{\pi} \text{Re} \, (0| X[i\omega]|0) \tag{18}$$

$$= \lim_{\varepsilon \to 0+} \frac{1}{\pi} \text{Re} \, (0| X[i\omega + \varepsilon]|0)$$

where the second expression is a more exact definition of the first one.

III. TWO SIMPLE EXAMPLES

First we will discuss two simple examples of the theory summarized in the previous section. They can be applied to a number of problems of physics and chemistry and also are very helpful for obtaining a general understanding of our subject. These simple examples are (a) a two-state-jump modulation and (b) a Gaussian modulation. [6,7]

In the first example, the frequency Ω is assumed to take only two values,

$$\Omega = \pm\omega_1 \quad \text{or} \quad \Omega = \begin{pmatrix} \omega_1 & 0 \\ 0 & -\omega_1 \end{pmatrix} \tag{19}$$

corresponding to two states, say a and b, of the environment. Transitions between two states are described in terms of the transition matrix,

$$\Gamma = \frac{\gamma}{2} \begin{bmatrix} -1 & 1 \\ 1 & -1 \end{bmatrix} \tag{20}$$

which has the equilibrium bra and ket vectors,

$$|0) = \begin{pmatrix} 1 \\ 1 \end{pmatrix}, \qquad (0| = (\tfrac{1}{2}, \tfrac{1}{2}) \tag{21}$$

We assume, for simplicity, equal equilibrium population; generalization to unequal equilibrium populations is straightforward.

Thus Eq. (14) takes the form,

$$\dot{X}(t) = \left[i \begin{pmatrix} \omega_1 & 0 \\ 0 & -\omega_1 \end{pmatrix} + \frac{\gamma}{2} \begin{pmatrix} -1 & 1 \\ 1 & -1 \end{pmatrix} \right] X(t) \tag{22}$$

and Eq. (17) becomes

$$X[s] = \begin{pmatrix} s - i\omega_1 + \dfrac{\gamma}{2} & -\dfrac{\gamma}{2} \\[2mm] -\dfrac{\gamma}{2} & s + i\omega_1 + \dfrac{\gamma}{2} \end{pmatrix}^{-1} \tag{23}$$

The line shape function is easily found to be

$$I(\omega) = \frac{1}{\pi} \frac{\omega_1{}^2}{(\omega^2 - \omega_1{}^2)^2 + \omega^2\gamma^2} \tag{24}$$

In the second example of a Gaussian modulation, the frequency Ω takes continuous values and is a Gaussian process. If further it is assumed to be Markovian, the Doob theorem[8] tells us that its correlation function has a simple exponential decay,

$$\langle \Omega(0)\Omega(t) \rangle = \Delta^2 \exp[-\gamma |t|\} \tag{25}$$

It is also described by a Fokker-Planck equation defined by the evolution operator,

$$\Gamma = \gamma \frac{\partial}{\partial\Omega} \left(\Delta^2 \frac{\partial}{\partial\Omega} + \Omega \right) \tag{26}$$

for which the equilibrium bra and ket vectors are

$$|0) \equiv f_0(\Omega) = \frac{1}{(2\pi)^{1/2} \Delta} \exp\left[-\Omega^2/2\,\Delta^2\right], \qquad (0| = 1 \tag{27}$$

Thus Eq. (14) takes the form

$$\frac{\partial}{\partial t} X(\Omega, t) = i\Omega X + \gamma \frac{\partial}{\partial\Omega} \left(\Delta^2 \frac{\partial}{\partial\Omega} + \Omega \right) X \tag{28}$$

and Eq. (18) for the line shape function gives

$$I(\omega) = \frac{1}{\pi} \operatorname{Re} \int_{-\infty}^{\infty} d\Omega \frac{1}{i(\omega - \Omega) - \Gamma} \frac{\exp|-\Omega^2/2\,\Delta^2|}{(2\pi\,\Delta^2)^{1/2}} \tag{29}$$

This equation can be written as

$$I(\omega) = \frac{1}{\pi} \operatorname{Re} \int_{-\infty}^{\infty} d\Omega f(\Omega, \omega) \tag{30}$$

where $f(\Omega, \omega)$ is the solution of the equation

$$\left[(i\omega - \Omega) + \gamma \frac{\partial}{\partial \Omega}\left(\Delta^2 \frac{\partial}{\partial \Omega} + \Omega\right)\right] f(\Omega, \omega) = f_0(\Omega) \qquad (31)$$

It is more convenient to rewrite these equations by introducing the transformation,

$$f = \exp\left[-\frac{\Omega^2}{4\Delta^2}\right] g$$

$$\bar{\Gamma} = \exp\left[\frac{\Omega^2}{4\Delta^2}\right]\Gamma \exp\left[-\frac{\Omega^2}{4\Delta^2}\right] = \gamma\left\{\Delta^2 \frac{\partial^2}{\partial \Omega^2} - \frac{\Omega^2}{4\Delta^2} + \frac{1}{2}\right\} \qquad (32)$$

Eqs. (30) and (31) then become

$$I(\omega) = \frac{1}{\pi} \operatorname{Re} \int_{-\infty}^{\infty} d\Omega \exp\left[-\frac{\Omega^2}{4\Delta^2}\right] g(\Omega, \omega) \qquad (33)$$

$$[i(\omega - \Omega) + \bar{\Gamma}]g(\Omega, \omega) = g_0(\Omega) \qquad (34)$$

where the operator $\bar{\Gamma}$ has the harmonic oscillator eigenfunctions as its eigenfunctions with the eigenvalues $n\gamma$ ($n = 0, 1, 2, \ldots$). On the right-hand side of Eq. (34), the function $g_0(\Omega)$ is the zeroth eigenfunction of $\bar{\Gamma}$. When the function $g(\Omega), \omega)$ is expanded in terms of the eigenfunctions of Γ Eq. (34) becomes a set of infinite algebraic equations; this form is useful for numerical computations.

In this Gaussian modulation case, the normalized correlation function of the moment $x(t)$ is given by

$$\frac{\langle x^*(0)x(t)\rangle}{\langle x^*x\rangle} = \exp\left\{-\int_0^t dt_1 \int_0^{t_1} dt_2 \langle \Omega(t_1)\Omega(t_2)\rangle\right\}$$

$$= \exp\left\{-\Delta^2 \int_0^t d\tau(t - \tau)e^{-\gamma\tau}\right\}$$

$$= \exp\left\{-\frac{\Delta^2}{\gamma^2}(e^{-\gamma t} - 1 + \gamma t)\right\} \qquad (35)$$

The Gaussian assumption yields the first equality. Assumption (25) is used in the second expression on the right-hand side. Thus the line shape function $I(\omega)$ can also be written as

$$I(\omega) = \frac{1}{\pi} \operatorname{Re} \int_0^{\infty} \exp\left\{-\frac{\Delta^2}{\gamma^2}(e^{-\gamma t} - 1 + \gamma t) - i\omega t\right\} dt \qquad (36)$$

It should be mentioned that the line shape function $I(\omega)$ can also be expressed as a continued fraction[9]; namely

$$I(\omega) = \frac{1}{\pi} \cfrac{1}{i\omega + \cfrac{\Delta^2}{i\omega + \gamma + \cfrac{2\Delta^2}{i\omega + 2\gamma + \cdots}}} \qquad (37)$$

This is most convenient for computer calculation.

Figure 1 shows the line shape for the two-state-jump modulation case.

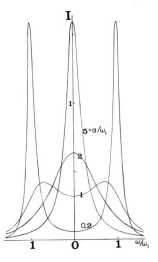

Fig. 1. Line shape for the two-state-jump model. The frequencies are in units of ω_1, $\pm\omega_1$ being the frequencies of the two states. The numbers on curves indicate the modulation rate, $\alpha = \gamma/\omega_1$.

Intensity curves $I(\omega)$ are plotted against the frequency measured in units of ω_1 for various values of the parameter

$$\alpha = \gamma/\omega_1$$

In slow modulation,

$$\alpha \ll 1$$

the shape function is peaked around two resonance frequencies, ω_1 and $-\omega_1$, the width of each line being $\gamma/2$. When the modulation becomes faster, the peaks are broadened, approach each other, then merge into a single peak, and finally, in the fast modulation limit,

$$\alpha \gg 1$$

a sharp Lorentzian line appears at the center.

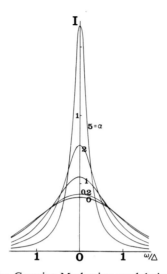

Fig. 2. Line shape for the Gaussian-Markovian modulation, for modulation rates, $\alpha = 5, 2, 1, 0.2, 0$.

Figure 2 is the line shape for a Gaussian modulation. In the slow modulation limit,

$$\alpha = \gamma/\Delta \ll 1$$

the line is Gaussian, reflecting the distribution of Ω itself. In the fast modulation limit,

$$\alpha \gg 1$$

the line becomes Lorentzian with the width equal to $\Delta^2\gamma$. Between the two limits, the line shape shows *motional narrowing* as the modulation rate increases.

IV. COLLAPSE OF AN NMR MULTIPLET

The line shape of an NMR spectrum often shows remarkable changes when physical or chemical conditions are varied. Narrowing of a doublet represented by Eq. (24) is observed in many cases. Here we consider a slightly more complicated example of a proton resonance coupled with another nucleus through an interaction of the type,

$$J\mathbf{I}_p \cdot \mathbf{I} \tag{38}$$

where $\mathbf{I}_p$ is the proton spin and $\mathbf{I}$ is the spin of a coupled nucleus.[10, 11] In the presence of a constant magnetic field, the proton resonance spectrum consists of a multiplet of $2I + 1$ lines corresponding to the $2I + 1$ states $(m = -I, \ldots, I)$ of the spin I. If there exists a relaxation process, for example, a quadrupole coupling of I to the lattice, transitions will be induced among the states causing random jumps of the effective field $JI_z = Jm$ acting on the proton, and hence jumps of the resonance frequencies

$$\Omega_m = mJ/\hbar, \ m = -I, \ldots, I$$

Under the assumption of quadrupole relaxation, the form of the transition matrix in Eq. (1) is easily determined. The transition rate is characterized by the time constant

$$\alpha = (e^2 qQ)^2 \tau_c / \hbar^2$$

where $e^2 qQ$ is the magnitude of the quadrupole interaction and τ_c is its correlation time. Thus the line shape function $I(\omega)$, Eq. (18), is obtained by first solving the equation[12]

$$i(\omega - \Omega_m)X_m - \sum_{m'} \Gamma_{mm'} X_{m'} = 1 \tag{39}$$

and then by computing the expression,

$$I(\omega) = \frac{1}{\pi} \text{Re} \sum_{m=-I}^{I} \frac{X_m(\omega)}{(2I + 1)} \tag{40}$$

The modulation of the proton field is *slow* if

$$\alpha = h\gamma/J = (e^2 qQ)^2 \tau_c / Jh \ll 1$$

and is *fast* if

$$\alpha \gg 1$$

In the first case, the multiplet skeleton is preserved. As the parameter α increases, the multiplet collapse proceeds. In Figures 3 and 4 there are shown examples of computed curves and the corresponding spectra

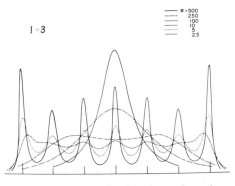

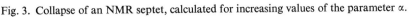

Fig. 3. Collapse of an NMR septet, calculated for increasing values of the parameter α.

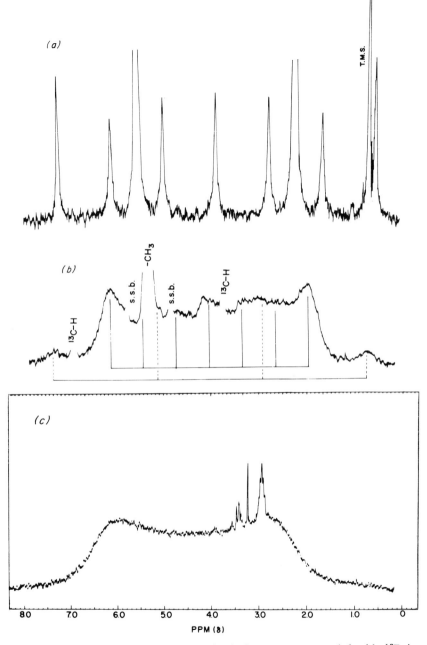

Fig. 4. Observed proton septet spectra, for hydrogen atoms coupled with ^{10}B in (a) lithium borohydride, (b) trimethylamineborane, and (c) N-tri(methyl-d_3) borazine.

observed for protons coupled to ^{10}B in various compounds[13]; Figure 4*a*
is an observation for lithium borohydride, Figure 4*b* for trimethylamina-
borane, and Figure 4*c* for *N*-tri(methyl-d_3) borazine. In the first and second
examples, ^{11}B—H quartets are superposed, and in the third case there is
a group of impurity peaks. The ^{10}B—H septets in these three observations correspond to the calculated curves with $\alpha = 2.5$, 10, and 100,
respectively.

V. LOW FIELD SPIN RESONANCE[9,14]

In a condensed system, the local field on a magnetic spin can be considered as a stochastic process. If a constant magnetic field H_0 is present in
the *z*-direction, the local field $\mathbf{H}(t)$ can be decomposed into the parallel
and the perpendicular components. If the constant field is strong enough,
this decomposition is meaningful; the parallel component $H_z(t)$ causes
adiabatic shifts of the resonance frequency, whereas the perpendicular
component $H_\perp(t)$ produces nonadiabatic effects.[6] If only the adiabatic
part is considered, the problem is just that treated in Section II, and if the
local field $H_z(t)$ is assumed to be a Gaussian process, then the Gaussian
model of Section III can be adopted.

When the constant field is weak and the fluctuating field is comparable
to or even larger than the constant field, the above decomposition becomes
meaningless. There is no way of distinguishing between the adiabatic and
nonadiabatic effects. In order to obtain an understanding of this rather
complex situation, we have examined a stochastic model,[14] extending the
theory in Section II. The stochastic equation of motion of a spin in a
random local field is written as

$$\dot{\mathbf{m}}(t) = (\mathbf{\Omega}_0 + \mathbf{\Omega}(t)) \times \mathbf{m} \qquad (41)$$

where $\mathbf{\Omega}_0$ represents the constant magnetic field and $\mathbf{\Omega}(t)$ the random field,
the gyromagnetic ratio being included. The corresponding stochastic
Liouville equation takes the form,

$$\frac{\partial}{\partial t} W(\mathbf{m}, \lambda, t) = -(\mathbf{\Omega}_0 + \mathbf{\Omega}) \times \mathbf{m} \frac{\partial}{\partial \mathbf{m}} W + \Gamma W \qquad (42)$$

where, as before, λ is the set of random variables required to complete
$\mathbf{\Omega}(t)$ to a Markovian process and Γ is its evolution operator, a matrix with
respect to the variables λ. The equilibrium distribution $P_0(\lambda)$ is characterized by

$$\begin{aligned}
\Gamma|0) &= 0, & (\lambda|0) &\equiv P_0(\lambda) \\
(0|\Gamma &= 0, & (0|\lambda) &\equiv 1, & (0|0) &\equiv \sum_\lambda P_0(\lambda) = 1 \qquad (43)
\end{aligned}$$

Now the expectation of the moment at the time t is defined by

$$\mathbf{M}(\lambda, t) = \int W(\mathbf{m}, \lambda, t)\mathbf{m} \, d\mathbf{m} \tag{44}$$

this quantity obeys the equation,

$$\frac{\partial \mathbf{M}(\lambda, t)}{\partial t} = \{(\mathbf{\Omega}_0 + \mathbf{\Omega})x + \mathbf{\Gamma}\}\mathbf{M} \tag{45}$$

with the initial condition,

$$\mathbf{M}(\lambda, 0) = \mathbf{m}'P_0(\lambda). \tag{46}$$

More explicitly we write Eq. (45) as

$$\left(\frac{\partial}{\partial t} - \Gamma\right)M_x + (\Omega_z + \omega_0)M_y - \Omega_y M_z = 0$$

$$-(\Omega_z + \omega_0)M_x + \left(\frac{\partial}{\partial t} - \Gamma\right)M_y + \Omega_x M_z = 0$$

$$\Omega_y M_x - \Omega_x M_y + \left(\frac{\partial}{\partial t} - \Gamma\right)M_z = 0, \tag{47}$$

where we have chosen the z axis along the constant magnetic field and denoted the corresponding Zeeman frequency by ω_0. Equation (47), with the initial condition of Eq. (46), can be solved by Laplace transformation. The line shape functions are found by inserting the result into a form Eq. (18) suitably generalized to apply to this case. The longitudinal and the transverse spectral functions are then given by

$$I_{zz}(\omega) = \frac{1}{\pi} \text{Re} \int d\mathbf{\Omega} f_{zz}(\mathbf{\Omega}, \omega) \tag{48}$$

and

$$I_{xx}(\omega) = \frac{1}{\pi} \text{Re} \int d\mathbf{\Omega} f_{xx}(\mathbf{\Omega}, \omega) \tag{49}$$

where $f_{zz}(\mathbf{\Omega}, \omega)$ and $f_{xx}(\mathbf{\Omega}, \omega)$ are determined by the equations,

$$\left\{i\omega - \Gamma + \tfrac{1}{2}(\Omega_x + i\Omega_y) \frac{1}{i\omega - \Gamma + i(\Omega_z + \omega_0)} (\Omega_x - i\Omega_y)\right.$$

$$\left. + \tfrac{1}{2}(\Omega_x - i\Omega_y) \frac{1}{i\omega - \Gamma - i(\Omega_z + \omega_0)} (\Omega_x + i\Omega_y)\right\} f_{zz}(\mathbf{\Omega}, \omega) = P_0(\mathbf{\Omega}) \tag{50}$$

and

$$\left\{ i\omega - \Gamma + \tfrac{1}{2}(\Omega_y + i(\Omega_z + \omega_0)) \frac{1}{i\omega - \Gamma + i\Omega_x} (\Omega_y - i(\Omega_z + \omega_0)) \right.$$

$$\left. + \tfrac{1}{2}(\Omega_y - i(\Omega_z + \omega_0)) \frac{1}{i\omega - \Gamma - i\Omega_x} (\Omega_y + i(\Omega_z + \omega_0)) \right\} f_{xx}(\Omega, \omega)$$

$$= P_0(\Omega) \quad (51)$$

If we assume a Gaussian-Markovian process for the random field, the evolution operator in Eq. (42) becomes

$$\Gamma = \frac{\partial}{\partial \Omega} \left(\Delta^2 \frac{\partial}{\partial \Omega} + \Omega \right) \tag{52}$$

which is a three-dimensional version of the expression (26); Eqs. (48)–(51) are generalizations of Eqs. (30) and (31). Here we summarize qualitative results of the calculation. Some examples of calculated line shapes are shown in Figures 5–7. Figure 5 shows zero-field resonance curves. The

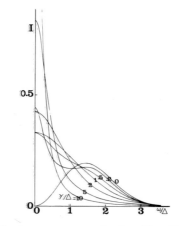

Fig. 5. Zero-field spin resonance spectra for $\gamma/\Delta = 10, 5, 2, 1, 0.5, 0.2, 0$.

curve marked by ∞ is the static modulation limit ($\gamma = 0$) and consists of a delta function at the origin and a broad curve which reflects the distribution of the random field. In the narrowed limit of large γ, the two branches merge into a single peak around the center. For intermediate values of γ, the resonance is broad and may have two peaks or an extended shoulder. Figure 6 shows the longitudinal resonance for the case $\omega_0/\Delta = 3$. General behavior is similar to that of zero-field resonance. The main peak is at the

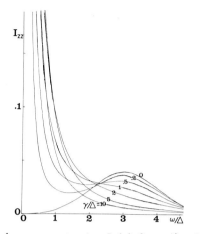

Fig. 6. Longitudinal spin resonance spectra, $I_{zz}(\omega)$, for $\omega_0/\Delta = 3$ and $\gamma/\Delta = 10, 5, 2, 1,$ 0.5, 0.2, 0.

origin and the satellite is around $\omega/\Delta \sim 3$. The satellite peak disappears as the modulation becomes faster. The transverse resonance curves are shown in Figure 7 for $\omega_0/\Delta \sim 1$. There, the main peak is around the Zeeman

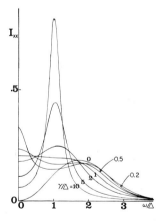

Fig. 7. Transverse spin resonance spectra, $I_{xx}(\omega)$, for $\omega_0/\Delta = 1$ and $\gamma/\Delta = 10, 5, 2, 1,$ 0.5, 0.2, 0.

frequency, around $\omega/\Delta \sim 1$ in the figure, while the satellite resonance is found near the center. The main peak grows as the modulation becomes faster, whereas the satellite peak decreases and finally disappears.

VI. SPECTRUM OF EXCITATIONS TO A DOUBLET
WITH A RANDOM MODULATION[15]

Consider an atomic system with a singlet ground state a and doublet excited states b, the members of which are denoted by b_1 and b_2. The Hamiltonian for the states (b_1, b_2) is assumed to be

$$H(t) = \begin{bmatrix} \omega_0 & \Omega(t) \\ \Omega(t) & -\omega_0 \end{bmatrix} \tag{53}$$

where the off-diagonal element Ω is supposed to be a random process with a vanishing average, i.e.,

$$\langle \Omega \rangle = 0$$

This random modulation may be caused, for example, by a coupling of the electronic states to the lattice vibrations. The Hamiltonian for the state a is just a constant and may be set, for convenience, to zero.

Now we ask the excitation spectrum from the state a to the excited states. The (un-normalized) shape function is given by

$$I(\omega) = \frac{1}{\pi} \, \mathrm{Re} \int_0^\infty dt \, \exp\left[-i\omega t\right] \langle (a|\mu(0)\mu(t)|a) \rangle_{\mathrm{av}} \tag{54}$$

Here μ is the dipole moment with the matrix elements,

$$(a|\mu|b_1) = (b_1|\mu|a) = \mu_1$$

$$(a|\mu|b_2) = (b_2|\mu|a) = \mu_2$$

Now, the Heisenberg equation of motion for $\mu(t)$,

$$\dot{\mu}(t) = \frac{1}{i}(\mu H - H\mu) \tag{55}$$

takes the form,

$$(b'|\dot{\mu}(t)|a) = i \sum_{b''} (b'|H(t)|b'')(b''|\mu(t)|a)$$

We introduce here the transformation matrix $v(t)$ defined by

$$(b'|\mu(t)|a) = \sum_{b''} (b'|v(t)|b'')(b''|\mu|a) \tag{56}$$

Then the matrix $v(t)$ obeys the equation of motion,

$$\dot{v}(t) = iH(t)v(t) \tag{57}$$

with the initial condition

$$v(0) = \mathbf{1}$$

Equation (57) is the stochastic equation of motion for $v(t)$, in which the matrix element $\Omega(t)$ is a random process. This is similar to Eq. (2). This may be written as a stochastic Liouville equation in the form

$$\frac{\partial}{\partial t} W(v, \lambda, t) = -\sum_{jl} \frac{\partial}{\partial v_{jl}} i(H(\Omega)v)_{jl} W + \Gamma W \qquad (58)$$

where Γ is the evolution operator for the set of random variables λ that complete Ω to a Markovian process. Corresponding to Eq. (14), we have the equation

$$\dot{V}(t) = iH(\Omega)V + \Gamma V \qquad (59)$$

where the matrix $V(t)$ is defined by the equation,

$$V_{jl}(t) = \int \cdots \int (\Pi \, dv_{mn}) v_{jl}(v, \lambda \,|W(t)|\, v', \lambda'), \qquad v' = 1 \qquad (60)$$

which is a conditional expectation of the matrix $v(t)$. The line shape function (54) is then written as

$$I_c(\omega) = \frac{1}{\pi} \operatorname{Re} \int_0^\infty dt \exp\left[-i\omega t\right](0|\sum_{jl} \mu_j V_{jl}(t)\mu_1 |0) \qquad (61)$$

or as

$$I(\omega) = \frac{1}{\pi} \operatorname{Re} \sum_{jl} \mu_j(0|\, V_{jl}[i\omega]\, |0)\mu_l \qquad (62)$$

where $V[i\omega]$ is the Laplace transform of $V(t)$; it obeys the equation

$$(s - iH + \Gamma)V[s] = 1 \qquad (63)$$

Remember that the vector space for the equation is the direct product of two spaces, the space of the electronic states and the space of the random variables λ. It is obvious that the above equation can be applied not only to a doublet but to any multiplet as long as the ground state is a singlet.

Let us now consider the case where the dipole moment couples only one of the excited states, say b_1, to the ground state; namely

$$\mu_1 \neq 0, \quad \text{and} \quad \mu_2 = 0 \qquad (64)$$

As another simplification, we assume that the modulation Ω takes only two values $\pm\omega_1$. This is a generalization of the two-state jump model mentioned in Section III. The basic space for Eq. (63) is then 2×2 dimension. It is convenient to write Eq. (63) as

$$(s - i\omega_0)\xi - i\Omega\eta + \Gamma\xi = \xi_0 \qquad (65)$$
$$(s + i\omega_0)\eta - i\Omega\xi + \Gamma\eta = \eta_0$$

where ξ is the component for the state b_1 and η that for the state b_2, each being vectors with two components corresponding to $\Omega = \pm \omega_1$. Solving Eq. (65) for ξ by setting $\xi_0 = 1$, $\eta_0 = 0$, we obtain the element $V_{11}[i\omega]$ in the form

$$V_{11}[i\omega] = \cfrac{1}{i(\omega + \omega_0) - \Gamma + \Omega \cfrac{1}{i(\omega - \omega_0) - \Gamma} \Omega} \tag{66}$$

where Ω and Γ are operators in the space of the variables λ. For our two-state-jump model they are given by Eqs. (19) and (20). By the assumption (64), the expression (62) is easily found to be

$$I(\omega) = \frac{1}{\pi} \frac{\gamma \omega_1^2}{(\omega_0^2 + \omega_1^2 - \omega^2)^2 + (\omega - \omega_0)^2 \gamma^2} \tag{67}$$

In the static limit ($\gamma = 0$), which may usually be called the adiabatic case, the perturbation Ω is constant ($\pm \omega_1$) and the excited states are split into a doublet with the energies

$$\varepsilon = \pm (\omega_0^2 + \omega_1^2)^{1/2}$$

The excitation spectrum consists of two sharp lines. The lower line at $\omega = -(\omega_0^2 + \omega_1^2)^{1/2}$ borrows its intensity from the upper line thanks to the mixing caused by the perturbation.

When the modulation becomes faster, i.e., γ increases, the adiabatic approximation becomes worse. In the first stage, each line will broaden; at the same time the lower line loses its intensity. If the modulation is very fast, the random modulation is averaged out, and the spectrum is narrowed to a sharp line at the unshifted position with the full intensity. In this problem, however, there are essentially two parameters, ω_1/ω_0 and γ/ω_0, which determine the condition for narrowing, so that the narrowing process is not simple. If γ is small and the condition

$$4\left(\frac{1}{3}\left(1 + \frac{\omega_1^2}{\omega_0^2}\right) + \frac{1}{6}\frac{\gamma^2}{\omega_0^2}\right)^{3/2} > \frac{\gamma^2}{\omega_0^2} \tag{68}$$

is satisfied, two peaks are noticeable. As γ becomes larger and the sign of the above inequality is reversed, the spectrum is singly peaked, but there remains a long shoulder extending to lower frequencies. As γ becomes even larger, this shoulder disappears. Figure 8 gives a few examples of the calculated spectra.

Similar calculations can be made for the continuous modulation case. If the process $\Omega(t)$ is Gaussian and Markovian, the operator Γ takes the

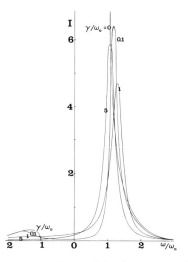

Fig. 8. Excitation spectra to a doublet modulated by a two-state-jump process; for $\omega_1/\omega_0 = 1$ and $\gamma/\omega_0 = 5, 1, 0.1, 0$.

form given by Eq. (26). The line shape function is given by Eq. (62), where we insert, for example, Eq. (66) and the equilibrium state vectors (27). The line shape functions can thus be calculated by using transformations similar to those used in Section III.

Figure 9 shows some examples of the spectrum. In the static limit, the

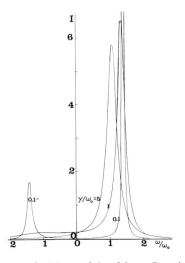

Fig. 9. Excitation spectra to a doublet modulated by a Gaussian-Markovian process; for $\omega_1/\omega_0 = 1$ and $\gamma/\omega_0 = 5, 1, 0.1, 0$.

spectrum consists of two branches; one in the region $\omega > \omega_0$ having an infinite peak at ω_0 and the other in the region $\omega < -\omega_0$. This static spectrum is an image of the Gaussian distribution of Ω. As the modulation becomes faster, this adiabatic picture loses its meaning. The process of narrowing is qualitatively the same as that in the two-state-jump model given by Eq. (67).

VII. RANDOM STARK MODULATION OF A HYDROGEN ATOM[16]

In a gaseous plasma, the electric field fluctuates in space and time as the ions and electrons move in a complicated fashion. If a hydrogen atom is put into such a plasma, it serves as a probe to detect this fluctuating field. The $2s$ and $2p$ states of a hydrogen atom are nearly degenerate, but they are split by the Stark effect in the presence of an electric field. The absorption or emission spectrum due to transitions between the $1s$ and $2p$ levels of a hydrogen atom is thus broadened by the random fluctuation of the electric field. This is a well-known example of pressure broadening,[17,18] but a complication in this problem is that the modulation of the electric field affects not only the spacing of split energy levels but also the direction of the quantization axis. Thus the simple-minded adiabatic approach cannot be used.

From our point of view, this problem is, however, quite the same as that treated in the previous section. We take the excited states to be the four states, $2s$, $2p_x$, $2p_y$, and $2p_z$. The Hamiltonian in this subspace is written as

$$H(t) = \begin{pmatrix} 0 & \Omega_x & \Omega_y & \Omega_z \\ \Omega_x & 0 & 0 & 0 \\ \Omega_y & 0 & 0 & 0 \\ \Omega_z & 0 & 0 & 0 \end{pmatrix} \tag{69}$$

where

$$\Omega = -\mu' E(t) \tag{70}$$

is the electric field times the factor μ' representing the matrix elements of the dipole moment; namely

$$\mu' = (2s|\mu_x|2p_x) = (2s|\mu_y|2p_y) = (2s|\mu_z|2p_z)$$

If the spectrum is observed for radiation linearly polarized in the x direction, the dipole moment in Eq. (54) is its x component, μ_x, which has a matrix element between $1s$ and $2p_x$ states. Thus, Eq. (61) now reads

$$I(\omega) = \frac{1}{\pi} \text{Re} \, (0| V_{xx}[i\omega] |0) \tag{71}$$

where the suffix x means $2p_x$. Instead of Eq. (62), it is more convenient to solve the equation,

$$(i\omega - iH(\Omega) + \Gamma)\Psi = \Psi_0$$

by using the expansion

$$\Psi = U|2s) + X|2p_x) + Y|2p_y) + Z|2p_z)$$

and by imposing the initial condition

$$\Psi_0 = |2p_x)$$

When the components, U, Y, and Z are eliminated, we obtain the solution for X, which is identified with the element $V_{xx}[i\omega]$ in Eq. (71). In this way, the line shape function is found to be

$$I(\omega) = \frac{1}{\pi} \operatorname{Re} (0| \frac{1}{i\omega} \left\{ 1 - \Omega \frac{1}{i\omega + \Gamma - \Omega \dfrac{1}{i\omega + \Gamma} \Omega} \Omega \right\} |0) \qquad (72)$$

where $(0|$ and $|0)$ are, as before, the equilibrium bra and ket states for the operator Γ.

The hardest part of the problem is the determination of the process $E(t)$ or more precisely the reduction of the complete Markovian process to a tractable process. The simplest approximation to the equilibrium distribution is the Holtzmark distribution which ignores the interaction between ions and electrons.[19] Corrections can be made in successive approximations. Much less is known, however, about the temporal behavior of $E(t)$. For practical purposes, an extreme limit is commonly assumed.[17] The motion of ions is considered to be slow and the electric field E_i produced by ions is regarded as *static*. On the other hand, electrons are moving very fast so that the electric field E_e produced by electrons changes very *fast*. Therefore, this part of the electric field is treated as a perturbation causing transition between the quantum levels of a hydrogen atom split by the static field E_i. Strictly speaking, this is not very accurate, because there are also slow components in the electron field $E_e(t)$ which cannot be treated in the extreme narrowing approximation.

Here, we shall not go any further into the analysis of this sort. Instead, we show a few examples of line shape functions calculated by Eq. (72) for the Gaussian models, which are characterized by the operator Γ given by Eq. (52). The Gaussian models are not very adequate for the electric field in a plasma, as is seen by the fact that the Holtzmark distribution is far from Gaussian. Still, it may serve to give one an understanding of the

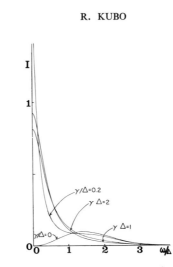

Fig. 10. Random Stark broadening of a hydrogen atom in a Gaussian random field with different modulation speeds ($\gamma/\Delta = 2$, 1, 0.2, 0).

general character of our problem. Figure 10 shows the spectral distribution for a few values of the parameter γ/Δ corresponding to different degrees of narrowing. In the slow modulation case, there exist a sharp peak at the center and two broad side peaks. These side peaks are the image of the distribution of the electric field strength. As the modulation becomes faster, the spectrum merges into a single peak. In Figure 11, two kinds of electric fields are assumed; one is a static field corresponding to the ion field, and the other is a nonstatic field due to the electrons. Both fields are assumed

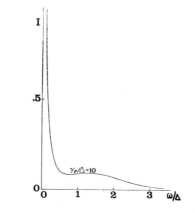

Fig. 11. Random Stark broadening of a hydrogen atom in the superposition of a static Gaussian field E_i and a fluctuating Gaussian field E_e. The modulation rate of E_e is as large as $\gamma_e/\omega = 10$.

to be Gaussian with the same variance. The modulation of electron field is fast, the parameter γ/Δ being chosen as 10. The static field determines the structure, a central peak and two side peaks, which are broadened by electron impacts.

VIII. LINE SHAPE OF MÖSSBAUER SPECTRA

Let us consider, for example, the Mössbauer spectra of ^{57}Fe in a solid. A ^{57}Fe nucleus may feel spin interactions with its neighboring nuclei, or a quadrupole interaction with the electric field gradient produced by the motion of surrounding ions. In the process of gamma-ray emission, these interactions give rise to perturbations of the excited nuclear states as well as to the ground states. The line shape of a Mössbauer multiplet can be treated by the present theory if these interactions are considered as random modulations. The line shape function is now given by

$$I_c(\omega) = \frac{1}{\pi} \operatorname{Re} \int_0^\infty dt \exp\left[-i\omega\right] \sum_{a'} \sum_{b'} \langle (a'|\mu|b')(b'|\mu(t)|a') \rangle_{av} \qquad (73)$$

where μ is the dipole moment for the gamma-ray transition. We ignore the natural width in this expression because we shall mostly be interested in broadenings larger than the natural widths. But it may be included, if necessary.

The motion of the dipole moment obeys Eq. (56), which is written as

$$(b'|\mu(t)|a') = i\left\{ \sum_{b''} (b'|H(t)|b'')(b''|\mu(t)|a') - \sum_{a''} (b'|\mu(t)|a'')(a''|H(t)|a') \right\} \qquad (74)$$

As in Eq. (57), we introduce the transformation matrix $v(t)$, defined by

$$(b'|\mu(t)|a') = \sum_{a'} \sum_{b''} (a'b'|v(t)|a''b'')(b''|\mu|a'') \qquad (75)$$

with the initial condition,

$$v(0) = \mathbf{1}$$

Then we find the equation of motion,

$$(a'b'|\dot{v}(t)|a''b'') = i\left\{ \sum_{b'''} (b'|H(t)|b''')(a'b'''|v(t)|a''b'') \right.$$

$$\left. - \sum_{a'''} (a'''|H(t)|a')(a'''b'|v(t)|a''b'') \right\} \qquad (76)$$

or

$$\dot{v}(t) = i\overline{H}(t)v(t) \qquad (77)$$

where the modified Hamiltonian $\bar{H}(t)$ is defined by the explicit expressions in Eq. (76).

The stochastic equation of motion of $v(t)$, Eq. (77), can be transformed into a stochastic Liouville equation of the type Eq. (7) if a Markovian process can be properly defined to generate the process of $H(t)$. Then we again obtain Eq. (63) for the conditional expectation $V(t)$ defined by Eq. (60). The line shape function is then given by

$$I(\omega) = \frac{1}{\pi} \operatorname{Re} \sum_{a'a''} \sum_{b'b''} (a'|\mu|b')(b''|\mu|a'')(0|(a'b'|V[i\omega]|a''b'')|0) \quad (78)$$

Recently, the stochastic models for the Mössbauer line shape problem have been discussed by several investigators.[20] Such models can be treated in a systematic way as we have described in the above. For example, in a ^{57}Fe nucleus, the spin in the excited state is $I = \frac{3}{2}$ and that in the ground state is $I = \frac{1}{2}$, so that the Hamiltonian is a 6×6 matrix. If a two-state-jump model is adopted, the dimension of the matrix equation, Eq. (63), is $6 \times 2 = 12$. If the stochastic operator is of the type (26), then the equation is a set of six differential equations. These equations can be solved, if necessary, by computers to yield the line shape functions for various values of parameters.

Figure 12 shows two examples of line shape functions for Fe Mössbauer spectra calculated by Tjon and Blume using a similar method.[21] It is assumed that a quadrupole interaction splits the excited state levels and a random hyperfine field is superposed on this. For simplicity the hyperfine field is assumed to take only two values. Figure 12a is the case where the hyperfine field is along the direction of the electric field gradient, and Figure 12b is the case where it is perpendicular. It is interesting to note that in the intermediate narrowing the spectrum may appear singly peaked, but is again split into two peaks in the extreme narrowing limit.

IX. CONCLUDING REMARKS

In the preceding sections, we have tried to show that our theory has a very wide range of applicability to various physical and chemical problems. The theory is essentially based upon the two equations, (16) and (18). In addition to classical examples such as treated in Sections III–V, it can, with suitable generalizations, be applied to quantum-mechanical systems as discussed in the later sections. In a previous paper of the author,[3] an analysis was made on the equation of the type (16) in order to investigate the structure and some general properties of the inverse operator (17). This analysis showed, in particular, how the narrowing occurs when the

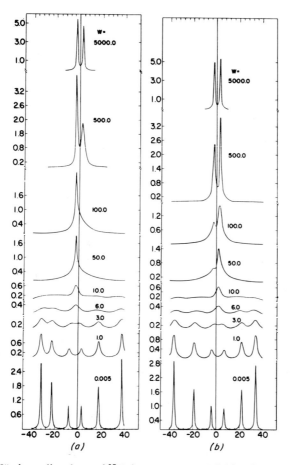

Fig. 12. Mössbauer line shape of ^{57}Fe in a constant eqQ field and a random hyperfine field assumed to be a two-state-jump process for different values of the jump rate W. (a) The random hyperfine field along the eqQ axis. (b) Perpendicular to the eqQ axis. (Calculations of Tjon and Blume.)

random modulation becomes fast. In the limit of fast modulation, extreme narrowing is realized and the line shape approaches a Lorentzian form. Here we do not repeat this analysis, but only mention that such an analysis can be extended to more general cases where the operators in Eq. (16) are replaced by more complicated ones, as for example, those in Sections V–VIII. It should be kept in mind, however, that, for computational purposes, the basic equation (Eq. (18)), is convenient; it may be that some transformation of the equations is useful, but elaborate manipulation of the equations is not necessarily required.

The strength of the theory has been acquired by making a sacrifice. As already mentioned in Section II, we made the simplification that the evolution operator Γ is independent of x, or the motion of the system under observation; in other words, the reaction of the system to its environment is ignored. This obviously limits the range of applicability of the theory, although it still covers a very large area. A difficulty arising from this simplification is that our theory, in its present form, does not satisfy the requirement that the system approaches equilibrium with its environment in the course of time. For example, consider a spin in a fluctuating local field. It may be assumed to satisfy the equation of motion, Eq. (41). Starting from a given state, the stochastic process of the spin should approach a stationary state which represents thermal equilibrium if the spin is in contact with a large heat bath. This requirement imposes some conditions which must be satisfied by the fluctuating field. In the simple theory of Brownian motion, based on the familiar Langevin equation or its generalization,[22] such conditions appear as the fluctuation–dissipation theorem, which gives a relation between the friction term and the random force. In the spin problem, if the forces on the spin are only the fluctuating local field appearing in the equation of motion, the situation is not so simple as this. It is possible to introduce a friction term into the equation of motion in order to guarantee the approach to equilibrium,[23] but this would not be a final solution of the problem. One side of the problem is related to the generalization of the Brownian motion theory to nonlinear systems, which is discussed in this volume by Professor van Kampen. The problem may be even deeper when we consider quantum-mechanical systems. How can we construct a general theory of Brownian motion of a nonlinear quantum-mechanical system which is in contact with a heat bath and react to external perturbations? To my knowledge this is an unsolved question.

References

1. R. Kubo, in *Fluctuation, Relaxation and Resonance in Magnetic Systems*, D. ter Haar, Ed., Oliver & Boyd, Edinburgh, 1962, p. 23.
2. P. W. Anderson, *J. Phys. Soc. Japan*, **9**, 316 (1954).
3. R. Kubo, *J. Phys. Soc. Japan*, **9**, 935 (1954).
4. R. Kubo, *Nuovo Cimento Suppl.*, **6**, 1063 (1957).
5. R. Kubo, *J. Math. Phys.*, **4**, 174 (1962).
6. P. W. Anderson and P. R. Weiss, *Rev. Mod. Phys.*, **25**, 316 (1954).
7. R. Kubo and K. Tomita, *J. Phys. Soc. Japan*, **9**, 888 (1954).
8. See for example, M. C. Wang and G. E. Uhlenbeck, *Rev. Mod. Phys.*, **17**, 323 (1945).
9. T. Toyabe, Master's Thesis, Department of Physics, University of Tokyo, 1966.
10. J. A. Pople, *Mol. Phys.*, **1**, 168 (1958).

11. K. Ito, H. Watanabe, and M. Kubo, *Bull. Chem. Soc. Japan*, **33**, 1588 (1960); *J. Chem. Phys.*, **32**, 947 (1960).
12. M. Suzuki and R. Kubo, *Mol. Phys.*, **7**, 201 (1964).
13. H. Watanabe, T. Totani, M. Ohtsuka, and M. Kubo, *Mol. Phys.*, **14**, 367 (1968).
14. R. Kubo and T. Toyabe, *Magnetic Resonance and Relaxation* (Proc. XIV-ieme Colloque Ampere, Ljubljana, 1966), North-Holland Publ. Co., Amsterdam, p. 785.
15. R. Kubo, unpublished.
16. R. Kubo and T. Toyabe, unpublished.
17. M. Baranger, in *Atomic and Molecular Processes*, D. R. Bates, Ed., Academic Press, New York, 1962, p. 493.
18. H. R. Griem, *Plasma Spectroscopy*, McGraw-Hill, New York, 1964, Chap. 4.
19. See, for example, S. Chandrasekhar, *Rev. Mod. Phys.*, **15**, 1 (1943).
20. M. Blume, *Phys. Rev. Letters*, **14**, 96 (1965); F. van der Woude and A. J. Dekker, *Phys. Stat. Solidi*, **9**, 9777 (1965); H. H. Wickman, M. P. Klein, and D. A. Shirley, *Phys. Rev.*, **152**, 345 (1966).
21. M. Blume and J. A. Tjon, *Phys. Rev.*, **165**, 446 (1968).
22. R. Kubo, *Rept. Progr. Phys.*, **24** Part 1, 255 (1966).
23. R. Kubo, Preprint for the NMR International Conference 1965, Tokyo.

A STOCHASTIC MODEL FOR NEUTRON SCATTERING BY SIMPLE LIQUIDS

RASHMI C. DESAI and SIDNEY YIP

*Massachusetts Institute of Technology,
Cambridge, Massachusetts*

Because there is no general microscopic theory of liquids, the analysis of inelastic neutron scattering experiments must proceed on the basis of model calculations. Recently[1] we have derived a simple interpolation model for single particle motions in simple liquids. This derivation, which was based on the correlation function formalism, depends on dispersion relation and sum rule arguments and the assumption of simple exponential decay for the damping function. According to the model, the linear response in the displacement, $\chi(t)$, satisfies the equation

$$\frac{d^2\chi(t)}{dt^2} + \omega_0{}^2\left\{\chi(t) - \frac{1}{\tau_0}\int_0^t dt'\chi(t')\exp\left[-\frac{(t-t')}{\tau_0}\right]\right\} = \frac{1}{M}\delta(t) \qquad (1)$$

Physically this description corresponds to putting an atom (mass M) in an external time-dependent harmonic potential (frequency ω_0). The potential relaxes exponentially in time (time constant $1/\tau_0$) so that eventually the atom experiences only a frictional force. Compared with other models[2] which have been proposed for neutron scattering calculation, the present model treats oscillatory and diffusive motions of an atom in terms of a single equation. Both types of motion are governed by the shape of the potential and the manner in which it decays. The model yields the same velocity auto-correlation function $\psi(t)$ as that obtained by Berne, Boon, and Rice[3] using the memory function approach.

The same model also can be obtained using the continued fraction representation.[4] Following Mori,[5] the Laplace transform of the velocity autocorrelation function, $f(z)$, can be expressed as

$$f(z) = \int_0^\infty \frac{\langle v(t)v \rangle}{\langle v^2 \rangle} \exp\left[-zt\right] dt \tag{2a}$$

$$= \cfrac{1}{z + \cfrac{\Delta_1{}^2}{z - i\omega_1 + \cfrac{\Delta_2{}^2}{z - i\omega_2 + \cdots}}} \tag{2b}$$

where ω_j, $\Delta_j{}^2$ are formally defined in terms of $v(t)$ and the Liouville operator. In the classical limit all ω_j vanish. One of the simplest approximations one can make is to replace $\Delta_2{}^2/z + (\Delta_3{}^2/z + \cdots)$ by a constant $1/\tau_0$. Notice that this approximation does not affect the asymptotic behavior of $f(z)$ for small z. It can be shown that Δ_1 is related to the mean square force on an atom.

$$\Delta_1{}^2 = \omega_0{}^2 = \frac{1}{3M} \langle \nabla^2 U \rangle \tag{3}$$

where U is the interaction potential. The constant τ_0 is related to the self diffusion constant through $f(0)$,

$$\tau_0 = \langle v \rangle^2 / D\omega_0{}^2 \tag{4}$$

The real part of $f(z = -i\omega)$ is just the spectral density $f(\omega)$ which is the Fourier transform of $\psi(t)$. We thus get for $f(\omega)$ and $\psi(t)$,

$$f(\omega) = \frac{2}{\pi} \frac{\omega_0{}^2/\tau_0}{(\omega^2 - \omega_0{}^2)^2 + (\omega/\tau_0)^2}$$

$$\psi(t) = \exp\left[-t/2\tau_0\right]\left[\cos \Omega t + \frac{1}{2\tau_0\Omega} \sin \Omega t\right] \tag{5}$$

where

$$\Omega^2 = \omega_0{}^2 - 1/4\tau_0{}^2 \tag{6}$$

These results have also been obtained by Berne, Boon, and Rice[3] as previously mentioned. For a stationary process, we have the relation between the mean square displacement, $\langle r^2(t) \rangle$, and $\psi(t)$,

$$\frac{\langle r^2(t) \rangle}{6\langle v^2 \rangle} = \int_0^t dt'(t - t')\psi(t') \tag{7a}$$

$$= \frac{\omega_0^2 - \frac{1}{\tau_0^2}}{\omega_0^4} + \frac{t}{\omega_0^2 \tau_0} + \frac{1}{\omega_0^4} \exp\left[-t/2\tau_0\right]$$

$$\times \left[\left(\frac{1}{8\tau_0^3 \Omega} - \frac{3\Omega}{2\tau_0}\right) \sin \Omega t - \left(\omega_0^2 - \frac{1}{\tau_0^2}\right) \cos \Omega t\right] \tag{7b}$$

The results given by the interpolation model have been tested[1] by comparing with neutron scattering experiments and molecular dynamics studies on liquid argon.

For a more direct experimental test of the interpolation model one should consider an incoherent scattering measurement. Recently neutron scattering from liquid argon containing hydrogen as an impurity has been measured,[6] and the data are well suited for comparison with our model. Hydrogen is a predominantly incoherent scatterer (ratio of coherent to incoherent cross section is about 0.02) and its cross section (about 160 b/molecule) is much larger compared to that for argon (about 0.6 b/atom). In this case, the observed spectra should reflect the motion of a hydrogen molecule in the liquid argon environment. In addition to translational motions, one must also consider the rotational motions of the hydrogen molecule; a theoretical study of this problem was given by Sears.[7] In the present analysis we have used the interpolation model for the translational motion and have treated the rotational motion in exactly the same way as Sears.[7] The major contributions to the observed cross sections are expected to come from the *ortho–ortho*, *ortho–para*, and *para–para* transitions. If one assumes free rotation and neglects the rotation–translation coupling, one obtains for these contributions the following:

$$\left(\frac{d^2\sigma}{d\Omega\,d\omega}\right)_{1,1} = 13.1 \frac{k}{k_0} \{[j_0(\tfrac{1}{2}\kappa r_e)]^2 + 2[j_2(\tfrac{1}{2}\kappa r_e)]^2\} S_S(\kappa, \omega) \tag{8a}$$

$$\left(\frac{d^2\sigma}{d\Omega\,d\omega}\right)_{1,0} = 6.35 \frac{k}{k_0} \{j_1(\tfrac{1}{2}\kappa r_e)\}^2 S_S(\kappa, \omega + \tilde{\omega}) \tag{8b}$$

$$\left(\frac{d^2\sigma}{d\Omega\,d\omega}\right)_{0,0} = 0.14 \frac{k}{k_0} \{j_0(\tfrac{1}{2}\kappa r_e)\}^2 S_S(\kappa, \omega) \tag{8c}$$

where r_e is the intranuclear separation of the hydrogen molecule (0.75 Å) and $\hbar\tilde{\omega} = 14.7$ meV, the *ortho* →*para* transitions energy, $j_n(x)$ is the nth order spherical Bessel function, k and k_0 are the final and initial neutron wave numbers, and $S_s(\kappa, \omega)$ refers to the translational motion of the hydrogen molecule. In the Gaussian approximation, it is related to the mean square displacement $\langle r^2(t) \rangle$ through the relation

$$S_S(\kappa, \omega) = \exp\left[-\beta\hbar\omega/2\right] \exp\left[-\beta\hbar^2\kappa^2/8M\right]$$

$$\times \frac{1}{\pi} \int_0^\infty dt \cos \omega t \exp\left[-\kappa^2\langle r^2(t)\rangle/6\right] \quad (9)$$

where $\hbar\kappa$ and $\hbar\omega$ are the momentum and energy gains by the neutron, and β is inverse temperature in energy units. The exponential factors account for detailed balance and recoil effects.

Experimentally, scattering cross sections are measured as a function of the time of flight, t, of scattered neutron over a fixed distance, l. Final neutron energy, $\hbar\omega_f$ is related to (t/l) as

$$\hbar\omega_f = \tfrac{1}{2}m_n(l/t)^2 \quad (10)$$

Moreover, the incident neutrons have a normalized distribution, $F(\omega_i)$. The measured intensity, $d^2\sigma/d\Omega\, dt$ is then given by

$$\frac{d^2\sigma}{d\Omega\, dt} = \frac{m_n}{\hbar} \frac{l^2}{t^3} \frac{d^2\sigma}{d\Omega\, d\omega_f} = \frac{m_n}{\hbar^2} \frac{l^2}{t^3} \int d\omega_i\, F(\omega_i) \frac{d^2\sigma}{d\Omega\, d\omega} \quad (11)$$

where m_n is the neutron mass and $d^2\sigma/d\Omega\, d\omega$ is the sum of the three contributions in Eq. (8). The full width at half-height of $F(\omega_i)$ was about 11 % for the experiment.[6]

For hydrogen in liquid argon, neither the diffusion constant, D, nor the mean square force is known. Using the law of corresponding states and the value of ω_0 for argon as found by computer molecular dynamics calculations, we obtain for hydrogen in argon, $\omega_0 = 23.4 \times 10^{12}$ sec^{-1}. From infrared measurements,[8] localized mode frequencies of about 18 and 30×10^{12} sec^{-1} have been observed. The neutron data[9] appear to suggest $\omega_0 = 13 \times 10^{12}$ sec^{-1} and $D = (10 \pm 2) \times 10^{-5}$ cm^2/sec. The small step diffusion approximation using $\omega_0 = 30 \times 10^{12}$ sec^{-1} gives $D = 13.7 \times 10^{-5}$ cm^2/sec. Using these values as a guide, we found that a reasonable agreement with the neutron experiments is obtained for $D = 12 \times 10^{-5}$ cm^2/sec and $\omega_0 = 15 \times 10^{12}$ sec^{-1}. The comparison of absolute scattering intensity is shown in Figure 1 for six scattering angles as a function of the time of flight. The experimental curves and the calculations for Sears' model are taken from the work of Eder et al.[6]

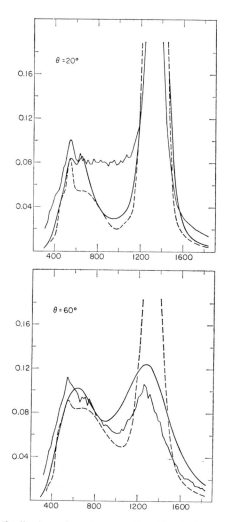

Fig. 1. Energy distribution of neutrons scattered by hydrogen in liquid argon at 100°K and 26.5 atm, as a function of time of flight for various scattering angles, θ. Solid curve, interpolation model. Dashed curve, Sears' itinerant oscillator model. Jagged curve, Experiment. Abscissa is time of flight in μsec/m and ordinate is cross section in mb sr^{-1} μsec^{-1}.

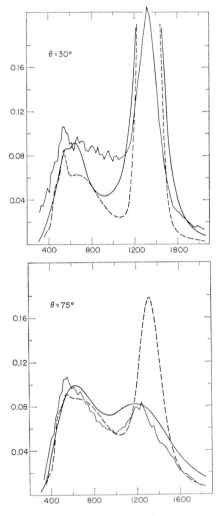

Fig. 1. (*continued*)

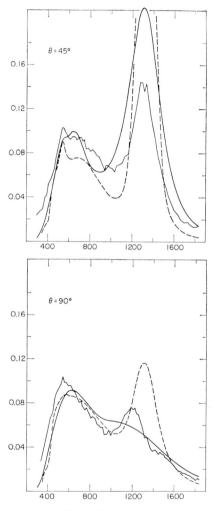

Fig. 1. (*continued*)

It is clear that the qualitative features of the experiments are reproduced by the model. The analysis also confirms the suggestion of Eder et al.[6] that D for the translational motion of hydrogen in argon environment, is much larger than the self-diffusion coefficient of argon. Neutron scattering data are sensitive to the details of the translational motion; in particular, the ratio of quasi-elastic to inelastic scattering intensities is a sensitive function of dynamics and has a nontrivial variation with scattering angle. At small scattering angle, the interpolation model overestimates the quasi-elastic intensity. Also it appears to be inadequate in predicting the shape of the low frequency part of inelastic spectrum. This indicates that for quantitative agreement with experiment, an improved treatment of rotation is probably required and that the assumption of a single relaxation process may be inadequate.

Acknowledgments

We would like to thank Dr. O. J. Eder for sending us the experimental results and Prof. S. H. Chen for helpful discussions. This work was supported by Project SQUID of the U.S. Office of Naval Research, the National Science Foundation, and Army Research Office, Durham. We are also grateful to V. F. Sears and B. Berne for calling to our attention an incorrect statement in the original manuscript.

References

1. R. C. Desai and S. Yip, *Phys. Rev.*, **166**, 129 (1968).
2. (a) V. F. Sears, *Proc. Phys. Soc.*, **86**, 953 (1965); Y. Nakahara and H. Takahashi, *Proc. Phys. Soc.*, **89**, 747 (1966); P. S. Damle, K. S. Singwi, and A. Sjolander, *Phys. Rev.*, **165**, 277 (1968). (b) A. Rahman, K. S. Singwi, and A. Sjolander, *Phys. Rev.*, **126**, 997 (1962). (c) V. Ardente, G. F. Nardelli, and L. Reatto, *Phys. Rev.*, **148**, 124 (1966).
3. B. J. Berne, J. P. Boon, and S. A. Rice, *J. Chem. Phys.*, **45**, 1086 (1966).
4. H. Mori, *Progr. Theoret. Phys.* (*Kyoto*), **34**, 399 (1965).
5. See Eqs. (3.1), (3.5), and (3.7) of Ref. 4.
6. O. J. Eder, S. H. Chen, and P. A. Egelstaff, *Proc. Phys. Soc.*, **89**, 833 (1966); also O. J. Eder, private communication.
7. V. F. Sears, *Proc. Phys. Soc.*, **86**, 965 (1965).
8. G. E. Ewing and S. Trajmar, *J. Chem. Phys.*, **41**, 814 (1964).
9. See Table 3 of Ref. 6.

FLUCTUATIONS IN AUTOCORRELATION FUNCTIONS IN DIFFUSING SYSTEMS

PETER H. VERDIER

National Bureau of Standards, Washington, D.C.

CONTENTS

INTRODUCTION

It has recently been pointed out by Gordon[1] that the root-mean-square fluctuations in the sampled values of the autocorrelation function of a dynamical variable do not necessarily relax to their equilibrium values at the same rate as the autocorrelation function itself relaxes. It is the purpose of this paper to investigate the relative rates of relaxation of autocorrelation functions and their fluctuations in certain systems that can be described by Smoluchowski equations,[2] i.e., Fokker-Planck equations in coordinate space. We exhibit the fluctuation and autocorrelation functions for several simple systems, and show that they usually relax at different rates.

II. DEFINITIONS

The autocorrelation function[3] $\rho(f, t)$ for a scalar dynamical variable $f(\mathbf{r})$ may be written:

$$\rho(f, t) = (\langle f(\mathbf{r}_0) \cdot f(\mathbf{r}_t) \rangle - \langle f \rangle^2)/(\langle f^2 \rangle - \langle f \rangle^2) \qquad (1)$$

where the angular brackets denote ensemble averages over equilibrium states, and the quantity $\langle f(\mathbf{r}_0) \cdot f(\mathbf{r}_t) \rangle$ is just the average of the product of pairs of values of f observed a time t apart. (The definition is easily extended to vector functions by taking the products involved to be dot products.) Following Gordon,[1] we define a fluctuation function $F(f, t)$ in terms of its square

$$F^2(f, t) = \left\langle \left[\frac{f(\mathbf{r}_0) \cdot f(\mathbf{r}_t) - \langle f \rangle^2}{\langle f^2 \rangle - \langle f \rangle^2} - \rho(f, t) \right]^2 \right\rangle$$

$$= B^{-2}\{\langle [f(\mathbf{r}_0) \cdot f(\mathbf{r}_t)]^2 \rangle - \langle f(\mathbf{r}_0) \cdot f(\mathbf{r}_t) \rangle^2\} \qquad (2)$$

where

$$B = \langle f^2 \rangle - \langle f \rangle^2 \qquad (3)$$

At a given value of t, $F^2(f, t)$ is thus just the variance associated with repeated sampling of the random variable $[f(\mathbf{r}_0) \cdot f(\mathbf{r}_t) - \langle f \rangle^2]/B$, whose mean is $\rho(f, t)$. The limiting values of F^2 at short and long times may be seen to be

$$F^2(f, 0) = B^{-2}(\langle f^4 \rangle - \langle f^2 \rangle^2)$$

and

$$F^2(f, \infty) = B^{-2}(\langle f^2 \rangle^2 - \langle f \rangle^4) = 1 + 2\langle f \rangle^2/B$$

We may note that although applying a linear transformation to f leaves ρ unchanged, i.e., $\rho(af + b, t) = \rho(f, t)$, where a and b are constants and a is nonzero, $F^2(f, t)$ does not have this property. In fact, as may readily be verified from Eqs. (1)–(3)

$$F^2(af + b, t) = F^2(f, t)$$

$$+ 2\beta B^{-2}\{\langle f(\mathbf{r}_0(\cdot f(\mathbf{r}_t)[f(\mathbf{r}_0) + f(\mathbf{r}_t)]\rangle - 2\langle f^2 \rangle\langle f \rangle\}$$

$$+ 2\beta B^{-1}(\beta - 2\langle f \rangle)\rho(f, t) + 2\beta B^{-1}(\beta + 2\langle f \rangle) \qquad (4)$$

where $\beta = b/a$. Thus any linear transformation applied to f, other than simply scaling without translation, modifies F^2 by the addition of a term which for scalar f is proportional to the cross-correlation between f and f^2 (the second term on the right-hand side of Eq. (4)), a term proportional to the autocorrelation in f, and a constant. In the following sections, we shall see that these changes in the form of F^2 can produce appreciable changes in the apparent relaxation time of F.

III. METHOD

It is clear from Eqs. (1) and (2) that calculation of ρ and F is essentially a matter of obtaining averages of the forms $\langle f(\mathbf{r}_0) \cdot f(\mathbf{r}_t) \rangle$ and $\langle [(f(\mathbf{r}_0) \cdot f(\mathbf{r}_t)]^2 \rangle$. These may sometimes be obtained without solving the Smoluchowski equation explicitly, by means of a method we have used previously.[4] We now restate this method in the slightly more general form needed for our present purpose.

Consider a system consisting of a particle diffusing in a viscous medium and under the influence of external forces. Such a system may be described[2] by a Smoluchowski equation of the form

$$\partial \psi / \partial t = D \nabla^2 \psi - \nabla \cdot [\mathbf{K}(\mathbf{r})\psi] \tag{5}$$

where $\psi(\mathbf{r}, t)$ is the distribution function, D is the diffusion constant, and $\mathbf{K}$ is the external force divided by the friction constant. For a scalar function $f(\mathbf{r})$, we multiply both sides of Eq. (5) by $f\,dv$ and integrate over the entire space, obtaining

$$\frac{d\langle f \rangle}{dt} = D \int f \nabla^2 \psi \, dv - \int f \nabla \cdot (\mathbf{K}\psi) \, dv \tag{6}$$

Applying Green's theorems to the right-hand side of Eq. (6), we obtain

$$\frac{d\langle f \rangle}{dt} = D\langle \nabla^2 f \rangle - \langle \mathbf{K} \cdot \nabla f \rangle + \int_S [D(f\nabla\psi - \psi\nabla f) + f\psi\mathbf{K}] \cdot d\mathbf{S} \tag{7}$$

In a given problem, characterized by a force-function and boundary condition, we look for sets $\{f_n\}$ of functions for which the surface integral in Eq. (7) vanishes and for which, if f_n is a member of such a set, $\nabla^2 f_n$ and $\mathbf{K} \cdot \nabla f_n$ can be written as linear combinations of members of the set. Then Eq. (7) may become a recursion relation which in principle (and sometimes in practice) can be solved for the time-dependent behavior of the quantities $\langle f_n \rangle$ in terms of their values at $t = 0$. Let $\langle f \rangle_t$ denote the expectation of f at time t, and $\langle f \rangle_0$ its expectation at $t = 0$. In the absence of a subscript, the angular brackets will denote the usual ensemble average over equilibrium states.

Given a function $g(\mathbf{r}_0, \mathbf{r}_t)$ which depends explicitly upon the state of the system both at time 0 and at time t (denoted by the variables $\mathbf{r}_0$ and $\mathbf{r}_t$, respectively), the quantity $\langle g(\mathbf{r}_0, \mathbf{r}_t) \rangle$ is given by

$$\langle g(\mathbf{r}_0, \mathbf{r}_t) \rangle = \int P_e(\mathbf{r}_0) \int P(\mathbf{r}_0 | \mathbf{r}_t, t) g(\mathbf{r}_0, \mathbf{r}_t) \, d\mathbf{r}_t \, d\mathbf{r}_0 \tag{8}$$

where $P(\mathbf{r}_0 | \mathbf{r}_t, t)$ is the particular solution $\psi(\mathbf{r}_t, t)$ of the appropriate

Smoluchowski equation and boundary conditions for which $P(\mathbf{r}_0 \mid \mathbf{r}_t, 0) = \delta(\mathbf{r}_0 - \mathbf{r}_t)$, and $P_e(\mathbf{r}_0) = P(\mathbf{r}' \mid \mathbf{r}_0, \infty)$. By an obvious extension of the argument used previously,[4] we see that the inner integral is just the expectation $\langle g \rangle_t$ of g at time t when $\mathbf{r}_t$ is known to be equal to $\mathbf{r}_0$ at $t = 0$. The outer integral is then just the average of $\langle g \rangle_t$ over the equilibrium distribution of initial states $\mathbf{r}_0$. This gives us a recipe for calculating $\langle g(\mathbf{r}_0, \mathbf{r}_t) \rangle$ in cases where g can be expressed in terms of sets of functions f_n, in both $\mathbf{r}_0$ and $\mathbf{r}_t$, for which Eq. (7) can be solved. First, combine appropriate solutions of Eq. (7) to obtain $\langle g \rangle_t$ as a function of parameters $\mathbf{r}_0$ and initial values $\langle f_n \rangle_0$ in the variable $\mathbf{r}_t$. Then, because of the delta function nature of P at $t = 0$, replace averages $\langle f_n \rangle_0$ in $\mathbf{r}_t$ by the corresponding quantities f_n in $\mathbf{r}_0$. Finally, take the ensemble average of the resulting expression, which now depends only upon the state $\mathbf{r}_0$ and the time.

In the following section, we illustrate this method by applying it to a number of simple systems for the special cases $g = f(\mathbf{r}_0) \cdot f(\mathbf{r}_t)$ and $g = [f(\mathbf{r}_0) \cdot f(\mathbf{r}_t)]^2$, in order to obtain the autocorrelation functions and their fluctuations, defined in Eqs. (1) and (2).

IV. RESULTS

A. Harmonically Bound Particle

We consider first a particle under the influence of Brownian motion and attached to the origin by a Hooke's law spring of zero equilibrium length. Although the complete solution for this case has previously been given by Wang and Uhlenbeck,[5] we can obtain the averages we need without using it. The Smoluchowski equation is given by Eq. (5), with $\mathbf{K}(\mathbf{r}) = -K\mathbf{r}$, where K is the spring constant divided by the friction constant. For sufficiently well-behaved ψ and f, the surface integral in Eq. (7) vanishes, and we have

$$d\langle f \rangle_t / dt = D\langle \nabla^2 f \rangle_t - K\langle \mathbf{r} \cdot \nabla f \rangle_t \qquad (9)$$

We first obtain autocorrelation and fluctuation functions for the function $f(\mathbf{r}) = r^2$. For this purpose, we shall need to find $\langle r_0^2 r_t^2 \rangle$ and $\langle (r_0^2 r_t^2)^2 \rangle = \langle r_0^4 r_t^4 \rangle$. From Eq. (9) we write immediately

$$d\langle r^m \rangle_t / dt = m(m + 1)D\langle r^{m-2} \rangle_t - mK\langle r^m \rangle_t \qquad (10)$$

from which, for the equilibrium case, we have

$$\langle r^m \rangle = (m + 1)(D/K)\langle r^{m-2} \rangle$$

and in particular,

$$\langle r^2 \rangle = 3(D/K)$$
$$\langle r^4 \rangle = 15(D/K)^2$$
$$\langle r^6 \rangle = 105(D/K)^3$$
$$\langle r^8 \rangle = 945(D/K)^4 \tag{11}$$

In the time-dependent case, we have

$$\frac{d\langle r^2 \rangle_t}{dt} = 6D - 2K\langle r^2 \rangle_t$$

$$\frac{d\langle r^4 \rangle_t}{dt} = 20D\langle r^2 \rangle_t - 4K\langle r^4 \rangle_t \tag{12}$$

The first of these yields immediately

$$\langle r^2 \rangle_t = (\langle r^2 \rangle_0 - \langle r^2 \rangle) \exp[-2Kt] + \langle r^2 \rangle \tag{13}$$

and substituting this into the second, we find

$$\langle r^4 \rangle_t = [\langle r^4 \rangle_0 - \langle r^4 \rangle - 10(D/K)(\langle r^2 \rangle_0 - \langle r^2 \rangle)] \exp[-4Kt]$$
$$+ 10(D/K)(\langle r^2 \rangle_0 - \langle r^2 \rangle) \exp[-2Kt] + \langle r^4 \rangle \tag{14}$$

Averaging over $\mathbf{r}_0$ gives

$$\langle r_0^2 r_t^2 \rangle = (\langle r^4 \rangle - \langle r^2 \rangle^2) \exp[-2Kt] + \langle r^2 \rangle^2$$
$$\langle r_0^4 r_t^4 \rangle = [\langle r^8 \rangle - \langle r^4 \rangle^2 - 10(D/K)(\langle r^6 \rangle - \langle r^2 \rangle\langle r^4 \rangle)] \exp[-4Kt]$$
$$+ 10(D/K)(\langle r^6 \rangle - \langle r^2 \rangle\langle r^4 \rangle) \exp[-2Kt] + \langle r^4 \rangle^2 \tag{15}$$

Then we can write immediately $\rho(r^2, t) = \exp[-2Kt]$, and from Eqs. (2), (11), and (15), we find

$$F^2(r^2, t) = \tfrac{1}{3}\{7 \exp[-4Kt] + 41 \exp[-2Kt] + 12\} \tag{16}$$

A related quantity of interest is $f(\mathbf{r}) = r^2 - \langle r^2 \rangle$. Its autocorrelation function is just $\rho(r^2, t)$, and we may use Eq. (4) to obtain the result

$$F^2(r^2 - \langle r^2 \rangle, t) = \tfrac{1}{3}\{7 \exp[-4Kt] + 8 \exp[-2Kt] + 3\} \tag{17}$$

Next, we consider the case $f(\mathbf{r}) = \mathbf{r}$. Since Eq. (7) is not directly applicable to vector functions, we express the averages we need in terms of averages of the Cartesian components

$$\langle \mathbf{r}_0 \cdot \mathbf{r}_t \rangle = \langle x_0 x_t \rangle + \langle y_0 y_t \rangle + \langle z_0 z_t \rangle$$
$$\langle (\mathbf{r}_0 \cdot \mathbf{r}_t)^2 \rangle = \langle (x_0 x_t + y_0 y_t + z_0 z_t)^2 \rangle$$

From Eq. (9) we obtain the equilibrium averages we shall need

$$\langle x \rangle = \langle xy \rangle = 0; \qquad \langle x^2 \rangle = D/K$$
$$\langle x^2 y^2 \rangle = (D/K)\langle x^2 \rangle = (D/K)^2$$
$$\langle x^4 \rangle = 3(D/K)\langle x^2 \rangle = 3(D/K)^2 \tag{18}$$

In the time-dependent case, we have

$$\frac{d\langle x \rangle_t}{dt} = -K\langle x \rangle_t$$

$$\frac{d\langle xy \rangle_t}{dt} = -2K\langle xy \rangle_t$$

$$\frac{d\langle x^2 \rangle_t}{dt} = 2D - 2K\langle x^2 \rangle_t \tag{19}$$

from which we write immediately

$$\langle x \rangle_t = \langle x \rangle_0 \exp\left[-Kt\right]$$
$$\langle xy \rangle_t = \langle xy \rangle_0 \exp\left[-2Kt\right]$$
$$\langle x^2 \rangle_t = \langle x^2 \rangle + (\langle x^2 \rangle_0 - \langle x^2 \rangle) \exp\left[-2Kt\right]$$
$$= D/K + (\langle x^2 \rangle_0 - D/K) \exp\left[-2Kt\right] \tag{20}$$

Then

$$\langle x_0 x_t \rangle = \langle x^2 \rangle \exp\left[-Kt\right]$$
$$\langle x_0 x_t y_0 y_t \rangle = \langle x^2 y^2 \rangle \exp\left[-2Kt\right]$$
$$\langle x_0^2 x_t^2 \rangle = \langle x^2 \rangle^2 + (\langle x^4 \rangle - \langle x^2 \rangle^2) \exp\left[-2Kt\right]$$

from which we find

$$\langle \mathbf{r}_0 \cdot \mathbf{r}_t \rangle = \langle r^2 \rangle \exp\left[-Kt\right] = 3(D/K) \exp\left[-Kt\right]$$
$$\langle (\mathbf{r}_0 \cdot \mathbf{r}_t)^2 \rangle = \langle r^4 \rangle \exp\left[-2Kt\right] + \tfrac{1}{3}\langle r^2 \rangle^2 [1 - \exp\left(-2Kt\right)]$$
$$= 3(D/K)^2 [1 + 4\exp\left(-2Kt\right)] \tag{21}$$

Then from Eqs. (1) and (2), we find

$$\rho(\mathbf{r}, t) = \exp\left[-Kt\right]$$
$$F^2(\mathbf{r}, t) = \tfrac{1}{3}[1 + \exp\left(-2Kt\right)] \tag{22}$$

B. Particle in a Box

We consider next the case of a diffusing particle contained in a box, but otherwise without external forces. For the sake of simplicity, we consider only the one-dimensional case. We suppose that the walls of the box lie at $x = 0$ and $x = b$. Equation (5) then takes on the simple form

$$\frac{\partial \psi}{\partial t} = \frac{D \, \partial^2 \psi}{\partial x^2}, \qquad 0 \le x \le b \qquad (23)$$

with the usual boundary conditions for reflecting barriers[2]:

$$\frac{\partial \psi}{\partial x} = 0 \quad \text{at} \quad x = 0 \quad \text{and} \quad x = b \qquad (24)$$

Equation (7) then becomes

$$\frac{(1/D) \, d\langle f \rangle t}{dt} = \langle f'' \rangle_t - [f' \psi]_0^b \qquad (25)$$

where the primes denote differentiation with respect to x. Because of the second term on the right-hand side, Eq. (25) is not generally helpful. However, let us restrict ourselves to functions f with the property $f'(0) = f'(b) = 0$, for which Eq. (25) simplifies to become

$$\frac{d\langle f \rangle_t}{dt} = D\langle f'' \rangle_t \qquad (26)$$

To simplify further, let us set $b = \pi$, and consider a set of functions f_n, defined by

$$f_n(x) = \cos(nx) \qquad (27)$$

Then, by inspection of Eq. (26), we write immediately

$$\langle f_{n0} f_{nt} \rangle = \langle f_n^2 \rangle \exp[-n^2 Dt]$$

$$\rho(f_n, t) = \exp[-n^2 Dt] \qquad (28)$$

For the fluctuation function, we obtain

$$\frac{d\langle f_n^2 \rangle_t}{dt} = -2n^2 D(2\langle f_n^2 \rangle_t - 1)$$

$$\langle f_n^2 \rangle_t = \langle f_n^2 \rangle + (\langle f_n^2 \rangle_0 - \langle f_n^2 \rangle) \exp[-4n^2 Dt]$$

$$\langle f_{n0}^2 f_{nt}^2 \rangle = \langle f_n^2 \rangle^2 + (\langle f_n^4 \rangle - \langle f_n^2 \rangle^2) \exp[-4n^2 Dt] \qquad (29)$$

The equilibrium averages needed are readily obtained from Eq. (26), and we find

$$\frac{d\langle f_n^m \rangle_t}{dt} = Dmn^2[(m-1)\langle f_n^{m-2} \rangle_t - m\langle f_n^m \rangle_t]$$

and

$$\langle f_n^2 \rangle = \tfrac{1}{2}; \qquad \langle f_n^4 \rangle = \tfrac{3}{8}$$

Equation (29) then becomes

$$\langle f_{n0}^2 f_{nt}^2 \rangle = \tfrac{1}{4} + \tfrac{1}{8} \exp\left[-4n^2 Dt\right],$$

and finally

$$F^2(f_n, t) = \tfrac{1}{2} \exp\left[-4n^2 Dt\right] - \exp\left[-2n^2 Dt\right] + 1 \qquad (30)$$

In particular, for $n = 1$ we have

$$\rho(\cos x, t) = \exp\left[-Dt\right] \qquad (31)$$

$$F^2(\cos x, t) = \tfrac{1}{2} \exp\left[-4Dt\right] - \exp\left[-2Dt\right] + 1 \qquad (32)$$

The method used here cannot be applied to the function $f(x) = x$, since it does not satisfy the boundary conditions needed to make Eq. (25) tractable. However, we may consider the function $f(x) = 1 - \cos x$, which "behaves like" x in that it goes through the origin and is monotonic increasing with x in the interval $(0, \pi)$. The autocorrelation function of $1 - \cos x$ is just that of $\cos x$, and is given by Eq. (31). However, by the use of Eqs. (4) and (32), we find that:

$$F^2(1 - \cos x, t) = \tfrac{1}{2} \exp\left[-4Dt\right] - \exp\left[-2Dt\right] + 4 \exp\left[-Dt\right] + 5 \qquad (33)$$

C. Plane Rotor

We next consider the case of a plane rotor. The Smoluchowski equation is identical with Eq. (23) for the particle in a box, if we replace x by ϑ and let the interval in ϑ be $(0, 2\pi)$. However, the only boundary condition now is periodicity, and this is also a sufficient condition on f for Eq. (26) to apply. The functions $\cos n\vartheta$ and $1 - \cos(\vartheta)$ are again acceptable, and yield the same results as were obtained for the particle in a box.

D. Spherical Rotor

As a final example we consider a rotating sphere. We take $f(\mathbf{r}) = \mathbf{r}/|\mathbf{r}|$, i.e., a unit vector in the direction of $\mathbf{r}$. As in the case of the harmonically bound particle, we write the definitions of the autocorrelation and fluctuation functions in terms of Cartesian components, expressed now in spherical polar coordinates. The analysis is straightforward, and yields

$$\rho(\mathbf{r}/|\mathbf{r}|, t) = \exp[-2Dt] \tag{34}$$

$$F^2(\mathbf{r}/|\mathbf{r}|, t) = \tfrac{2}{3}\exp[-6Dt] - \exp[-4Dt] + \tfrac{1}{3} \tag{35}$$

V. RELAXATION TIMES

In the simple cases worked out in the preceding section, the autocorrelation function always turned out to be a simple exponential. Its relaxation time τ is therefore unambiguously defined by $\rho(f, \tau) = e^{-1}$. In Table I we show the fluctuation functions $F^2(f, t)$ obtained in the

TABLE I

Squared Fluctuation Functions $F^2(f, t)$, Expressed in Terms of Autocorrelation Functions $\rho(f, t)$; and the Limiting Forms Taken by the Scaled rms Fluctuation Functions $U(f, t)$ at Short and Long Times, for the Functions f Shown and the Following Systems: (A) Harmonically bound particle. (B) One-dimensional particle in a box. (C) Plane rotor. (D) Spherical rotor. The limiting behaviour at short times is given in terms of $\varepsilon = 1 - \rho$.

System	Function	$F^2(f, t)$	Limiting behavior of $U(f, t)$ at	
			Short times	Long times
A	r^2	$\tfrac{1}{3}(7\rho^2 + 41\rho + 12)$	$1-0.83\varepsilon$	1.4ρ
	$r^2 - \langle r^2 \rangle$	$\tfrac{1}{3}(7\rho^2 + 8\rho + 3)$	$1-1.03\varepsilon$	0.92ρ
	$\mathbf{r}$	$\tfrac{1}{3}(\rho^2 + 1)$	$1-1.7\varepsilon$	$1.2\rho^2$
B	$\cos nx$	$\tfrac{1}{2}\rho^4 - \rho^2 + 1$	$1-4.8\varepsilon^2$	$1.7\rho^2$
	$1 - \cos x$	$\tfrac{1}{2}\rho^4 - \rho^2 + 4\rho + 5$	$1-1.01\varepsilon$	1.3ρ
C	$\cos \sigma$	$\tfrac{1}{2}\rho^4 - \rho^2 + 1$	$1-4.8\varepsilon^2$	$1.7\rho^2$
	$1 - \cos \sigma$	$\tfrac{1}{2}\rho^4 - \rho^2 + 4\rho + 5$	$1-1.01\varepsilon$	1.3ρ
D	$\mathbf{r}/|\mathbf{r}|$	$\tfrac{2}{3}\rho^3 - \rho^2 + \tfrac{1}{3}$	$1-1.7\varepsilon$	$1.5\rho^2$

preceding section, expressed in terms of $\rho(f, t)$. Since these functions are not simple exponentials, in order to discuss their relaxation we introduce a scaled rms fluctuation function $U(f, t)$, defined by:

$$U(f, t) = [F(f, t) - F(f, \infty)]/[F(f, 0) - F(f, \infty)] \tag{36}$$

We may then define a relaxation time τ' for the fluctuations by setting $U(f, \tau') = e^{-1}$. Using this definition and the functions in Table I, we can obtain the ratios τ'/τ of the relaxation time for U to that for ρ. The results are shown in Table II.

TABLE II

Comparison of Rates of Relaxation of Scaled rms Fluctuation Functions $U(f, t)$ and Autocorrelation Functions $\rho(f, t)$ at Short, Intermediate, and Long Times, for the Functions f Shown and the Systems Described in Table I

The quantities shown are as follows: For intermediate times, the ratios τ'/τ obtained by setting $U(f, \tau') = e^{-1}$; for short times, the same quantity inferred from the limiting slope of U at $t = 0$; for long times, the limiting value of the ratio U/ρ.

System	Function	$[(-dU/d\varepsilon)^{-1}]_{t=0}$ (Short times)	τ'/τ (Intermediate times)	$[U/\rho]_{t\to\infty}$ (Long times)
A	r^2	1.2	1.2	1.4
	$r^2 - \langle r^2 \rangle$	0.97	0.97	0.92
	$\mathbf{r}$	0.59	0.56	0
B	$\cos nx$	∞	0.73	0
	$1 - \cos x$	0.99	1.14	1.3
C	$\cos \sigma$	∞	0.73	0
	$1 - \cos \sigma$	0.99	1.14	1.3
D	$\mathbf{r}/|\mathbf{r}|$	0.58	0.57	0

We may also compare the limiting behavior of U with that of ρ at short and long times. If F^2 can be expressed as a polynomial in ρ, as it can for the systems studied here, the procedure is straightforward. We first write

$$F^2(f, t) = \sum_{k=0}^{n} c_k \rho^k \qquad (37)$$

For long times, we expand U in powers of ρ, and for short times, in powers of $\varepsilon = 1 - \rho$, which for exponential ρ may be equated to t/τ in the limit of sufficiently short time. Then from Eq. (36), we find for long times

$$U(f, t) \cong M c_0^{-1/2} V(\rho), \qquad \rho \ll 1 \qquad (38)$$

where

$$M = \frac{1}{2} \left[\left(\sum_{k=0}^{n} c_k \right)^{1/2} - c_0^{1/2} \right]^{-1}$$

and $V(\rho)$ is the lowest-order nonvanishing term in $\sum_{k=6}^{n} c_k \rho^k$.

For short times, expansion in powers of ε yields

$$U(f, t) \cong 1 + M\left(\sum_{k=0}^{n} c_k\right)^{-1/2} W(\varepsilon), \quad \text{for} \quad \sum_{k=0}^{n} c_k \neq 0$$

$$\cong 1 + 2MW(\varepsilon)^{1/2}, \quad \text{if} \quad \sum_{k=0}^{n} c_k = 0 \tag{39}$$

Here $W(\varepsilon)$ is the lowest-order nonvanishing term in

$$\sum_{j=1}^{n} (-\varepsilon)^j \sum_{k=j}^{n} \binom{k}{j} c_k$$

In Table I, we show the limiting behavior of U at short and long times implied by Eqs. (38) and (39).

VI. DISCUSSION

In Table II we show the ratios τ'/τ of the relaxation time for U to that for ρ inferred from the behavior of U at short and intermediate times, and the ratios U/ρ at long times. First we may note that the ratios at intermediate times range from 0.56 to 1.2. It is clear that if the functional forms for F^2 given in Table I are typical, strict equality of τ and τ' will occur only by coincidence. However, we may note that for the systems discussed here, τ and τ' are at least of the same order of magnitude.

The ratios of relaxation times implied by the limiting slopes at short times may be seen to follow the results at intermediate times in a general way, except for the cosine functions in the particle in a box and the plane rotor. Here the initial slope of U vs. time is horizontal, although U attains the value e^{-1} in a shorter time than does ρ. The behavior of the ratios U/ρ shows that at long times, U may be either greater or less than ρ, and need not be relaxing at the same rate. It appears that the natures of the relaxations of the fluctuations at short, intermediate, and long times are uncorrelated, so that information about relaxation in one region tells us little about relaxation in the other two.

We can also see in Tables I and II the effects of a change in the origin of f upon the relaxation of U. The difference between the U's for $\cos \vartheta$ and for $1 - \cos \vartheta$ in the case of the plane rotor (and the analogous case of the particle in a box) is perhaps especially striking. At intermediate times, the translation is seen to change the relative rate of relaxation of U from 0.73 to 1.14, but at short and long times, it changes the nature of the relaxation behavior completely. We can readily show from Eq. (4), in fact, that for any function f, a sufficiently large translation in the origin of f will eventually cause F^2 to relax as $1 + \rho$. This will lead to values of τ'/τ at short and intermediate times of 1.2 and 1.3 respectively, if ρ is a simple exponential, and to a limiting ratio U/ρ at long times of 1.2.

References

1. R. G. Gordon, *J. Chem. Phys.*, **47**, 1 (1967).
2. See, for example, S. Chandrasekhar, *Rev. Mod. Phys.*, **15**, 1 (1943); reprinted in *Selected Papers on Noise and Stochastic Processes*, N. Wax, Ed., Dover, New York, 1954.
3. See, for example, M. S. Bartlett, *An Introduction to Stochastic Processes*, Cambridge University Press, London, 1955, pp. 160ff; W. Feller, *An Introduction to Probability Theory and Its Applications*, Vol. 1, 2nd ed., Wiley, New York, 1957, pp. 221ff; R. Zwanzig, *Ann. Rev. Phys. Chem.*, **16**, 67 (1965).
4. P. H. Verdier, *J. Chem. Phys.*, **45**, 2118 (1966).
5. M. C. Wang and G. E. Uhlenbeck, *Rev. Mod. Phys.*, **17**, 323 (1945); reprinted in *Selected Papers on Noise and Stochastic Processes*, N. Wax, Ed. Dover, New York, 1954.

STOCHASTIC THEORY OF CHEMICAL RATE PROCESSES

DONALD A. McQUARRIE

Science Center/Aerospace and Systems Group,
North American Rockwell Corporation,
Thousand Oaks, California

CONTENTS

I. INTRODUCTION

The stochastic theory of chemical rate processes or chemical kinetics seems to be able to be divided into three main, almost mutually exclusive, groups. The first can be thought of as a stochastic treatment of the rate of transitions among the various states of individual molecules, where a reaction might be, for example, the transition from a bound state to a dissociated state, or the transition over a barrier from state A to state B. Such an approach was first presented by Kramers[1] in 1940, who used the Smoluchowski equation as a basis, and later by Shuler, Montroll, and others[2-4] who used a discrete random walk model on a finite number of states with an absorbing boundary representing dissociation. This type of approach will be discussed briefly in Section II. The second group is a study of elementary reactions such as A $\rightleftarrows$ B by a stochastic model. In this case one typically sets up differential-difference equations for the probability of finding x A molecules in the system at time t. From this, one can calculate the fluctuations as well as the mean, and so in some ways this represents an attempt to discuss fluctuations in chemical kinetics in a manner similar to that in which one uses statistical thermodynamics to discuss fluctuations in thermodynamics. As one would expect, these fluctuations are important essentially only in systems containing small numbers of molecules. An early example of this type of study is that of radioactive decay, in which one shows that the expected fluctuations go as $N^{-1/2}$, but from a more chemical point of view the stochastic approach was first popularized by Bartholomay[5-7] and then extended by Rényi,[8] Ishida,[9-11] McQuarrie and co-workers,[12,13] and more recently by Darvey, Ninham, and Staff.[14-16] Unfortunately, except for a few special systems or examples, there are really no experimental data to support this work, and so it is somewhat academic. A few simple examples, however, will be given in Section III. Lastly comes perhaps the most important application of stochastic techniques to chemical kinetics, that of more complicated systems which actually require such a description. The list of such examples is quite extensive, but some examples are the distribution of chain lengths and the distribution of copolymeric composition in polymer kinetics,[17-23] the kinetics of reactant isolation,[24] the polymerization kinetics of biological macromolecules on templates,[25-27] denaturation of polypeptides and proteins,[28-30] the degradation of linear chain molecules,[31-34] certain visual and blood clotting mechanisms in which a few activated molecules initiate an avalanche type reaction,[35-37] and photochemical reactions in RNA.[38] Some nonbiological or nonpolymeric examples are diffusion-controlled chemical reactions,[39-40] models of sterilization,[41] chromatography,[42-44] relaxation of vibrational nonequilibrium distributions in shock waves,[45-49] theory of homogeneous and heterogeneous nucleation,[50-56] the theory of absorption of gases onto solid surfaces,[57] the separation of molecular compounds by countercurrent dialysis,[58] the statistical processes of aggregation,[59] isotope exchange,[60] and random walk models of tarnishing reactions.[61] A few of these will be discussed in Section IV.

There are only a few existing review articles in this area. The earliest is that in Bharucha-Reid's book,[62] in which he discusses the early work of Singer,[63] Rényi,[8] and Bartholomay.[5-7] Recently three more have appeared, one by Montroll,[64] who concentrates mostly on random walk theories and applications of these to models of the kinetics of dissociation of diatomic molecules. He does devote some space, however, to the kinetics of growth and degradation of polymers and to diffusion controlled reactions. The second is by Weiss,[65] and reviews the various applications of the concept of mean first passage times to various problems in chemical physics. He discusses the work of Montroll and Shuler mentioned above and also an interesting example provided by Lifson and Jackson[66] in an attempt to explain long association times of sodium ions and polymer macroions observed in transference experiments for polyelectrolytes. The third is by McQuarrie,[67] who reviews in some detail the various elementary reactions that have been treated by stochastic methods and then discusses several more complicated systems such as the kinetics of reactant isolation, reaction kinetics of a long-chain molecule, copolymerization statistics, random walk model of unimolecular decomposition, and the kinetics of biological macromolecules. The reader is referred to this article for a fairly comprehensive list of references for the type of reactions to be discussed in Sections III and IV.

II. RANDOM WALK MODEL OF UNIMOLECULAR DECOMPOSITION

In this section we shall discuss at least briefly the work originally due to Montroll and Shuler[2] on the discrete random walk extension of a Brownian motion model used by Kramers[1] in 1940. They consider a collection of reactant molecules with quantized energy levels to be immersed in a large excess of chemically inert gas which acts as a constant temperature heat bath throughout the reaction. The reactant molecules are initially in a Maxwell-Boltzmann distribution, say, appropriate to a temperature T_0 such that $T_0 < T$, where T is the temperature of the heat bath. By collision with these heat bath molecules the reactants are excited in a stepwise process among their energy levels until they reach some upper level where they dissociate and are irreversibly removed as reactants. The collisional transition probabilities per unit time W_{mn} which govern the rate of transition of reactant molecules between levels with energies E_n and E_m are functions of the quantum numbers n and m and can, in principle, be calculated in terms of the interaction of the reactant molecules with the heat bath.

This corresponds to a one-dimensional random walk with an absorbing barrier, with the transition probabilities calculated from quantum mechanics. The time dependent distribution of the reactant molecules among the energy levels $n = 0, 1, \ldots, N$ is then given by the fraction of walkers in state n. The rate of activation is inversely proportional to the mean first passage time to the highest level, say the $(N + 1)$th. In general, the quantum-mechanical transition probabilities are quite difficult to obtain, but if the reactant molecules can be treated as simple harmonic oscillators, and if only weak interactions exist between the oscillators and heat bath molecules, an explicit calculation of the collisional transition probabilities can be carried out. The probability per collision of a transition of state n

to state m is given by

$$P_{mn} = [(m + 1) \delta_{n-1, m} + m \delta_{n+1, m}]P_{10} = P_{nm} \tag{1}$$

where P_{10} is the transition probability per collision for the $0 \to 1$ transition. Note that only transitions between neighboring levels are allowed. From the kinetic theory of gases, the transition probabilities per unit time, W_{mn}, are given by

$$
\begin{aligned}
W_{n+1, n} &= ZNe^{-\theta}P_{n, n+1} \\
W_{n-1, n} &= ZNP_{n, n-1}
\end{aligned}
\tag{2}
$$

The quantity Z is the number of collisions per unit time suffered by the oscillator when the gas density is one molecule per unit volume, N is the total concentration of heat bath molecules, and $\theta = hv/kT$, where h is Planck's constant, k the Boltzmann constant, T the absolute temperature, and v the fundamental vibrational frequency of the oscillators.

The potential energy curve of the dissociating harmonic oscillators is taken to be that of a truncated harmonic oscillator with a finite number of equally spaced energy levels such that level N is the last bound level. The dissociation or activation energy for the reaction is then $E_{N+1} = hv(N + 1)$. This potential energy curve is shown in Figure 1.

Let $F(t)$ be the fraction of molecules which have not yet reached $(N + 1)$ in the time interval $(0, t)$. Then if $x_n(t)$ is the fraction of molecules in level n,

$$F(t) = \sum_{n=0}^{N} x_n(t) \tag{3}$$

The fraction of molecules which dissociates in an infinitesimal time interval $(t, t + \delta t)$ is

$$-[F(t + \delta t) - F(t)] = -(dF/dt)\, \delta t \tag{4}$$

If $P(t)$ is the distribution of first passage times for transitions past level N, the number of molecules which pass N in the interval $(t, t + \delta t)$ is $P(t)\, \delta t$. Then

$$P(t) = -\frac{dF}{dt} = -\frac{d}{dt} \sum_{n=0}^{N} x_n(t) \tag{5}$$

The mean first passage time is

$$
\begin{aligned}
\bar{t} &= \int_0^\infty tP(t)\, dt = -\int_0^\infty t \frac{d}{dt} \sum_{n=0}^{N} x_n(t)\, dt \\
&= \int_0^\infty \sum_{n=0}^{N} x_n(t)\, dt
\end{aligned}
\tag{6}
$$

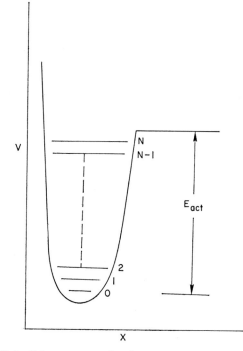

Fig. 1. Potential energy curve for the truncated harmonic oscillator.

The differential-difference transport equations which determine the $x_n(t)$ are

$$\frac{dx_0}{dt} = -W_{10}x_0 + W_{01}x_1$$

$$\frac{dx_j}{dt} = W_{j,j-1}x_{j-1} - (W_{j-1,j} + W_{j+1,j})x_j + W_{j,j+1}x_{j+1}$$
$$j = 1, 2, \ldots, N-1 \tag{7}$$

$$\frac{dx_N}{dt} = W_{N,N-1}x_{N-1} - (W_{N-1,N} + W_{N+1,N})x_N$$

The distribution of first passage times can be found by summing these equations to give

$$P(t) = -\frac{d}{dt}\sum_{n=0}^{N} x_n(t) = W_{N+1,N}x_N(t) \tag{8}$$

and so the mean first passage time is

$$\bar{t} = W_{N+1,N} \int_0^\infty t x_N(t)\, dt \tag{9}$$

Write Eqs. (7) in the form

$$\frac{dX(t)}{dt} = AX(t) \tag{10}$$

where $X(t)$ is a vector with components $x_0(t)$, $x_1(t)$, $\ldots$, $x_N(t)$. The solution is

$$X(t) = e^{At}X(0) \tag{11}$$

Now express the exponential matrix as a linear combination of the characteristic matrices of A, the $f_j(A)$'s which satisfy the relations

$$Af_j(A) = \lambda_j f_j(A) \qquad j = 0, 1, 2, \ldots, N$$
$$f_K(A)f_j(A) = \delta_{kj} f_j(A) \tag{12}$$
$$\sum_{j=0}^N f_j(A) = I$$

where I is the identity matrix and the λ_j's are the eigenvalues of A. Since the first of these equations implies that $G(A)f_j(A) = G(\lambda_j)f_j(A)$, then

$$e^{At}I = e^{At}\sum_{j=0}^N f_j(A)$$
$$= \sum_{j=0}^N e^{At}f_j(t) = \sum_{j=0}^N e^{\lambda_j t}f_j(A) \tag{13}$$

and

$$\int_0^\infty X(t)\, dt = \sum_{j=0}^N \left\{ \int_0^\infty e^{\lambda_j t}\, dt \right\} f_j(A)X(0)$$
$$= -\sum_{j=0}^N \lambda_j^{-1} f_j(A)X(0) = -\sum_{j=0}^N A^{-1} f_j(A)X(0) \tag{14}$$
$$= -A^{-1}X(0)$$
$$= \frac{(-)^{N+1}}{\det A}\{a_N I + a_{n-1}A + \cdots + A^N\}X(0)$$

In the last line we have made use of the Cayley-Hamilton theorem. The

a_j's are the coefficients in the secular equation of A. In particular

$$a_N = (-)^N \sum_i \lambda_0 \lambda_1 \cdots \lambda_{i-1}\lambda_{i+1} \cdots \lambda_N$$

$$= (-)^N \det A \sum_{i=0}^{N} \lambda_i^{-1} = (-)^N \det A \text{ trace } A^{-1} \tag{15}$$

Let $\langle i|A^m|j\rangle$ be the elements in the ith row and jth column of the matrix A^m. Then the mean first passage time from an initial jth state is

$$\bar{t} = \int_0^\infty \sum_{n=0}^{N} x_n(t)\, dt = -\sum_{i=0}^{N} \langle i|A^{-1}|j\rangle$$

$$= \frac{(-)^{N+1}}{\det A} \sum_{l=0}^{N} a_l \sum_{i=0}^{N} \langle i|A^{N-l}|j\rangle \tag{16}$$

When all the molecules are initially in the ground state and when $\det A$ is a continuant, Montroll and Shuler[2] show that Eq. (16) reduces to

$$\bar{t} = -\text{trace } A^{-1}$$

We now explicitly consider the model of the unimolecular decomposition, that of a truncated harmonic oscillator. Using Eq. (1), we write

$$\frac{dx_n}{dt} = \kappa\{ne^{-\theta}x_{n-1} - [n + (n+1)e^{-\theta}]x_n + (n+1)x_{n+1}\} \tag{17}$$

$$n = 0, 1, 2, \ldots, N-1$$

$$\frac{dx_N}{dt} = \kappa\{Ne^{-\theta}x_{N-1} - [N + (N+1)e^{-\theta}]x_N\} \tag{18}$$

where $\kappa = P_{10}$. These equations can be symmetrized by introducing $y_n = x_n \exp[\frac{1}{2}n\theta]$ which gives

$$\frac{dY}{dt} = BY \tag{19}$$

where B is now a symmetrical matrix. Using the symmetrical and continuant properties of B, Montroll and Shuler show that

$$\kappa\bar{t} = -\kappa \text{ trace } B^{-1}$$

$$= \sum_{j=1}^{N+1} e^{j\theta}\left(\frac{1}{j} + \frac{1}{j+1} + \cdots + \frac{1}{N+1}\right) \tag{20}$$

As $N \to \infty$,

$$\kappa\bar{t} = \frac{e^{(N+1)\theta}}{(N+1)(e^{-\theta}-1)^2}\left\{1 + \frac{e^{-\theta}}{N(1-e^{-\theta})} + O(N^{-2})\right\} \tag{21}$$

The standard theories of chemical kinetics are equilibrium theories in which a Maxwell-Boltzmann distribution of reactants is postulated to persist during a reaction.[68] The equilibrium theory first passage time is the $N \to \infty$ limit in Eq. (6). Corrections to it then are to be expected when the second term in this equation is no longer negligible, i.e., when N is not much greater than $e^{-\theta}(1 - e^{-\theta})^{-1}$. The mean first passage time and rate of activation deviate from their equilibrium value by more than 10% when

$$N(1 - e^{-\theta}) < 10e^{-\theta}$$

or roughly when $E_{\text{activation}}/kT < 10$. This result is in agreement with other statistical mechanical estimates of this effect.

Montroll and Shuler were also able to solve Eqs. (17) and (18) for $x_n(t)$. They found that

$$x_n(t) = \sum_{j=0}^{N} a_j l_n(\mu_j) \exp\left[\mu_j(e^{-\theta} - 1)t\kappa\right] \tag{22}$$

where the $l_n(z)$ are Gottlieb polynomials[2] and the μ_j are the zeros of $l_{N+1}(z)$. By means of the orthogonality relations of the Gottlieb polynomials, the a_j are found to be given by

$$a_j = \frac{\sum\limits_{n=0}^{N} x_n(0) l_n(\mu_j) e^{n\theta}}{\sum\limits_{n=0}^{N} l_n^2(\mu_j) e^{n\theta}} \tag{23}$$

When all the molecules are initially in state m,

$$x_n(t) = \sum_{j=0}^{N} \left\{ \frac{l_m(\mu_j) l_n(\mu_j) e^{m\theta}}{\sum\limits_{s=0}^{N} l_s^2(\mu_j) e^{s\theta}} \right\} \exp\left[\mu_j(e^{-\theta} - 1)t\kappa\right] \tag{24}$$

When $x_n(0)$ is a Boltzmann distribution with an initial temperature such that the population of levels greater than N is completely negligible,

$$x_n(t) = \sum_{j=0}^{N} \left\{ l_n(\mu_j) \left[\frac{1 - e^{-[\theta_0 - \theta]}}{1 - e^{-\theta_0}} \right]^{\mu_j} \middle/ \sum_{m=0}^{N} l_m^2(\mu_j) e^{m\theta} \right\} \exp\left[-\mu_j(1 - e^{-\theta})t\kappa\right] \tag{25}$$

Using Eq. (8) for $P(t)$, mean first passage times may then be calculated and compared to either the equilibrium result ($N \to \infty$) to test the range of validity of this assumption or to experiment. The agreement with experiment is not very good[3,4] but then again the model outlined here is only a first step. The obvious refinement is the use of a more realistic model for the oscillators and a calculation of transition probabilities for strong interactions. Kim[3] has studied an anharmonic oscillator model, but no numerical results have appeared. He did consider in some detail, however, the conditions under which the macroscopic rate law

$$-\frac{dc}{dt} = kc$$

is valid. Montroll also refers to Osipov and Stupochenko[69] and Widom[68] for a further discussion of such extensions. The effect of recombination on the reaction has recently been considered by Keck and Carrier.[70]

III. EXACTLY SOLVABLE ELEMENTARY REACTIONS

In this section we shall present a few of the elementary type reactions that have been solved exactly. By elementary we mean unimolecular and bimolecular reactions, and simple extensions of them. In a more classical stochastic context, these reactions may be thought of as birth and death processes, unimolecular reactions being linear birth and death processes and bimolecular being quadratic. These reactions may be described by a finite or infinite set of states, $\{x\}$, each member of which corresponds to a specified number of some given type of molecule in the system. One then describes a set of transition probabilities of going from state x to $x - i$, which in unimolecular reactions depend linearly upon x and in bimolecular reactions depend quadratically upon x. The simplest example is that of the unimolecular irreversible decay of A into B, which occurs particularly in radioactive decay processes. This process seems to have been first studied in a chemical context by Bartholomay.[6]

Let the random variable $X(t)$ be the number of A molecules in the system at time t. The stochastic model is then completely defined by the following assumptions.

(a) The probability of transition $(x) \to (x - 1)$ in the interval $(t, t + \Delta t)$ is $kx\Delta t + o(\Delta t)$, where k is a constant and $o(\Delta t)$ means that $o(\Delta t)/\Delta t \to 0$ as $t \to 0$.

(b) The probability of a transition $(x) \to (x - j)$, $j > 1$, in the interval $(t, t + \Delta t)$ is at least $o(\Delta t)$, since the time interval is considered to be small enough that only one molecule undergoes a transition.

(c) The reverse reaction occurs with probability zero.

A detailed balance gives

$$P_x(t + \Delta t) = k(x + 1)\,\Delta t P_{x+1}(t) + (1 - kx\,\Delta t)P_x(t) + o(\Delta t) \qquad (26)$$

where $P_x(t) = \text{Prob}\,\{X(t) = x\}$. By the standard procedure of transposing

$P_x(t)$ from the right-hand side, dividing by Δt, and then taking the limit $\Delta t \to 0$, one easily gets the differential-difference equation

$$\frac{dP_x}{dt} = k(x + 1)P_{x+1}(t) - kxP_x(t) \tag{27}$$

We assume that this procedure is valid. By means of the generating function of $P_x(t)$, viz.,

$$F(s, t) = \sum_{x=0}^{\infty} P_x(t)s^x \qquad |s| < | \tag{28}$$

Eq. (27) may be transformed into a partial differential equation,

$$\frac{\partial F}{\partial t} = k(1 - s)\frac{\partial F}{\partial s} \tag{29}$$

It should be mentioned here that even though the system we are considering has a finite number of states, the sum in Eq. (27) runs from zero to infinity. This introduces no difficulty since we know physically that $P_x(t)$ must vanish for all time when $x \geq x_o$, where x_o is the total number of particles in the system, and so the sum is really finite. This same reasoning applies to later cases as well. The solution of this, subject to the initial condition $F(s, 0) = s^{x_o}$, is

$$F(s, t) = [1 + (s - 1)e^{-kt}]^{x_o} \tag{30}$$

By noting the easily proved relations

$$E\{X(t)\} = (\partial F/\partial s)_{s=1} \tag{31}$$

$$D^2\{X(t)\} = (\partial^2 F/\partial s^2)_{s=1} + (\partial F/\partial s)_{s=1} - (\partial F/\partial s)_{s=1}$$

where $E\{X(t)\}$ is the expectation value or mean of $X(t)$, and $D^2\{X(t)\}$ is the variance, one gets

$$E\{X(t)\} = x_0 e^{-kt}$$
$$D^2\{X(t)\} = x_0 e^{-kt}(1 - e^{-kt}) \tag{32}$$

Note that the mean value of the stochastic representation is the deterministic result, showing that the two representations are "consistent in the mean." We shall see later that this is true only for unimolecular reactions. The stochastic model, however, also gives higher moments and so fluctuations can now be included in chemical kinetics. One sees that the stochastic approach is to chemical kinetics as statistical thermodynamics is to thermodynamics. An expansion of Eq. (30) gives for $P_x(t)$,

$$P_x(t) = \binom{x_0}{x} e^{-xkt}(1 - e^{-kt})^{x_0 - j}$$

which is first due to Bartholomay.[6]

The reversible case, viz., $A \rightleftarrows B$, is little more difficult, and if we again let $X(t)$ be the concentration of A molecules at time t and let k_1 and k_2 be the forward and backward rate constants, respectively, then we get[12]

$$\frac{dP_x}{dt} = k_2(x_0 - x + 1)P_{x-1}(t) + k_1(x + 1)P_{x+1}(t)$$

$$- [k_1 x + k_2(x_0 - x)]P_x(t) \quad (33)$$

where x_0 is the total number of A and B molecules. The partial differential equation becomes

$$\frac{\partial F}{\partial t} = [k_1 + (k_2 - k_1)s - k_1 s^2]\frac{\partial F}{\partial s} + x_0 k_2(s - 1)F \quad (34)$$

If we assume that there are x_o A molecules at time zero, then the solution of Eq. (34) is

$$F(s, t) = \left[\frac{(\lambda e^{-kt}(s - 1) + \lambda - s)}{\lambda}\right]^{x_0} \quad (35)$$

where $\lambda = k_1/k_2$ and $k = k_1 + k_2$. Equations (31) give for the mean and variance;

$$E\{X(t)\} = [x_0/(k_1 + k_2)](k_1 e^{-kt} + k_2) \quad (36)$$

$$D^2\{X(t)\} = [x_0 \omega/(1 + \lambda)](1 - [\omega/(1 + \lambda)]) \quad (37)$$

where $\omega = \lambda e^{-kt} + 1$. Such a reversible system at equilibrium $(t \rightarrow \infty)$, can be studied by equilibrium statistical thermodynamics, which predicts that[71]

$$\overline{N_A^2} - (\overline{N_A})^2 = \overline{N_A}\,\overline{N_B}/N = \overline{N_B^2} = (\overline{N_B})^2 \quad (38)$$

where N_A and N_B are the numbers of A and B molecules, respectively, and $N = N_A + N_B$. The stochastic model shows that this is valid not only at equilibrium, but in fact for all values of t. For large λ, i.e., the forward rate constant much larger than the reverse one, Eq. (35) reduces to Eq. (30).

A number of other unimolecular cases have been solved, such as parallel reactions, those with more general initial conditions, triangular reactions, unimolecular decomposition through a number of internal states, and those with time dependent rate constants.[67] Ishida[9] has, in fact, used this last case to approximate the solutions of the more complicated bimolecular reactions. All of these unimolecular reactions can be solved exactly since they lead to first-order partial differential equations for the generating functions. Such general linear stochastic processes have been solved by Kreiger and Gans[72] and by Gans.[73] Their motivation was a study of the relaxation of multistate systems and not chemical kinetics *per se*, but the mathematical formulation is the same. They also showed that a system relaxing by a first-order process from one equilibrium state to another will maintain, at all times, a multinomial distribution. A stochastic model for the general system of first-order chemical reactions involving n chemical species was derived later by Darvey and Staff,[15] from which the multinomial distribution was again shown to represent the probability time course of the components of the reaction. They show that the expected value for the number of molecules of any particular component of the general system of first-order reactions given by the stochastic model is consistent with the exact number of molecules predicted by the deterministic model obtained by using the principle of mass action, provided the probability parameters of the former model are interpreted as the rate constants of the latter model. This can be seen by multiplying their Eq. (4), viz.,

$$\frac{dP_{x_1 x_2 \cdots x_n}(t)}{dt} = \sum_{\substack{i=1 \\ i \neq j}}^{n} \sum_{j=1}^{n} k_{ij}(x_i + 1)P_{x_1 \cdots x_i+1, \, x_j-1, \ldots, x_n}(t)$$

$$- \sum_{\substack{i=1 \\ i \neq j}}^{n} \sum_{j=1}^{n} k_{ij} x_k P_{x_1 x_2 \cdots x_n}(t) \quad (39)$$

by x_m, say, and summing over all the x's. If this is done, one gets after some manipulation,

$$\frac{d\langle x_i \rangle}{dt} = \sum_{\substack{j=1 \\ j \neq i}}^{n} k_{ji}\langle x_j \rangle - \sum_{\substack{j=1 \\ i \neq j}}^{n} k_{ij}\langle x_i \rangle \qquad i = 1, =, \ldots, n \qquad (40)$$

which is the deterministic equivalent of the process described by Eq. (39).

Another way of deriving equations for the moments is to use the technique of the cumulant generating function[12] which generates the cumulants or semiinvariants of the process. Let $K(u, t) = \ln F(e^u, t)$. The partial differential equation for $F(s, t)$ may then be transformed into one for $K(u, t)$. Since

$$K(u, t) = uE\{X(t)\} + \frac{u^2}{2!} D^2\{X(t)\} + \cdots \qquad (41)$$

both sides of the equation for $K(u, t)$ may be expanded in terms of the dummy variable u, and coefficients of like powers of u may be compared. This procedure produces a hierarchy of ordinary differential equations for the cumulants in which the equation of the nth cumulant

$$\frac{d\chi_n}{dt} = f(\chi_n, \chi_{n-1}, \ldots, \chi_1) \tag{42}$$

Unfortunately, this technique is applicable only to first-order processes, since the hierarchy does not uncouple in the case of processes of higher order. In particular, for a second-order process, Eq. (42) becomes

$$\frac{d\chi_n}{dt} = f(\chi_{n+1}, \chi_n, \ldots, \chi_1) \tag{43}$$

A similar situation exists in the molecular-distribution function theory of liquids and one usually resorts to a superposition approximation. This amounts to assuming that, e.g., $\langle x^2 \rangle = \langle x \rangle^2$ or something similar. It will be seen shortly that, contrary to unimolecular reactions, for bimolecular reactions the stochastic mean is not the same as the classical kinetic expression for the concentration.

Just as in the unimolecular cases, the basis for the stochastic approach is to consider the reaction $2A \rightarrow B$ as being a pure death process with a continuous time parameter and transition probabilities for the elementary events that make up the reaction process. Letting the random variable $X(t)$ be the number of A molecules in the system at time t, the stochastic model is then completely defined by the following assumptions:

(a) The probability of the transition $(x + 2) \rightarrow (x)$ in the interval $(t, t + \Delta t)$ is $\frac{1}{2}k(x + 2)(x + 1) \Delta t + o(\Delta t)$, where k is a constant and $o(\Delta t)/\Delta t \rightarrow 0$ as $\Delta t \rightarrow 0$.

(b) The probability of the transition $(x + j) \rightarrow (x)$, $j > 2$ in the interval $(t, t + \Delta t)$ is $o(\Delta t)$.

(c) The probability of the transition $(x - j) \rightarrow (x)$, $j > 0$, in the interval $(t, t + \Delta t)$ is zero.

(d) The probability of the transition $x \rightarrow x$, in the interval $(t, t + \Delta t)$ is $\{1 - \frac{1}{2}kx(x - 1) \Delta t\} + o(\Delta t)$. This set of transition probabilities leads to

$$\frac{dP_x}{dt} = \frac{1}{2}k(x + 2)(x + 1)P_{x+2}(t) - \frac{1}{2}kx(x - 1)P_x(t) \tag{44}$$

where $P_x(t) = \text{Prob}\{X(t) = x, \ x = 0, 2, 4, \ldots, x_o\}$, and x_o is the initial number of A molecules.

The partial differential equation for the generating function is

$$\frac{\partial F}{\partial t} = \frac{k}{2}(1 - s^2)\frac{\partial^2 F}{\partial s^2} \tag{45}$$

which may be solved by separation of variables to give

$$F(s, t) = \sum_{n=0}^{\infty} A_n C_n^{-1/2}(s) T_n(t) \tag{46}$$

where $C_n^{-1/2}(s)$ is a Gegenbauer polynomial,[74] i.e., a solution of

$$(1 - s^2) \frac{d^2 C_n^{-1/2}(s)}{ds^2} + n(n - 1) C_n^{-1/2}(s) = 0 \tag{47}$$

and

$$T(t) = \exp\{-\tfrac{1}{2} kn(n - 1)t\} \tag{48}$$

The coefficients A_n can be determined most easily from the boundary condition

$$\frac{\partial F}{\partial s} = x_0 s^{x_0 - 1} \qquad \text{at} \quad t = 0. \tag{49}$$

Using this boundary condition together with the relation,

$$-\frac{dC_n^{-1/2}}{ds} = -C_n^{1/2} = P_{n-1}(s)$$

where $P_n(s)$ is a Legendre polynomial, one can show that

$$A_n = \frac{(1 - 2n)}{2} \int_{-1}^{1} x_0 s^{x_0 - 1} P_{n-1}(s) \, ds$$

$$= \frac{1 - 2n}{2^n} \left\{ \frac{\Gamma(x_0 + 1)\Gamma[(x_0 - n + 1)/2]}{\Gamma(x_0 - n + 1)\Gamma[(x_0 + n + 1)/2]} \right\} \tag{50}$$

$$n = 2, 4, \ldots, x_0$$

It can be easily shown that

$$\langle x \rangle = - \sum_{\substack{n=2 \\ \text{even}}}^{x_0} A_n T_n(t) \tag{51}$$

$$\langle x(x - 1) \rangle = - \sum_{\substack{n=2 \\ \text{even}}}^{x_0} \frac{n(n - 1)}{2} A_n T_n(t) \tag{52}$$

The coefficient of variation, $CV(t)$, is used to measure the relative extent of fluctuations, i.e., fluctuations relative to the mean,

$$CV(t) = \left\{ \frac{\text{var}}{\langle x \rangle^2} \right\}^{1/2} \tag{53}$$

Numerical results show that the stochastic mean and deterministic result approach each other quite rapidly as the number of particles increases. Figures are shown in Refs. 13 and 67.

The irreversible reaction $A + B \rightarrow C$ has also been solved exactly. If $X(t)$ represents the number of A molecules at time t, and $Y(t) = Z_0 + X(t)$, the number of B molecules where $Z_0 = Y(0) - X(0)$ and $Y(0) > X(0)$, the differential-difference equation for this bimolecular process is

$$\frac{dP_x}{dt} = k(x + 1)(Z_0 + x + 1)P_{x+1}(t) - kx(Z_0 + x)P_x(t) \qquad (54)$$

and the corresponding partial differential equation is

$$\frac{\partial F}{\partial t} = ks(1 - s)\frac{\partial^2 F}{\partial s^2} + k(Z_0 + 1)(1 - s)\frac{\partial F}{\partial s} \qquad (55)$$

Application of the method of separation of variables yields

$$F(s, t) = \sum_{n=0}^{\infty} A_n S_n(s) T_n(t) \qquad (56)$$

where $S_n(s) = J_n(Z_0, Z_0 + 1, s)$ are Jacobi polynomials and solutions to the differential equation,[75]

$$s(1 - s)\frac{d^2 J_n(p, q, s)}{ds^2} + [q - (p + 1)s]\frac{dJ_n(p, q, s)}{ds}$$
$$+ n(n + p)J_n(p, q, s) = 0 \qquad (57)$$

and $T_n(t) = \exp\{-n(n + Z_0)kt\}$.

Using the boundary condition given by Eq. (49) together with the relation,

$$\frac{dJ_n(p, q, s)}{ds} = [-n(n + p)/c]J_{n-1}(p + 2, q + 1, s) \qquad (58)$$

and the orthogonality relation,

$$\int_0^1 s^{q-1}(1 - s)^{p-q}J_n(p, q, s)J_m(p, q, s)\,ds = \frac{n!\{\Gamma(q)\}^2\Gamma(n + p - q + 1)}{(2n + p)\Gamma(n + p)\Gamma(n + q)}\delta_{mn} \qquad (59)$$

one gets

$$A_n = \frac{(-)^n(2n + Z_0)\Gamma(n + Z_0)\Gamma(x_0 + 1)\Gamma(x_0 + Z_0 + 1)}{\Gamma(n + 1)\Gamma(Z_0 + 1)\Gamma(x_0 - n + 1)\Gamma(x_0 + Z_0 + n + 1)} \qquad (60)$$

where $n = 1, 2, 3, \ldots, x_0$.

The first moment and the second factorial moment are

$$\langle x \rangle = \sum_{n=0}^{x_0} \frac{(2n + Z_0)\Gamma(x_0 + 1)\Gamma(x_0 + Z_0 + 1)T_n(t)}{\Gamma(x_0 - n + 1)\Gamma(x_0 + Z_0 + n + 1)} \tag{61}$$

$$\langle x(x - 1) \rangle =$$

$$\sum_{n=2}^{x_0} \frac{(n - 1)(n + Z_0 + 1)(2n + Z_0)\Gamma(x_0 + 1)\Gamma(x_0 + Z_0 + 1)}{\Gamma(x_0 - n + 1)\Gamma(x_0 + Z_0 + n + 1)} \times T_n(t) \tag{62}$$

If it is assumed that Z_o is very large, that is $Y(o) \gg X(o)$, it can be easily shown that the bimolecular process changes to a "pseudo-first-order" process.

This same pair of reactions was also studied by Ishida,[10] who used a Laplace transform technique. Although superficially quite different results were obtained, they are in fact identical to those presented above.

Reversible bimolecular reactions such as $A + B \rightleftarrows C + D$ can be solved exactly by the method of separation of variables and the ordinary differential equations in the variable s are Lamé equations. This makes the evaluation of the Fourier-type coefficients very difficult since derivative formulas and orthogonality conditions do not seem to exist or at least are not easily used. In addition to this, even if such formulas did exist, it seems unlikely that numerical results could be easily obtained. It does turn out, however, that these reversible bimolecular processes can be solved exactly and conveniently in the equilibrium limit, and this was done by Darvey, Ninham, and Staff.[14]

They showed that if the variance of a bimolecular process is zero or negligible, the deterministic results and the stochastic means are identical. This was also shown by Rényi in his early study of the irreversible bimolecular reaction $A + B \rightleftarrows C$. If the concentrations of A, B, and C are given by the random variables $X_1(t)$, $X_2(t)$, and $X_3(t)$, respectively, then it is easy to show that

$$\frac{dE\{X_3(t)\}}{dt} = kE\{X_1(t)\}E\{X_2(t)\} + kD^2\{X_3(t)\} \tag{63}$$

where E and D^2 are the mean and variance. By simple manipulation he showed that Eq. (63) can be put in the form

$$\frac{dE\{X_3(t)\}}{dt} = kE\{X_1(t)X_2(t)\} \tag{64}$$

which is to be compared to the deterministic equation, viz.,

$$\frac{dC}{dt} = kAB \qquad (65)$$

Equation (64) is immediately "derivable" from Eq. (65) by simply "taking the average" of both sides of Eq. (65). The deterministic approach always assumes that $E\{AB\}$ can be replaced by $E\{A\}E\{B\}$, and as Eq. (63) shows, this amounts to setting $D^2\{C(t)\} = 0$, and this is true only for a delta function type of density function, i.e., one in which all central moments vanish. By a similar heuristic argument, it can be seen that the deterministic solution and the stochastic mean values are always the same for unimolecular processes. This was pointed out (but never really proved in general) by McQuarrie.[12]

This concludes a discussion of exactly solvable second-order processes. As one can see, only a very few second-order cases can be solved exactly for their time dependence. The more complicated reversible reactions such as $2A \rightleftarrows C$ seem to lead to very complicated generating functions in terms of Lamé functions and the like. This shows that even for reasonably simple second- and third-order reactions, approximate techniques are needed. This is not only true in chemical kinetic applications, but in others as well, such as population and genetic models. The actual models in these fields are beyond the scope of this review, but the mathematical problems are very similar. Reference 62 contains a discussion of many of these models. A few of the approximations that have been tried are discussed in Ref. 67. It should also be pointed out at this point that the application of these intuitive methods to chemical kinetics have never been justified at a fundamental level and so the results, although intuitively plausible, can be reasonably subject to doubt.

This concludes our discussion of elementary type reactions. Again we say that unfortunately there are few real applications of these to chemical or physical systems. On the other hand, such simple models or slight extensions of them have found use in other fields. In the next section we shall discuss a selected group of more complicated processes which do in fact have direct application to physical or chemical systems.

IV. SELECTED APPLICATIONS

In this final section we shall outline a few examples of the application of stochastic models to systems of physical chemical interest. Two of these appear in the author's previous review[67] but the others do not. These examples are chosen to be representative of the general approach.

A. Kinetics of Reactant Isolation[24]

There are a number of examples of systems in which species firmly attached to sites can react with one another. The reaction is usually confined to groups that occupy adjacent sites. A classic example of such a system is the polymer, polyvinyl chloride, whose structure is

$$-CH_2-CH-CH_2-CH-CH_2-CH-CH_2-CH-CH_2-CH-$$
$$\quad\quad\; | \quad\quad\quad\; | \quad\quad\quad\; | \quad\quad\quad\; | \quad\quad\quad\; |$$
$$\quad\quad Cl \quad\quad\; Cl \quad\quad\; Cl \quad\quad\; Cl \quad\quad\; Cl$$

The addition of zinc to a solution of polyvinyl chloride extracts chlorines in a paired manner to give, for example,

$$\quad\quad CH_2 \quad\quad\quad\; Cl \quad\quad\quad\; CH_2$$
$$\quad\quad \wedge \quad\quad\quad\quad\quad\quad \wedge$$
$$-CH_2-CH-CH-CH_2-CH-CH_2-CH-CH-$$

Now the lone chlorine atom has found itself isolated since the zinc only extracts two adjacent chlorines. Such a result is called reactant isolation, and one wishes to predict the chlorine concentration left in the polymer as a function of time. It was shown by Flory[76] that the fraction of chlorines unreacted should approach e^{-2}, and this was used in fact by Marvel[77] to determine the structure of polyvinyl chloride. Other examples are the condensation of the polymer of methyl vinyl ketone[76] and the vulcanization of natural rubber.[78] The vulcanization studies supply another example where a molecular structure was determined by a kinetic scheme. The complete time dependence of the process was recently derived by Cohen and Reiss[24] using a novel method of multiplets, which will now be outlined.

Consider a chain of N sites between which bonds are formed. A single unbonded site is referred to as a "singlet," a run of two unbonded sites as a "doublet," etc. In general, a run of n unbonded sites is termed an "n-tuplet." It should be noted that an "n-tuplet" may contain two distinct "$(n-1)$-tuplets," three distinct "$(n-2)$-tuplets," etc. This is illustrated in Figure 2.

Consider an ensemble of M identical chains of N sites. Denote the number of n-tuplets in the jth chain at time t by $C_n^j(t)$. Let $k(t)\,dt$ be the probability that a bond forms between two unreacted neighbors in the time interval $(t, t+dt)$, the same for all pairs of neighbors. The rate of change of $C_n^j(t)$ with time is

$$-\frac{dC_n^{(j)}(t)}{dt} = k(t)\{(n-1)C_n^{(j)} + 2C_{n+1}^{(j)}\} \tag{66}$$

The minus sign appears because the reaction is irreversible and n-tuplets can only be destroyed, never created. This, in fact, is exactly the useful

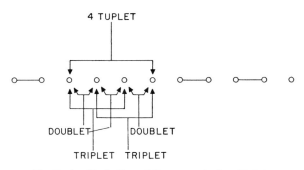

Fig. 2. An illustration of the concept of multiplets.

property of the concept of an n-tuplet. If this were formulated in terms of the more obvious quantity, viz. runs or clusters, this equation would involve summations on the right-hand side and would seriously complicate things. The first term on the right corresponds to the destruction of n-tuplets by the formation of a bond within the n-tuplet itself. Since there are $(n - 1)$ possible bonds within an n-tuplet, the rate of destruction is proportional to $k(t)(n - 1)C_n^j$. The second term on the right corresponds to the destruction of n-tuplets by the formation of a bond between either its terminal sites and a site not belonging to an n-tuplet.

If we denote the mean number of n-tuplets averaged over the M identical chains by

$$\bar{C}_n(t) = M^{-1} \sum_{j=1}^{M} C_n^{(j)}(t) \tag{67}$$

and sum (66) over j and divide by M, one gets

$$-\frac{d\bar{C}_n}{dt} = k(t)\{(n - 1)\bar{C}_n + 2\bar{C}_{n+1}\} \tag{68}$$

Initially there are $N - n + 1$ n-tuplets so that the initial conditions are

$$\bar{C}_n(0) = N - n + 1 \tag{69}$$

By introducing the variable

$$z = \int_0^t k(t)\, dt \tag{70}$$

Eq. (68) becomes

$$-\frac{d\bar{C}_n}{dz} = (n - 1)\bar{C}_n + 2\bar{C}_{n+1} \tag{71}$$

whose solution, subject to Eq. (69), is

$$\bar{C}_n = \exp\left[-(n-1)z\right]\sum_{s=0}^{N-n}(N-n-s+1)\frac{[2e^{-z}-2]^s}{s!} \tag{72}$$

The fraction of n-tuplets which survive, or the probability of survival of an n-tuplet, is

$$P_n(z) = \frac{\bar{C}_n}{N-n+1}$$

$$= \exp\left[-(n-1)z\right]\sum_{s=0}^{N-n}\left(1-\frac{s}{N-n+1}\right)\frac{[2e^{-z}-2]^s}{s!} \tag{73}$$

In the case of an infinitely long chain ($N \to \infty$), we have for all finite n,

$$P_n(z) = \exp\left[-(n-1)z\right]\exp\left\{-2[1-\exp(-z)]\right\} \tag{74}$$

At infinite time ($z \to \infty$), $P_1(\infty)$ is

$$P_1(\infty) = e^{-2} \tag{75}$$

which is the result obtained by Flory.[76]

Cohen and Reiss also considered a system in the form of a ring, end effects in a linear chain, the effect of diluents, and the generating function for particle survival, but these will not be given here. To the author's knowledge, however, the reversible process has not been solved.

B. Reaction Kinetics on Linear Lattices with Neighbor Effects

Consider a long-chain molecule again, each segment of which carries a reactive substituent or group. In many cases, the reactivity of each substituent depends upon the states of its two nearest neighbors. For example, the reactivity might be greater if one or both neighbors have reacted than if neither has. We wish to formulate a model for this process which produces the average fraction of reacted groups at time t. In 1963 there was a spurt in this area,[79-83] and some confusion or disagreement arose, but the problem was finally settled. It was later formulated in terms of the multiplets of the previous discussion in a study of polypeptide denaturation[28] and this will be outlined now. Let unity denote a reactive group that has undergone its reaction and a zero denote one that has not reacted yet. If one considers only the effect of nearest-neighbors, there are three elementary steps, with rate constants k_1, k_2, and k_3, viz.

$$1\ 0\ 0\ 0\ 1 \xrightarrow{k_1} 1\ 0\ 1\ 0\ 1$$

$$1\ 0\ 0\ 1\ 1 \xrightarrow{k_2} 1\ 1\ 0\ 1\ 1 \tag{76}$$

$$1\ 1\ 0\ 1\ 1 \xrightarrow{k_3} 1\ 1\ 1\ 1\ 1$$

We are interested in determining the time dependence of the number of unreacted groups. We now introduce the idea of a j-tuplet again. We denote the number of j-clusters by B_j and the number of j-tuplets by P_j. Since there are j 1-tuplets in a j-cluster, j-1 2-tuplets (doublets) in a j-cluster, etc., one gets for the relation between the P_j and B_j,

$$P_1 = B_1 + 2B_2 + 3B_3 + \cdots + NB_N$$

$$P_2 = B_2 + 2B_3 + 3B_4 + \cdots + (N - 1)B_N$$

$$P_3 = B_3 + 2B_4 + 3B_5 + \cdots + (N - 2)B_N \qquad (77)$$

$$.$$
$$.$$
$$.$$

$$P_N = B_N$$

or

$$P_j = \sum_{i=0}^{N-j} (i + 1)B_{j+i} \qquad (78)$$

These equations may be inverted by inspection to give

$$B_j = P_j - 2P_{j+1} + P_{j+2} \qquad 1 \leq j \leq N \qquad (79)$$

if we set P_n, $n > N$, identically zero.

It is now most convenient to proceed by deriving a set of equations for the rate of change of the number of j-tuplets, dP_j/dt, in terms of the number of j-clusters, B_j, and then transforming this into a set of equations for the dP_j/dt in terms of the P_j. Figure 2 serves as a guide for the derivation of the first few equations. Clearly,

$$\frac{dP_1}{dt} = -k_3 B_1 - 2k_2 B_2 - 2k_2 B_3 - k_1 B_3 - 2k_2 B_4 - 2k_1 B_4 + \cdots$$

$$= -k_1 P_3 - 2k_2(P_2 - P_3) - k_3(P_1 - 2P_2 + P_3) \qquad (80)$$

and

$$\frac{dP_2}{dt} = -2k_2 B_2 - 2k_2 B_3 - 2k_1 B_3 - 2k_2 B_4 - 4k_1 B_4 + \cdots$$

$$= -2k_2(P_2 - P_3) - 2k_1 P_3 \qquad (81)$$

The terms on the right-hand side of the first of Eqs. (80) and (81) are arrived at in the following manner: $2k_2 B_2$ since each of the two zeros in a 2-cluster can transform with a rate constant k_2; $2k_2 B_3$ since each of the two end zeros in a 3-cluster can transform with a rate constant k_2; $2k_1 B_3$ because the one middle zero in a 3-cluster eliminates two 2-tuplets when it transforms; $2k_2 B_4$ because of the two end zeros in a 4-cluster; $4k_1 B_4$ since each of the two middle zeros of a 4-cluster eliminates two doublets upon transforming. Proceeding in a like manner,

$$\frac{dP_3}{dt} = -2k_2 B_3 - k_1 B_3 - 2k_2 B_4 - 4k_1 B_4 - 2k_2 B_5 - 7k_1 B_5 + \cdots$$

$$= -2k_2(P_3 - P_4) - k_1(P_3 + 2P_4) \tag{81}$$

The general pattern may not be apparent at this stage, but if several more equations are written out the general term may be seen to be

$$\frac{dP_j}{dt} = -2k_2(P_j - P_{j+1}) - k_1[(j-2)P_j + 2P_{j+1}] \qquad j \geq 2 \tag{83}$$

We place no upper bound on j since we assume that the chain is long enough to neglect the end effect, which manifests itself in separate equations for dP_N/dt and dP_{N-1}/dt.

We are now faced with the problem of solving this system of equations. Assume that

$$P_j(t) = e^{-jk_1 t}\psi(t) \qquad j \geq 2 \tag{84}$$

where $\psi(t)$ is to be determined. We substitute this into Eq. (83) to get

$$\frac{d\psi}{dt} = 2(k_1 - k_2)(1 - e^{-k_1 t})\psi(t) \tag{85}$$

which gives

$$P_j(t) = e^{-jk_1 t} \exp\{2(k_1 - k_2)[t - (1 - e^{-k_1 t})/k_1]\} \qquad j \geq 2 \tag{86}$$

where we have used the initial condition $P_j(0) = 1$ for all finite j. The value 1 results from normalization, i.e., by dividing every $P_j(t)$ by $N - j$. What we wish is an expression for $P_1(t)$, which is the total number of zeros, or unreacted groups, as a function of time. This is obtained by substituting $P_2(t)$ and $P_3(t)$ from Eq. (86) into Eq. (80) and solving the resultant first-order linear differential equation. Equation (80) becomes

$$\frac{dP_1}{dt} + k_3 P_1 = 2(k_3 - k_2)P_2 + (2k_2 - k_1 - k_3)P_3 \tag{87}$$

and[67]

$$P_1(t) = e^{-k_3 t}\left(1 - \frac{2(k_3 - k_1)\exp\{2(k_2 - k_1)/k_1\}}{k_1[2(k_2/k_1 - 1)]^{2(k_2 - k_3)/k_1}}\right.$$

$$\times \left\{\gamma\left[\frac{2k_2 - k_3}{k_1}, 2\left(\frac{k_2}{k_1} - 1\right)e^{-k_1 t}\right] - \gamma\left[\frac{2k_2 - k_3}{k_1}, 2\left(\frac{k_2}{k_1} - 1\right)\right]\right\}$$

$$- \frac{(2k_2 - k_1 - k_3)\exp\{2(k_2 - k_1)/k_1\}}{k_1[2(k_2/k_1 - 1)]^{2(k_2 + k_1 - k_3)/k_1}}$$

$$\times \left\{\gamma\left[\frac{2k_2 + k_1 - k_3}{k_1}, 2\left(\frac{k_2}{k_1} - 1\right)e^{-k_1 t}\right]\right.$$

$$\left.\left.- \gamma\left[\frac{2k_2 + k_1 - k_3}{k_1}, 2\left(\frac{k_2}{k_1} - 1\right)\right]\right\}\right) \tag{88}$$

where $\gamma(a, x)$ is the incomplete gamma function,

$$\gamma(a, x) = \int_0^x u^{a-1} e^{-u}\, du \tag{89}$$

The initial slope of $P_1(t)$ vs. t is $-k_1$; that is, the process starts off behaving as if it had a single relaxation time k_1^{-1}. Likewise, the end of the reaction exhibits a single relaxation time k_3^{-1}. The physical meaning of this is that in all the initial processes an unreacted groups with unreacted neighboring groups reacts; whereas, toward the end of the reaction, the groups that react have both of their neighbors already reacted. This formalism has been applied to the irreversible renaturation of polypeptides by McQuarrie et al.[28] This is also similar to the time-dependent Ising model studies of Glauber.[84] To the author's knowledge, the reversible case has never been solved, in an exact analytical manner, although Gō[85-86] has recently applied the approximate method of Kikuchi[87] to the reversible polypeptide case, and Silberberg and Simha[88] have developed a procedure for the systematic derivation of the rate equations which can be programmed on a computer. This work is presumably reviewed in the chapter by Silberberg et al in this volume.

C. Kinetics of Photochemical Reactions in Nucleic Acid Derivatives

When polyuridylic acid is photolyzed with radiation in the 250 μ region, two types of photochemical reactions take place. One is the reversible formation of dimers between adjacent uracils and the other is a photohydration of the 5–6 double bond of the uracil. The position of the photochemical equilibrium of the first reaction is known to depend upon the wavelength of the radiation used and that of the latter is determined by conditions of temperature, pH, etc. The photohydration has commonly been considered to be irreversible. Burr[89] has recently reviewed the experimental aspects of these systems.

A consideration of the schematic view of a polyuridylic acid molecule shown below indicates that the formation of dimers in a random and

irreversible manner would leave some uracil sites isolated and thus unavailable for dimer formation. Such one-dimensional reactant isolation problems have already been discussed. However, the formation of dimers is *not* irreversible, and in addition, some sites will become hydrated in an almost irreversible manner, and thus are unable to undergo dimer formation, and so the problem of theoretically studying the kinetics of this process becomes more difficult. This has recently been started by Tanaka,[38] who considered the even more complicated case of natural RNA. It is this work which we shall outline in this section.

RNA has four kinds of bases along its polyribose–phosphate backbone and Tanaka assumes that only uracil is photochemically active, the other three bases being equivalently inert. In order to specify the statistical nature of the base sequence, the base composition and nearest neighbor frequencies are used, both of these being experimentally available quantities in many cases. If one assumes the sequence to be stationary, then p_u and p_i, the probabilities that an arbitrarily given site is a uracil or an inert (photochemically) base, respectively, and the conditional probabilities, e.g., p_{uu}, suffice to represent the sequence. Because of the relations governing these probabilties, viz.

$$
\begin{array}{ll}
p_u + p_i = 1 & p_{uu} + p_{ui} = 1 \\
p_{iu} + p_{ii} = 1 & p_u p_{ui} + p_i p_{ii} = p_i
\end{array}
\tag{90}
$$

one can use only $p_u (\equiv p)$ and $p_{uu} (\equiv q)$ as independent. One now introduces the state variables D_j and H_j, defined by

$D_j = 1$:   when a dimer consists of the jth and $(j+1)$th bases.

   $= 0$:   otherwise

$H_j = 1$:   when the jth base is hydrated

   $= 0$:   otherwise

Conditions such as $D_j D_{j+1} = D_j H_j = D_j H_{j+1} = 0$ follow immediately from the model. Let k_1 be the rate constant of dimer formation. Then the probability rates of dimer formation per radiation dose, $P_{ud}(S_j)$, which depend upon the nature of the occupation of a set of sites, S_j, are given in Table I. The probability of the reverse reaction of the dimer $(j, j+1)$,

TABLE I

Reaction Probabilities of Dimer Formation per Radiation Dose

Sequence $j-1\,j\,j+1\ \ j+2$	Probability of occurrence	$P_{ud}(S_j)$
$r\,r\,r\,r$	pq^3	$k_1(1 - D_{J-1})(1 - D_J)(1 - D_{J+_})(1 - H_J)$ $\times(1 - H_{J+1})$
$r\,r\,r\,i$	$pq^2(1-q)$	$k_1(1 - D_{J-1})(1 - D_J)(1 - H_J)(1 - H_{J+1})$
$i\,r\,r\,r$	$pq^2(1-q)$	$k_1(1 - D_J)(1 - D_{J+1})(1 - H_J)(1 - H_{J+1})$
$i\,r\,r\,i$	$pq(1-q)^2$	$k_1(1 - D_J)(1 - H_J)(1 - H_{J+1})$
others	$1-qp$	0

say $P_{du}(S_j)$, is simply given by $k_2 D_j$, which defines k_2. By similar reasoning, the reaction probabilities of the photohydration are given in Table II. We are now ready to set up the basic rate equations.

TABLE II

Reaction Probabilities of Photohydrations

Sequence $j-1\,j\,j+1$	Probability of occurrence	$P_{uli}(S_j')$
$r\,r\,r$	pq^2	$k_3(1 - D_{j-1})(1 - D_j)(1 - H_j)$
$r\,r\,i$	$pq(1-q)$	$k_3(1 - D_{j-1})(1 - H_j)$
$i\,r\,r$	$pq(1-q)$	$k_3(1 - D_j)(1 - H_j)$
$i\,r\,i$	$pq(1-q)^2$	$k_3(1 - H_j)$
others	$1-q$	0

Consider an ensemble of RNA molecules by base sequences specified by p and q. Then at the jth site, the fraction dimerized or hydrated (averaged over the ensemble) are given by $pq\langle D_j\rangle$ and $p\langle H_j\rangle$, respectively, and we can write

$$\frac{d(pq\langle D_j\rangle)}{dt} = \langle P_{ud}(S_j) - P_{du}(S_j)\rangle$$

$$= k_1\{pq^3\langle(1 - D_{j-1})(1 - D_j)(1 - D_{j+1})(1 - H_j)(1 - H_{j+1})\rangle$$
$$+ pq^2(1-q)\langle(1 - D_{j-1})(1 - D_j)(1 - H_j)(1 - H_{j+1})\rangle$$
$$+ pq^2(1-q)\langle(1 - D_j)(1 - D_{j+1})(1 - H_j)(1 - H_{j+1})\rangle$$
$$+ pq(1-q)^2\langle(1 - D_j)(1 - H_j)(1 - H_{j+1})\rangle\} \, dt$$
$$- k_2\, pq\langle D_j\rangle \, dt \tag{91}$$

and

$$\frac{d(p\langle H_j\rangle)}{dt} = \langle P_{uh}(S_j')\rangle$$

$$= k_3\{pq^2\langle(1 - D_{j-1})(1 - D_j)(1 - H_j)\rangle$$
$$+ pq(1 - q)\langle(1 - D_{j-1})(1 - H_j)\rangle$$
$$+ qp(1 - q)\langle(1 - D_j)(1 - H_j)\rangle + p(1 - q)^2\langle(1 - H_j)\rangle\} dt$$

Upon expanding and using conditions such as $D_j D_{j+1} = 0$, etc., one has

$$\frac{d\langle D_j\rangle}{dt} = k_1\{1 - \langle H_j\rangle - \langle H_{j+1}\rangle - \langle D_j\rangle - q\langle D_{j-1}\rangle - q\langle D_{j+1}\rangle$$

$$+ \langle H_j H_{j+1}\rangle + q\langle D_{j-1}H_{j+1}\rangle + q^2\langle D_{j-1}D_{j+1}\rangle\} - k_2\langle D_j\rangle \quad (92)$$

and

$$\frac{d\langle H_j\rangle}{dt} = k_3\{1 - \langle H_j\rangle - q\langle D_{j-1}\rangle - q\langle D_j\rangle\}$$

Using the assumption that the statistics of the distributions is stationary and neglecting end effects, the quantities $\langle D_j\rangle$ and $\langle H_j\rangle$ and the pair correlations $\langle D_j D_{j+2}\rangle$, etc. become independent of j. With the notation $\langle D_j\rangle = D$, $\langle H_j\rangle = H$, $\langle D_j D_{j+2}\rangle = \xi_2$, $\langle D_j H_{j+2}\rangle = \eta_2$, and $\langle H_j H_{j+1}\rangle = \zeta_1$, Eqs. (92)

$$\frac{dD}{dt} = k_1\{1 - 2H - (1 + 2q)D + \zeta_1 + q\eta_2 + q^2\xi_2\} - k_2 D$$

$$\frac{dH}{dt} = k_3\{1 - H - 2qD\}$$

(93)

These are actually the first members of a coupled hierarchy of equations for the successively higher order correlations.

Tanaka has solved these two simultaneous equations in two special approximate cases. In the first case he assumes that $\xi_2 = D^2$, $\eta_2 = DH$, and $\zeta_1 = H^2$. Equations (93) thus become coupled simultaneous nonlinear differential equations which were solved apparently only in the case where $k_3 = 0$, i.e., that in which there is no photohydration. In this case

$$D(t) = \frac{e^{k_1\alpha t} - e^{k_1\beta t}}{\alpha e^{k_1\alpha t} - \beta e^{k_1\beta t}} \quad (94)$$

where

$$\alpha = \tfrac{1}{2}[(1 + 2q + r) + \{(1 + 2q + r)^2 - 4q^2\}^{1/2}]$$

$$\beta = \tfrac{1}{2}[(1 + 2q + r) - \{(1 + 2q + r)^2 - 4q^2\}^{1/2}]$$

and $r = k_2/k_1$. Furthermore, for the irreversible case $(k_2 = 0)$ for the homopolymer, polyuridylic acid $(p = q = 1)$, $D(\infty) = 0.38196$, compared to 0.4323 for the exact solution to the irreversible case.

The other approximation discussed by Tanaka is a linearized pair of equations which he obtains from Eqs. (92) by neglecting the effects of the $(j + 1)$th site. This gives.

$$\frac{dD_0}{dt} = k_1\{1 - (1 + q)D_0 - H_0\} - k_2 D_0$$

$$\frac{dH_0}{dt} = k_3(1 - 2qD_0 - H_0) \tag{95}$$

which can be readily solved. The solutions are somewhat lengthy and are not given here. For the limit $k_2 = k_3 = 0$ and $q = 1$, $D(\infty) = 0.5000$, compared to the exact value of 0.4323 and the other approximate value of 0.3820. Tanaka has plotted $D(t)$ from both approximations and obtains the correct qualitative features, although quantitatively they differ appreciably. This is a first, interesting attempt at a complicated problem and so in that light it stands well. Nevertheless, there is much to be done here, as pointed out by Burr,[89] who writes:

> An attempt has been made to apply the Cohen and Reiss theory to dimer and hydrate formation in RNA. The results were inconclusive, probably because of a poor choice of example. Application of the theory to RNA was complicated by the necessity of estimating the distribution of uracil residues on the chain. The results are made still more tentative by the fact that Tanaka ignored the probability of dimer formation between cytosine residues, mixed dimers between cytosine and uracil, and hydrate formation in cytosine as well as the resultant deamination phenomena. A better choice of example would have been polyuridylic acid.

D. Nucleation Theory

A vapor, when compressed to the point where its pressure exceeds its vapor pressure at that temperature, will condense to form liquid droplets, so that the final stable pressure is just the equilibrium vapor pressure. This condensation usually and readily takes place on dust particles, container walls, or ions formed by extraneous cosmic radiation or the like. Under extremely clean and ion-free conditions, however, it is possible to avoid condensation and achieve a metastable state in which the actual pressure of the vapor is greater than its equilibrium vapor pressure at that temperature. Such a state is possible since the dust or ion nuclei on which the vapor molecules readily condense and grow are absent, and the vapor molecules must form clusters of themselves to act as nuclei. Such a process is called homogeneous nucleation. Homogeneous nucleation theory has been formulated as a birth and death process in which the states of the system correspond to specified numbers of molecules in a cluster. The transition probabilities for this process are not linear or quadratic, but are fractional powers. This seems to complicate matters enormously and most treatments assume a steady-state condition. Recently, however, several papers have appeared which explicitly treat the non-steady state behavior. We refer mainly to Courtney,[53] who solves a 100 or so differential—differential birth and death equations numerically on a computer. He was then able to study the effect of the steady-state assumption on classical homogeneous nucleation theory.[54,56] We also refer to Andres and Boudart,[51] who calculated the mean time to attain steady-state by a method similar to that of Montroll and Shuler[2] given in this review. Finally, we point out the work of Goodrich,[55] who treated nucleation formally as a birth and death process and was able to calculate lag times. This work constitutes perhaps the most complete treatment of nucleation from a stochastic standpoint and is well recommended. In view of the complex nature of the rate equations here, this is an example of a system to which approximate techniques can be quite useful.

All of these examples have been in homogeneous nucleation in the vapor phase. There is also a parallel field of nucleation in the solid state, and in this section we shall treat the most recent work, that of Allnatt and Jacobs.[50] We refer the reader to the references in their paper for bibliography of the previous work. Apparently, when a solid decomposes to yield a second phase, the chemical reaction initiates at certain discrete points called nucleus-forming sites. This results in the formation of submicroscopic particles of the solid product phase called nuclei. Further chemical reaction is localized at the interface between the nuclei and the reactant matrix so that the nuclei grow in size as the reaction proceeds. As the nuclei grow, the area of this interface increases, thus accounting for the rapid acceleratory stage which is usually a feature of the isothermal kinetics. Further growth leads to overlap of the nuclei, resulting in a reduction in the area of the interface and a consequent deceleration of the reaction, which continues until the reactant is consumed. If nucleation occurs over the whole surface, or if the growth of surface nuclei is unusually rapid, then the surface soon becomes covered by a product layer and the kinetics are governed by the rate of inward propagation of this contracting envelope. Thus the reaction is entirely deceleratory in character. A constant rate of propagation leads to the familiar "contracting volume" expression.

The conventional theory of the decomposition of solids distinguishes between formation and growth of nuclei in a very real way by ascribing different rate constants k_f and k_g to these two processes. This is a realistic procedure if a nucleus can be formed as a result of a single reaction step because the first molecular decomposition at a nucleus-forming site is clearly occurring in a different environment from that for subsequent ones.

An important advance over this picture was made by Bagdassarian,[50] who introduced the concept of multistep nucleation. He proposed, that in general, p successive molecular decompositions at a single site are required to form a stable growth nucleus and that nuclei containing less than p product atoms are not growth nuclei, but germ nuclei, which may become growth nuclei by acquiring the requisite number of product atoms. Bagdassarian considered only the special case

$$k_0 = k_1 = k_2 \cdots = k_{p-1}$$
$$k_p = k_{p+1} = k_{p+2} \cdots = k, \tag{96}$$

where k_i is the rate constant for the addition of a product atom to a nucleus containing i atoms. He recognized that this was an approximation, but did so because of mathematical convenience. The improvement due to Allnatt and Jacobs is to solve the general case in which all the k's are different. An especially important case which they consider is when the k's are different up to $i = r$ and then equal for $i > r$. Physically this means that a so-called germ nucleus forms in steps and then grows in a uniform manner once it has become a growth nucleus by becoming a nucleus of r atoms.

The differential equation controlling the number of nuclei n_i which contain i product atoms is

$$\frac{dn_i(t)}{dt} = k_{i-1} n_{i-1}(t) - k_i n_i(t) \tag{97}$$

This equation is to be solved subject to the boundary conditions $n_i = 0$ for $i < 0$; $n_i = 0$ for $i > 0$ at $t = 0$, $n_i = n_0(0)$ for $i = 0$ at $t = 0$; $n_i = 0$ for $i = 0$ at $t = \infty$. This can be solved by Laplace transforms to give

$$n_i(t) = n_0(0) k_0 k_1 k_2 \cdots k_{i-1} \left\{ \sum_{l=0}^{l=i} \frac{e^{-k_l t}}{\left(\prod_{\substack{j=0 \\ (j \neq l)}}^{i} (k_j - k_l) \right)} \right\} \tag{98}$$

They are then able to show by induction that for $k_j t \ll 1$ for all j,

$$n_i(t) = \frac{k_{i-1} k_{i-2} \cdots k_0 n_0(0)}{i!} t^i = K_i t^i \qquad (99)$$

which is the general power law for solid state nucleation. Equation (98) for $n_i(t)$ is inconvenient in the limiting case in which any two of the nucleation rate constants are equal. It is easier to consider the situation in which the k_i are all different for $i = 0, 1, 2, \ldots, r$, but $k_i = k$ for $i \geq r + 1$, by starting with Eq. (97) directly. Again, by means of Laplace transforms, one can show that

$$n_i(t) = n_0(0) k_0 k_1 k_2 \cdots k_r k^{i-r-1} I_i(t) \qquad (100)$$

where

$$I_i(t) = \sum_{l=0}^{r} \frac{e^{-k_l t}}{(k - k_l)^{i-r} \prod_{\substack{j=0 \\ (j \neq l)}}^{r} (k_j - k_l)}$$

$$\times \left[1 - e^{-(k-k_l)t} \left\{ \frac{[(k - k_l)t]^{i-r-1}}{(i - r - 1)!} + \frac{[(k - k_l)t]^{i-r-2}}{(i - r - 2)!} + \cdots 1 \right\} \right] \qquad (101)$$

These equations give the general solution to the problem of multistep nucleation when the rate constants are all different at the start, but after the nucleus contains more than r atoms, the nucleation rate constants have a constant value k for the addition of successive atoms of product. The limit for short times may be obtained by induction as before, and they obtain

$$n_i(t) = \frac{k^{i-r-1} k_r k_{r-1} \cdots k_0 n_0(0)}{(i - r - 1)!(r + 1)!} t^i = K_i t^i \qquad \text{provided} \quad kt, k_i t \ll 1 \qquad (102)$$

Thus the power law for nucleation is still valid, but the meaning of the constant K_i depends on whether the k_i are all unequal or whether $k_i = k$ for $i > r$.

The Bagdassarian model, see Eq. (96), then is given by

$$n_i(t) = \left(\frac{k_0}{k} \right)^p \left(\frac{k}{k_0 - k} \right)^i n_0(0) e^{-kt} \sum_{m=0}^{i-p} \frac{[(k_0 - k)t]^{i-p-m}}{(i - p - m)!} \frac{(m + p - 1)!}{m!(p - 1)!}$$

$$\times \left\{ 1 - e^{(k-k_0)t} \left[1 + \cdots + \frac{[(k_0 - k)t]^{m+p-2}}{(m + p - 2)!} + \frac{[(k_0 - k)t]^{m+p-1}}{(m + p - 1)!} \right] \right\}, \qquad (103)$$

which holds for $i \geq p$.

The total number of growth nuclei formed in time t is

$$n(t) = \sum_{i=p}^{\infty} n_i(t)$$

which can be shown to be

$$n(t) = n_0(0)\left\{1 - e^{-k_0 t} \sum_{j=0}^{p-1} \frac{(k_0 t)^j}{j!}\right\} \tag{104}$$

which was derived first by Bagdassarian in 1945. Bagdassarian's theory was one of photographic development but Allnatt and Jacobs utilize his basic idea of multistep nucleation in solid state thermal reactions. Thus in Bagdassarian's theory, nuclei go on growing after they contain p atoms of product but with a different rate constant k ($\neq k_0$). All nuclei with $i \geq p$ will then undergo development when the grains are exposed to the developer. In their theory, as soon as a nucleus reaches the size characterized by p atoms, it becomes a stable growth nucleus and no further assumptions about k_i, $i \geq p$, are necessary since k_i is automatically determined by whatever assumptions are made concerning the nuclear growth rates. For example, a constant growth rate means that $k_i \propto i^{2/3}$.

The two main theories of nucleus growth are those due to Avrami[90] and to Erofeev.[91] Avrami assumed that germ nuclei are converted into growth nuclei in a single activated step. However, some germ nuclei are lost through incorporation into growing nuclei, also some growth nuclei formed from germ nuclei, which happen to be near one another in the reactant, will impinge together and overlap during growth. This ingestion and overlap result in the fractional decomposition α being smaller than α_{ex}, the extended fractional decomposition, which Avrami defines as the fractional decomposition which would have occurred without ingestion and overlap. For spherical nuclei with a constant growth rate in a radial direction,

$$\alpha_{ex} = [V(\infty)]^{-1} \int_0^t d\tau \left(\frac{dn}{dt}\right)_{t=\tau} \frac{4\pi}{3} [G(t - \tau)]^3 \tag{105}$$

where G is the constant growth rate. The simplest expression that relates α to α_{ex} is given by

$$d\alpha = d\alpha_{ex}(1 - \alpha) \tag{106}$$

This is the simplest expression that satisfies the required boundary conditions $d\alpha/dt = d\alpha_{ex}/dt$ at $\alpha = 0$, $d\alpha/dt = 0$, but $d\alpha_{ex}/dt$ finite at $\alpha = 1$. The so-called Avrami equation is obtained by substituting $n(t)$ with $p = 1$

from Eq. (104) and integrating Eq. (106) to get

$$-\log (1 - \alpha) = Kn_0(0)\left\{e^{-k_0 t} - 1 + k_0 t - \frac{(k t_0)^2}{2!} + \frac{(k_0 t)^3}{3!}\right\} \quad (107)$$

where $K = 8\pi G^3/k_0{}^3 V(\infty)$. k_0 here is the nucleation rate constant. This equation was first derived by Avrami.

The Erofeev equation is obtained by using the small time behavior of $n(t)$, viz.,

$$\left(\frac{dn}{dt}\right)_{t=\tau} = \frac{n_0(0)k_0 k_1 \cdots k_{p-1}}{(p-1)!} t^{p-1} \quad (108)$$

which gives the Erofeev equation,

$$-\log (1 - \alpha) = (Kt)^{p+3} \quad (109)$$

where K is a combination of constants. This commonly used rate law of solid state reaction kinetics is frequently referred to as the Avrami-Erofeev equation since the Avrami equation reduces to this form for either short times or long times. Both the Avrami equation and the Erofeev equation are approximations that need not be made now since we have Eq. (100).

Suppose that nucleation is a multistep process characterized by rate constants $k_0, k_1, \ldots, k_p$, and that once a nucleus containing p atoms of product is formed it becomes an active growth nucleus. The rate of formation of *active growth nuclei* is therefore

$$\frac{dn_p(t)}{dt} = k_{p-1}n_{p-1}(t) = n_0(0)\sum_{l=0}^{p-1} B_{pl} e^{-k_l t} \quad (110)$$

where the general result has been used for $n_{p-1}(t)$ and

$$B_{pl} = k_l \prod_{\substack{j=0 \\ (j\neq l)}}^{p-1} \frac{k_j}{k_j - k_l}. \quad (111)$$

The extended fractional decomposition α_{ex} is then

$$\alpha_{ex} = \frac{4\pi}{3V(\infty)}\int_0^t d\tau \left[\frac{dn_p}{dt}\right]_{t=\tau} [G(t - \tau)]^3 \quad (112)$$

which gives

$$-\log (1 - \alpha) = 6\sigma[(V(\infty))]^{-1} n_0(0)G^3 \sum_{l=0}^{p-1} k_l{}^{-4} B_{pl}$$

$$\times \left\{e^{-k_l t} - 1 + k_l t - \frac{(k_l t)^2}{2!} + \frac{(k_l t)^3}{3!}\right\} \quad (113)$$

This is the general solution to the problem of multistep nucleation followed by a constant rate of growth in three dimensions. Equation (113) is of the same form as Eq. (107) and therefore is called the generalized Avrami equation. The limit for short times is

$$-\log(1 - \alpha) = 6\sigma[V(\infty)]^{-1}n_0(0)G^3 \sum_{l=0}^{p-1} B_{pl} \frac{(-k_l t)^{p+3}}{(p+3)!\,k_l} \qquad (k_l t \ll 1)$$

$$(114)$$

Thus $-\log(1 - \alpha)$ behaves like t^{p+3} when $k_l t \ll 1$, if there are p steps in forming a growth nucleus. But this is just Erofeev's equation, which is therefore exact in the limit of short times.

This concludes our discussion of nucleation and solid state nucleation, in particular. It is hoped that the examples chosen in this section illustrate to the reader some typical recent applications of stochastic processes to chemical rate processes, and indicates the utility, extent, and types of methods used.

References

1. H. A. Kramers, *Physica*, **7**, 284 (1940).
2. E. W. Montroll and K. E. Shuler, *Advan. Chem. Phys.*, **1**, 361 (1958).
3. S. K. Kim, *J. Chem. Phys.*, **28**, 1057 (1958).
4. K. E. Shuler and G. H. Weiss, *J. Chem. Phys.*, **38**, 505 (1963).
5. A. F. Bartholomay, *Bull. Math. Biophys.*, **20**, 97 (1958).
6. A. F. Bartholomay, *Bull. Math. Biophys.*, **20**, 175 (1958).
7. A. F. Bartholomay, *Bull. Math. Biophys.*, **21**, 363 (1959).
8. A. Rényi, *Magyar Tud. Akad. Alkalm. Mat. Közl.*, **2**, 93 (1954).
9. K. Ishida, *Bull. Chem. Soc. Japan*, **33**, 1030 (1960).
10. K. Ishida, *J. Chem. Soc.*, **41**, 2472 (1964).
11. K. Ishida, *J. Phys. Chem.*, **70**, 3806 (1966).
12. D. A. McQuarrie, *J. Chem. Phys.*, **38**, 433 (1963).
13. D. A. McQuarrie, C. J. Jachimowski, and M. E. Russell, *J. Chem. Phys.*, **40**, 2914 (1964).
14. I. G. Darvey, B. W. Ninham, and P. J. Staff, *J. Chem. Phys.*, **45**, 2145 (1966).
15. I. G. Darvey and P. J. Staff, *J. Chem. Phys.*, **44**, 990 (1966).
16. P. J. Staff, *J. Chem. Phys.*, **46**, 2209 (1967).
17. H. K. Frensdorff and R. Pariser, *J. Chem. Phys.*, **39**, 2303 (1963).
18. J. Hijmans, *Physica*, **29**, 1 (1963).
19. J. Hijmans, *Physica*, **29**, 819 (1963).
20. J. I. Lauritzen, E. A. DiMarzio, and E. Passaglia, *J. Chem. Phys.*, **45**, 4444 (1966).
21. L. Peller, *J. Chem. Phys.*, **36**, 2976 (1962).
22. L. Peller, *J. Chem. Phys.*, **43**, 2355 (1965).
23. F. P. Price, *J. Chem. Phys.*, **36**, 209 (1962).
24. E. R. Cohen and H. Reiss, *J. Chem. Phys.*, **38**, 680 (1963).
25. R. Simha, J. M. Zimmerman, and J. Moacanin, *J. Chem. Phys.*, **39**, 1239 (1963).
26. J. M. Zimmerman and R. Simha, *J. Theoret. Biol.*, **9**, 156 (1965).

27. J. M. Zimmerman and R. Simha, *J. Theoret. Biol.*, **13**, 106 (1966).
28. D. A. McQuarrie, J. P. McTague, and H. Reiss, *Biopolymers*, **3**, 657 (1965).
29. A. C. Pipkin and J. H. Gibbs, *Biopolymers*, **4**, 3 (1966).
30. G. Schwarz, *J. Mol. Biol.*, **11**, 64 (1965).
31. A. Amemiya, *J. Phys. Soc. Japan*, **17**, 1245 (1962).
32. A. Amemiya, *J. Phys. Soc. Japan*, **17**, 1694 (1962).
33. M. Gordon and L. R. Shenton, *J. Polymer Sci.*, **38**, 157 (1959).
34. M. Inokuti, *J. Chem. Phys.*, **38**, 1174 (1963).
35. S. N. Levine, *Science*, **152**, 651 (1966).
36. R. G. MacFarlane, *Nature*, **202**, 498 (1964).
37. G. Wald, *Science*, **150**, 1028 (1965).
38. M. Tanaka, *J. Phys. Soc. Japan*, **22**, 233 (1967).
39. R. M. Noyes, *Progr. Reaction Kinetics*, **1**, 129 (1961).
40. J. Yguerabide, M. A. Dillon, and M. Burton, *J. Chem. Phys.*, **40**, 3040 (1964).
41. A. G. Fredrickson, *Biotech. Bioeng.*, **8**, 167 (1966).
42. J. C. Giddings, *J. Chem. Phys.*, **31**, 1462 (1959).
43. J. C. Giddings and H. Eyring, *J. Phys. Chem.*, **59**, 416 (1955).
44. D. A. McQuarrie, *J. Chem. Phys.*, **38**, 437 (1963).
45. N. W. Bazley, E. W. Montroll, R. J. Rubin, and K. E. Shuler, *J. Chem. Phys.*, **28**, 700; **29**, 1185 (1958).
46. R. Herman and K. E. Shuler, *J. Chem. Phys.*, **29**, 366 (1958).
47. E. W. Montroll and K. E. Shuler, *J. Chem. Phys.*, **26**, 454 (1957).
48. R. J. Rubin and K. E. Shuler, *J. Chem. Phys.*, **25**, 68 (1956).
49. K. E. Shuler, *J. Phys. Chem.*, **61**, 849 (1957).
50. A. R. Allnatt and P. W. Jacobs, *Can. J. Chem.*, **46**, 111 (1968).
51. R. P. Andres and M. Boudart, *J. Chem. Phys.*, **42**, 2057 (1966).
52. B. K. Chakraverty, *Surface Sci.*, **4**, 205 (1966).
53. W. G. Courtney, *J. Chem. Phys.*, **36**, 2009 (1962).
54. J. Feder, K. C. Russell, J. Lothe. and G. M. Pound, *Advan. Phys.*, **15**, 111 (1966).
55. F. C. Goodrich, *Proc. Roy. Soc. (London) Ser. A*, **277**, 155 (1964).
56. J. P. Hirth and G. M. Pound, *Condensation and Evaporation*, Macmillan, New York, 1963.
57. K. Ishida, *Nippon Kagaku Zasshi*, **81**, 524 (1960).
58. M. A. Kastenbaum, *Biometrika*, **44**, 69 (1960).
59. P. Whittle, *Proc. Cambridge Phil. Soc.*, **61**, 475 (1965).
60. K. Ishida and Y. Yamamoto, *J. At. Energy Soc. Japan*, **4**, 322 (1962).
61. J. R. Anderson and I. M. Ritchie, *Proc. Roy. Soc. (London) Ser. A*, **299**, 354 (1967).
62. A. T. Bharucha-Reid, *Elements of the Theory of Markov Processes and Their Applications*, McGraw-Hill, New York, 1960.
63. K. Singer, *J. Roy. Statist. Soc.*, **B15**, 92 (1953).
64. E. W. Montroll, *Energetics in Metallurgical Phenomena*, Vol. 3, Gordon and Breach, New York, 1967.
65. G. H. Weiss, *Advan. Chem. Phys.*, **13**, 1 (1967).
66. S. Lifson and J. L. Jackson, *J. Chem. Phys.*, **36**, 2410 (1962).
67. D. A. McQuarrie, *J. Appl. Prob.*, **4**, 413 (1967).
68. B. Widom, *Advan. Chem. Phys.*, **5**, 353 (1962).
69. A. Osipov and E. Stupochenko, *Soviet Phys. Uspekhi*, **6**, 47 (1963).
70. J. Keck and G. Carrier, *J. Chem. Phys.*, **43**, 2284 (1965).
71. T. L. Hill, *Statistical Thermodynamics*, Addison-Wesley, Reading, Mass., 1960.

72. M. Krieger and P. J. Gans, *J. Chem. Phys.*, **32**, 247 (1960).
73. P. J. Gans, *J. Chem. Phys.*, **33**, 691 (1960).
74. A. Erdélyi, *Higher Transcendental Functions*, McGraw-Hill, New York, 1953.
75. P. M. Morse and H. Feshbach, *Methods of Theoretical Physics*, McGraw-Hill, N. Y., 1953.
76. P. J. Flory, *Principles of Polymer Chemistry*, Cornell University Press, Ithaca, N. Y., 1953.
77. C. S. Marvel, in *The Chemistry of Large Molecules*, R. E. Burk and O. Grummit, Eds., Interscience, New York, 1943.
78. D. F. Lee, J. Scanlan, and W. F. Watson, *Proc. Roy. Soc. (London) Ser. A*, **273**, 345 (1963).
79. T. Alfrey, Jr. and W. G. Lloyd, *J. Chem. Phys.*, **38**, 318 (1963).
80. C. B. Arends, *J. Chem. Phys.*, **38**, 322 (1962).
81. J. B. Keller, *J. Chem. Phys.*, **37**, 2584 (1962).
82. J. B. Keller, *J. Chem. Phys.*, **38**, 325 (1963).
83. L. Lazare, *J. Chem. Phys.*, **39**, 727 (1963).
84. R. J. Glauber, *J. Math. Phys.*, **4**, 294 (1963).
85. N. Gō, *J. Phys. Soc. Japan*, **22**, 413 (1967).
86. N. Gō, *J. Phys. Soc. Japan*, **22**, 416 (1967).
87. R. Kikuchi, *Ann. Phys. (N.Y.)*, **10**, 127 (1960).
88. A. Siberberg and R. Simha, (preprint).
89. J. G. Burr, in *Adv. in Photochem.*, **6**, 193 (1968).
90. J. Avrami, *J. Chem. Phys.*, **7**, 1103 (1939); **8**, 212 (1940); **9**, 177 (1941).
91. B. V. Erofeev, *Compt. Rend. Acad. Sci. U.R.S.S.*, **52**, 511 (1946).

THE KINETICS OF BIOPOLYMERIZATION ON NUCLEIC ACID TEMPLATES

JULIAN H. GIBBS

Metcalf Research Laboratory Brown University,
Providence, Rhode Island

CONTENTS

I. INTRODUCTION

The biosyntheses of the genetic substance DNA, of the various types ("messenger," "ribosomal," and "transfer") of RNA, and of both enzymatic and structural proteins are all effected on nucleic acid templates. In the case of the synthesis of DNA (gene "replication") and the various species of RNA ("transcription") the template is a DNA molecule; in the case of the synthesis of proteins ("translation") it is a messenger-RNA molecule. Despite this difference, which is probably rather important since DNA is normally a double-stranded helical polymer molecule whereas messenger-RNA is a less highly ordered single-stranded polymer molecule, there are striking similarities among these polymerization reactions. In particular, the enzymes (ribosomes in the case of protein synthesis) which catalyze these polymerizations all have the property that they will catalyze only the addition of monomers (as distinct from oligomers) to the end of a growing polymer chain, the process starting at a given end of the template.[1]

If the rate-controlling step in the addition of each monomer to a growing chain is, in all cases, assumed to be an enzymatically catalyzed chemical event rather than, for example, the unraveling of double helical template structure (in advance of the growing-chain end) where such exists, then the syntheses of DNA, RNA, and protein would, at first sight, all seem to represent similar, one-dimensional, stochastic processes. However, even

185

for the formal treatment of these syntheses as stochastic processes, one fundamental distinction between DNA and protein syntheses must be recognized. (The situation in the case of RNA synthesis is not yet clear on this point.) In the case of DNA synthesis, the already synthesized part of a growing DNA polymer chain remains bound along its full length to the DNA template strand on which it has been developed.[2] This blocks the template to the initiation of the synthesis of yet another polymer molecule; thus only one DNA strand at a time may be synthesized on each template strand. In the case of protein synthesis, however, the growing polypeptide chain remains attached to the messenger-RNA template molecule only through the most recently added amino acid monomer residue (and its still associated transfer-RNA which is not eliminated until the addition of the next amino acyl transfer RNA). That is, rather than covering the template from starting end to the farthest point that has been reached, as in the case of DNA synthesis, the growing chain "dangles" from the template at this "farthest point," where the last amino acid was added. (Each addition of an amino acid monomer unit shifts the point of attachment one template site[3] in the proper direction so that proper registration of growing chain with template is maintained.) In this case, therefore, more than one polypeptide chain can grow on a given template molecule at the same time.

In the latter case of multiple synthesis on a given template, the possibility of interference of one growing chain end with the motion of another must be considered in the establishment of a stochastic model for the process. That is, two growing chain ends cannot occupy the same template site at the same time. Furthermore, if the effective diameter of the ribosome catalyzing the polymerization events at a growing chain end is L, in units of numbers of template sites, then the distance of closest approach (in such units) of two growing chain ends is L template sites, although each growing-chain end moves but one site at each chemical event.

In each of these cases, the theorem of microscopic reversibility indicates that the only type of depolymerization event that need be considered in the establishment of a stochastic model for each of these processes is the back reaction in which a growing chain end moves back by one, and only one, site at a time.

Since a one-to-one correspondence exists between the distance, expressed as number of template sites, that a growing-chain end has progressed from the starting end of the template at a given time and the degree of polymerization of the growing chain at that time, an obvious analogy presents itself. In the case of DNA synthesis, the growth of the single new DNA chain on a given template strand may be related to the diffusion of a particle (representing the "growing-" or moving-chain end) on a one-dimensional lattice (representing the template).[4] In the case of protein synthesis, the allowed growth of several polypeptide chains on the same template may be related to the diffusion of several nonoverlapping segments of length L on a one-dimensional lattice.[5]

Therefore, each "system" in the ensemble requisite to a statistical discussion may be considered as a lattice with either one point-particle (DNA synthesis case) or many segment-particles (protein synthesis case) diffusing on it. In thermodynamic parlance, one may say that in the former case the system is closed with respect to both particles and lattices (one of each) whereas in the latter case the system is open with respect to particles, which, however, can only enter the system at a lattice end, though closed with respect to lattices (one only). In both cases each system is also closed with regard to lattice sites; the fixed template length $= K$.[6]

The case of protein synthesis, i.e., diffusion of many segments on the same one-dimensional lattice, is clearly recognized as a species of traffic problem. However, the existing traffic literature has been of no help to its solution. Indeed, only rather special types of solutions have presented themselves to date. On the other hand, methods for a full solution of the DNA synthesis problem, i.e., single-particle diffusion, are reasonably well known but not of much use, since they give solutions in terms of only slowly converging series. Nevertheless, the first two moments of the distribution of degrees of polymerization in the ensemble at each time are easily obtained.

Since detailed discussions of solutions obtained to date and of procedures for obtaining them have been published previously,[4,5] and since this article (like others in this volume) is based on the subject matter of a single oral presentation, only a brief review of treatments of the indicated stochastic models for these biopolymerizations will be given in the following discussion.

II. DNA REPLICATION

We designate the states available to each system as $1, 2, \ldots, i, \ldots K$. Thus, state i corresponds to a situation in which the excess of forward (polymerization) reaction events over backward (depolymerization) ones that have occurred is equal to i, so that the degree of polymerization of the new chain is i. In the analogous instance of a single particle diffusing on a lattice, state i corresponds to the particle resting on lattice site i, the lattice sites being numbered consecutively from the end where the particle begins its diffusion. The largest attainable degree of polymerization, equal to the degree of polymerization of the template, i.e., the number of lattice sites, is K. We further designate the number of systems in state i at time t as $N_i(t)$.

According to the discussion in the Introduction we may expect that, subject to certain restrictions described below, the polymerization involved in DNA replication may be described by the equations

$$N_i' = k_f N_{i-1} + k_b N_{i+1} - (k_f + k_b)N_i \qquad \text{for } 2 \leq i \leq K - 1 \qquad (1)$$

$$N_1' = + k_b N_2 - k_f N_1 \qquad (2)$$

$$N_K' = k_f N_{K-1} - k_b N_K \qquad (3)$$

Here k_f and k_b do not have solely their usual meanings as forward and backward chemical "rate constants," because the free monomer concentration has been included as a factor in k_f and the concentrations of the by-products of the forward reaction (inorganic pyrophosphate and water) have been absorbed into k_b. Since there are actually four different types of monomer, each template site specifying, according to the Watson-Crick base-pairing rules, which type is to be incorporated at that site, this use of the same k_f for each step is strictly valid only if all four monomer concentrations are equal, as well as essentially invariant during the duration of the process, and if the true rate constant for the incorporation of each type of monomer is independent not only of the nature of the monomer to be added but also of the nature of the sequence already incorporated.

Equations (1)–(3) with the initial conditions

$$N_1(O) = N = \text{constant}$$
$$N_i(O) = O \qquad \text{for } 2 \leq i \leq K \qquad (4)$$

describe one round of DNA replication and say nothing about events occurring during the period between completion of one round and initiation of the next. By a "round" of replication we may mean either the replication of a single DNA molecule once in a single cell, in which case we are adopting the usual Gibbsian view of imaginary replicas of the system to form an ensemble, or we may mean the single replication of each of a large number of identical DNA molecules all of which begin their replication in phase. The latter situation can be approximated by each set of identical DNA molecules, one molecule from each cell, that exists in a culture of cells of given genotype, provided that the cell divisions in the culture have initially been brought into common phase.

The problem posed by Eqs. (1)–(4) admits of solution in many forms. Montroll[7] has treated the initial-value problem for an equation of the same form as Eq. (1) but with $-\infty \leq i \leq \infty$ in place of our condition $2 \leq i \leq K - 1$. Montroll's method of solution, utilizing a generating function and an expansion involving Bessel functions of imaginary argument of the first kind of order K, has been extended[8] to treat the problem represented by Eqs. (1)–(4). Takacs[9] has given the matrix solution, useful only at small t, and the solution in terms of normal modes of relaxation, hardly useful at all in our case of large K for which the relaxation times are numerous and closely spaced. He has also given the solution in Montroll's form for the special case $K = \infty$.

Despite the availability of exact solutions, an intuitive comprehension of the results is more easily obtained from inspection of approximate solutions and special cases. For the former we consider the time evolution of the moments $\langle i^P \rangle$ of the distribution of degrees of polymerization N_i:

$$d\langle i^P \rangle/dt = \sum_{i=1}^{K} i^P N_i^1(t) \tag{5}$$

From Eqs. (1)–(3) we easily find $d\langle i^0 \rangle/dt = 0$, the condition of conservation of systems. It is convenient to normalize all the $N_i(t)$ such that

$$\sum_{i=1}^{K} N_i(t) = N = 1 \tag{6}$$

From Eqs. (1), (2), (3), (5), and (6) we obtain for the time dependence of the mean $\langle i \rangle$

$$d\langle i \rangle/dt = (k_f - k_b) + k_b N_1(t) - k_f N_K(t) \tag{7}$$

Also from Eqs. (1), (2), (3), (5), and (6) we can find an expression for $d\langle i^2 \rangle/dt$ (in terms of $\langle i \rangle$), which, when combined with Eq. (7), gives for the time evolution of the variance $\sigma^2 = \langle i^2 \rangle - \langle i \rangle^2$

$$d\sigma^2/dt = k_f + k_b - k_b N_1(2\langle i \rangle - 1) - k_f N_K(2K + 1 - 2\langle i \rangle) \tag{8}$$

Equation (7), with Eqs. (4) and (6), shows that the initial rate of increase of the average degree of polymerization is just k_f. As N_1 decreases toward 0 the rate of increase of this mean decreases toward $k_f - k_b$, a value which it sustains during a relatively long intermediate interval[4] (with large K) before N_K begins to become significantly large.

During this long intermediate interval, the variance grows at rate $k_f + k_b$, as shown by Eq. (8). We wish to determine whether the distribution spreads significantly during the time required for the mean to travel the full distance K. The latter time is approximately $K/(k_f - k_b)$ if the spreading is small (k_b not too close to k_f). Actually σ^2 increases at rate

$k_f + k_b$, so that, during this time, σ will reach the value

$$[(k_f + k_b)K/(k_f - k_b)]^{1/2}.$$

Considering spreading to be small if $\sigma \ll K$, or $\sigma^2 \ll K^2$, we see that it is small if $(k_f + k_b) \ll (k_f - k_b)K$. If the opposite be true, then the distribution changes more by spreading than by steady motion of the mean; in this case a reasonable estimate of the time required for a round of synthesis is the time for $\sigma^2 \approx K^2$, that is $K^2/(k_f + k_b)$.

To summarize, the time T for a round of synthesis is given by

$$T \sim \begin{cases} K/(k_f - k_b) & \text{if } (k_f - k_b)K \gg k_f + k_b \\ K^2/(k_f + k_b) & \text{if } (k_f - k_b)K \ll k_f + k_b \end{cases} \qquad (9)$$

These estimates have been given more rigorous justification elsewhere.[4]

In the case $k_b = 0$, a useful solution is available[10] not merely for the first few moments of the distribution $N_i(t)$ but actually for the distribution itself. This proves to be a Poisson distribution with parameter t for all states except the final state K:

$$N_i(t) = e^{-t}t^{i-1}/(i-1)! \qquad 1 \le i \le k-1$$

$$N_K(t) = \int_0^t e^{-\tau}\tau^{K-2}\, d\tau/(K-2)! \qquad (10)$$

Returning to the general case in which k_b is permitted to be nonzero, we comment on one more feature of this stochastic model, namely that the equilibrium distribution, considered as a function of k_f/k_b, displays a first order transition in the limit $K = \infty$. With $dN_i(\infty)/dt = 0$ the equilibrium solution to Eqs. (1)–(3) is seen to be of the form $N_i(\infty) = A(k_f/k_b)^i$. The conservation condition, Eq. (6), gives the value of A, and we have

$$N_i(\infty) = [(k_f/k_b) - 1](k_f/k_b)^i/[(k_f/k_b)^K - 1] \qquad (11)$$

which clearly undergoes a transition at $(k_f/k_b) = 1$.

Obviously Eq. (11) can also be derived directly from equilibrium thermodynamic considerations involving equilibrium constants. A statistical-mechanical derivation[4] of Eq. (11), utilizing an equilibrium (actually grand canonical) ensemble, points up the analogy between this transition and a special case of helix–coil transition, the latter being most usually treated with equilibrium ensembles.

The possibility that this transition might conceivably be involved in a mechanism controlling biopolymerization seems remote in view of the best estimates that one can make for $\Delta G°$, the standard free energy change of the individual reaction step, and the physiological concentrations of monomer and inorganic pyrophosphate, which, it will be recalled, are included in our k_f/k_b along with $k_{eq} = \exp\left(-\Delta G^\circ/RT\right)$.[11]

III. PROTEIN SYNTHESIS

We again number the lattice sites $1, 2, \ldots, K$ from beginning to end. Since the number of adjacent sites covered by the growing-chain end and ribosome (the "diffusing segment") is L, there are $L + 1$ states available to each lattice site (L distinguishable modes of occupation and one of emptiness). We stipulate that a particular lattice site j is in state 0 if it is empty and in state $s(1 \leq s \leq L)$ if the complete set of sites occupied by the segment covering j is $j - s + 1, \ldots, j - s + L$. For $s = 0, \ldots, L$, we let $n_j^{(s)}(t)$ be the fraction of systems in the ensemble which have site j in state s at time t.

Since site j must, at each time, be found in one and only one of these states we clearly have

$$\sum_{s=0}^{L} n_j^{(s)}(t) = 1 \tag{12}$$

The definition of the states s implies

$$n_j^{(s)}(t) = n_{j-s+L}^{(L)}(t) \qquad \text{for } 1 \leq s \leq L \tag{13}$$

Eqs. (11) and (12) together yield

$$n_j^{(0)}(t) = 1 - \sum_{s=1}^{L} n_j^{(s)}(t) = 1 - \sum_{s=1}^{L} n_{j-s+L}^{(L)}(t) = 1 - \sum_{s=1}^{L} n_{j+s-1}^{(L)}(t) \tag{14}$$

Thus the motion of each segment as a unit means, as shown by Eqs. (13) and (14), that we may express every $n_j^{(s)}(t)$ in terms of the $n_j^{(L)}(t)$.

We now define $q_j(t)$ to be the flux of occupancy of mode L between site j and site $j + 1$. We clearly have

$$dn_j^{(L)}(t)/dt = q_{j-1}(t) - q_j(t) \tag{15}$$

Allowing for possible backward, as well as forward, motion of a segment we write

$$q_j(t) = q_j^{(f)}(t) - q_j^{(b)}(t) \tag{16}$$

where the superscripts (f) and (b) indicate forward and backward fluxes, respectively.

Forward flux from j to $j+1$ is only possible if site j is in state L and site $j+1$ is in state 0. Thus,[12]

$$q_j^{(f)}(t) = k_f n_j^{(L)}(t) f_{j+1}(t)$$

where $f_{j+1}(t)$ is the conditional probability that site $j+1$ is in state 0 at time t, given that site j is in state L at the same time.

The assumed independence of the motions of the various growing-chain end ribosome complexes, when not actually in contact with one another, implies that $f_{j+1}(t)$ can be put, at least approximately, equal to the conditional probability that site $j+1$ is in state 0 (at time t) given that site j is simultaneously in either of the states compatible with $j+1$ in 0, that is, j in either L or 0. Since $n_j^{(0)}(t) + n_j^{(L)}(t) = n_{j+1}^{(0)}(t) + n_{j+1}^{(1)}(t)$, $f_{j+1}(t)$ may also be expressed as the probability that site $j+1$ is in state 0 given that it is in either state 0 or 1. Thus, we have $f_{j+1}(t) = n_{j+1}^{(0)}(t)/[n_{j+1}^{(0)}(t) + n_{j+1}^{(1)}(t)]$, or, from Eqs. (13) and (14),

$$f_{j+1}(t) = \frac{1 - \sum_{s=1}^{L} n_{j+s}^{(L)}(t)}{1 - \sum_{s=1}^{L} n_{j+s}^{(L)}(t) + n_{j+L}^{(L)}(t)} \tag{17}$$

We have thus found

$$q_j^{(f)}(t) = k_f \frac{n_j^{(L)}(t)\left[1 - \sum_{s=1}^{L} n_{j+s}^{(L)}(t)\right]}{1 - \sum_{s=1}^{L} n_{j+s}^{(L)}(t) + n_{j+L}^{(L)}(t)} \tag{18}$$

Similar considerations applied to the backward flux $q_j^{(b)}(t)$ give an analogous expression which, when combined with Eq. (18) according to Eq. (16), yields finally for $q_j(t)$

$$q_j(t) = k_f \frac{n_j^{(L)}(t)\left[1 - \sum_{s=1}^{L} n_{j+s}^{(L)}(t)\right]}{1 + n_{j+L}^{(L)}(t) - \sum_{s=1}^{L} n_{j+s}^{(L)}(t)} - k_b \frac{n_{j+1}^{(L)}(t)\left[1 - \sum_{s=1}^{L} n_{j-L+s}^{(L)}(t)\right]}{1 + n_{j-L+1}^{(L)}(t) - \sum_{s=1}^{L} n_{j-L+s}^{(L)}(t)} \tag{19}$$

Since it has been possible to write this flux equation in terms of only the $n_j^{(L)}(t)$, we drop the superscript and let $n_j^{(L)}(t) = n_j(t)$ in all subsequent discussion.

Equation (19) is valid for $2L - 1 \le j \le K - L$. At the ends it must be modified in accordance with the special boundary conditions.

We first investigate uniform density solutions of Eq. (19), because all steady-state solutions will be seen later to be closely related to these. If $n_j(t) = n(t)$ for all j, then Eq. (19) indicates $q_j(t) = q(t)$ for all j, which, substituted into Eq. (15), implies $n(t) = n$. When the latter is used in Eq. (19) we have

$$q(t) = q = (k_f - k_b)n(1 - Ln)/[1 - (L - 1)n] \qquad (20)$$

In order to be able to plot various uniform density solutions conveniently on the same scale, as in Figure 1, we define new variables $Q = Lq/(k_f - k_b)$ and $N = Ln$. Using these new variables Eq. (20) becomes

$$Q = N(1 - N)/[1 - N + (N/L)] \qquad (21)$$

which has a maximum value, $Q_{max} = N_{max}^2$, for $N = N_{max} = \sqrt{L}/(1 + \sqrt{L})$. The maximum true flux q_{max} is $(k_f - k_b)Ln_{max}^2$, where

$$n_{max} = 1/[\sqrt{L}(1 + \sqrt{L})].$$

For every flux q smaller than q_{max} there are two solutions; a low density solution, whose flux is less than the maximum possible because of the paucity of diffusing segments, and a high density solution, whose flux is restricted by the "traffic jam."

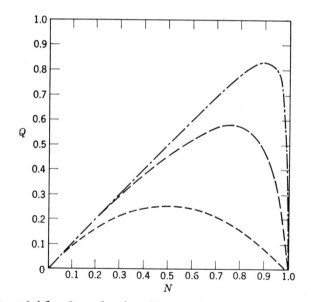

Fig. 1. The scaled flux Q as a function of the scaled density N in the case of uniform density solutions. (- - - -)$L = 1$. (— —)$L = 10$. (— . — . —)$L = 100$.

We now consider the wider class of steady state solutions defined by $dn_j(t)/dt = 0$. For these Eq. (15) gives $q_j(t) = q(t)$, and Eq. (19) gives $q(t) = q$. The latter has not yielded an analytical solution except for the case $L = 1$, to which we now restrict our attention.

With $L = 1$, as well as $dn_j(t)/dt = 0$, Eq. (19) reduces to

$$q = k_f n_j(1 - n_{j+1}) - k_b n_{j+1}(1 - n_j) \qquad (22)$$

This equation has three types of solutions. First, there are the uniform solutions, $n_j = n$, for which $q = (k_f - k_b)n(1 - n)$, as given by Eq. (20). Second, when q exactly equals the maximum flux permitted in the uniform density case, namely $\frac{1}{4}(k_f - k_b)$, the solutions are of the form

$$n_j = \frac{1}{2} + \frac{(k_f + k_b)}{(k_f - k_b)} \frac{1}{(2j + c)} \qquad 1 \leq j \leq k. \qquad (23)$$

This solution includes the uniform solution $n_j = \frac{1}{2}$ as the limit $C = \infty$. Third, for $q \neq \frac{1}{4}(k_f - k_b)$, the solutions can be seen to be of the form

$$n_j = n + \frac{1 - 2n}{1 + C'[f(n)]^j} \qquad 1 \leq j \leq K$$

with $\qquad\qquad\qquad\qquad\qquad\qquad\qquad\qquad\qquad\qquad\qquad (24)$

$$f(n) = \frac{n + (k_b/k_f)(1 - n)}{1 - n + (k_b/k_f)n}$$

and n here defined by $q = (k_f - k_b)n(1 - n)$. This includes the uniform solutions $n_k = n$ (as the limits $C' = \pm\infty$) and $n_k = 1 - n$ (as the limit $C' = 0$). It also includes the solutions of Eq. (23) by a special limiting process.

All these solutions are nearly uniform except for a limited range of values of k. To see this we write C as $-2j_0$ in Eq. (23) and C' as $\pm[f(n)]^{-j_0}$ in Eq. (24). In both cases it is clear that n_j varies significantly only in the neighborhood of $j = j_0$.

Detailed discussion of the solutions (23) and (24), for various values of the constants C and C' (i.e., j_0), may be found in Ref. 5, along with an analytic procedure for deriving them and an alternative graphical method of solution.

The various types of steady state solution are plotted in Figures 2–7. In any particular case the choice among these solution curves (or portions thereof) is naturally dictated by the boundary conditions. An extensive discussion of special boundary conditions for irreversible initiation and irreversible termination is also given in Ref. 5.

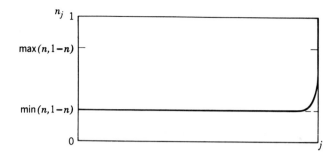

Fig. 2. Solution of Eq. (22) for a case of slow initiation, i.e., slow arrival at beginning of template, with polymerization somewhat faster than termination (release).

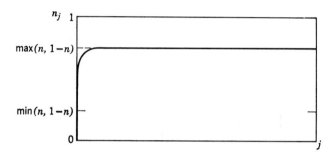

Fig. 3. Solution of Eq. (22) for a case of slow termination, i.e., slow release of completed chain from end of template, with polymerization somewhat faster than initiation (arrival).

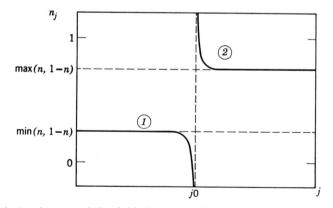

Fig. 4. Another case of slow initiation (curve *1*) and another of slow termination (curve *2*). Curve *1* differs from Figure 2 because here termination is faster than polymerization. Curve *2* differs from Figure 3 because here initiation is faster than polymerization.

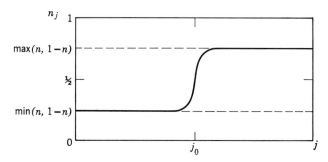

Fig. 5. Solution of Eq. (22) for a case in which initiation and termination rates are nearly equal and both slow compared to polymerization.

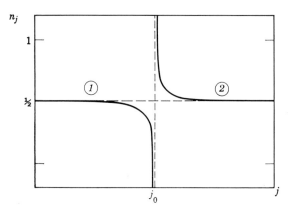

Fig. 6. Curve *1*: a case in which polymerization and initiation rates are nearly equal and both slow compared to termination. Curve *2*: a case in which polymerization and termination rates are nearly equal and both slow compared to initiation.

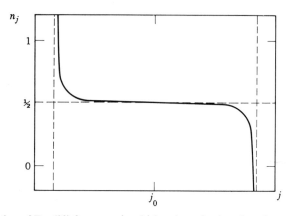

Fig. 7. Solution of Eq. (22) for a case in which polymerization alone is rate controlling.

It should suffice here to observe simply that the solutions shown in Figures 2 and 4 (curve *1*) correspond to cases in which initiation is rate limiting, that the ones shown in Figures 3 and 4 (curve *2*) correspond to cases in which termination is rate limiting, that the one shown in Figure 5 corresponds to a case in which both initiation and termination are rate limiting, and finally that the ones shown in Figures 6 and 7 correspond to cases in which the polymerization steps are partly and exclusively rate limiting, respectively.

For the very low density varieties of the cases shown in Figure 2 and, more particularly, Figure 4 (curve *1*), for which initiation is slow compared to both termination (release from end of template) and polymerization, a simpler treatment, in which the interference of one ribosome with another is totally neglected, should suffice. In this case an equation of the form of Eq. (1), herein only applied to the problem of DNA synthesis, should be valid, but Eqs. (2) and (3) should be modified to account for repetitive initiation at site 1 and continuing release from site K, respectively; Eqs. (4) and (6) will not apply. In the even more restricted (but perhaps biochemically relevant) case in which, in addition to neglecting ribosome interference, one may also neglect the back reaction ($k_b \approx 0$), one may solve this system of equations (Eq. (1), plus Eqs. (2) and (3) modified as described) very easily by taking Laplace transforms.[13] This is the only case with repetitive initiation for which we have been able to find solutions for the transient, as well as steady state, behavior.

In the general case, in which both back reaction and ribosome interference are accounted for, the influence of larger values of L on steady state solutions, analogous to those shown in Figures 2–7, has recently been determined[14] via machine computations of Eq. (19) with $n_j(t) = n_j$ and $q_j(t) = q$, as indicated by Eq. (15) with $dn_j(t)/dt = 0$.

The principal effect of larger L is to introduce into the regions of high density (traffic jams) an oscillation in the density n_j as a function of lattice site number j. As would be expected, these solutions are progressively damped in the direction of decreasing j.

Acknowledgment

As the references indicate, the work reviewed here was performed in collaboration with A. C. Pipkin and C. T. MacDonald, whose contributions are gratefully acknowledged by the author. This review was prepared while the author was on sabbatical leave from Brown University at the Max Planck Institute for Physical Chemistry in Göttingen, Germany, and was receiving support from the John Simon Guggenheim Memorial Foundation and from the governments of the United States and the Federal Republic of Germany under the Fulbright-Hays Act. The author wishes to thank all of these institutions and particularly his host, the director of the Max Planck Institute, Dr. Manfred Eigen.

References

1. H. M. Dintzis and P. M. Knopf, in *Informational Macromolecules*, H. J. Vogel, V. Bryson, and J. O. Lampen, Eds., Academic, New York, 1963, p. 376.
2. M. Meselson and F. Stahl, *Proc. Natl. Acad. Sci. U.S.*, **44**, 671 (1958).
3. In accordance with coding requirements each site is actually a triplet of nucleotide residues, but this feature need not concern us here.
4. A. C. Pipkin and J. H. Gibbs, *Biopolymers*, **4**, 3 (1966).
5. C. T. MacDonald, J. H. Gibbs and A. C. Pipkin, *Biopolymers*, **6**, 1 (1968).
6. In this respect, these template directed biopolymerizations differ from vinyl polymerizations with which they have in common the property of progressing via the accretion of monomers only.
7. E. W. Montroll, *J. Math. Phys.*, **25**, 37 (1946).
8. Appendix D of Ref. 4.
9. W. Takacs, *Introduction to the Theory of Queues*, Oxford, New York, 1962, pp. 12–26.
10. R. Simha, J. M. Zimmerman and J. Moacanin, *J. Chem. Phys.*, **39**, 1239 (1963).
11. In this standard relation k_{eq} is the equilibrium constant for the individual reaction step, and, of course, R is the gas constant and T the absolute temperature.
12. As in the case of DNA synthesis, discussed in Section II, the quantity k_f is the product of the usual chemical forward reaction rate constant and the monomer concentration. Again we are treating here only the special case in which it is assumed that all monomer concentrations, as well as all forward rate constants, are equal and invariant. An analogous comment applies to the quantity k_b, utilized below for the back reaction. In this case of protein synthesis, which probably involves 60-different types of monomer unit (amino-acyl transfer-RNA species), some of which may be present in only minor amounts, this restriction may be a very severe one.
13. J. Maniloff and J. H. Gibbs, unpublished.
14. C. T. MacDonald and J. H. Gibbs, *Biopolymers*, in press.

SOME MODELS FOR THE DECAY OF INITIAL CORRELATIONS IN DYNAMICAL SYSTEMS

GEORGE H. WEISS

Division of Computer Research and Technology,
National Institutes of Health, Public Health Service,
Department of Health, Education and Welfare, Bethesda, Maryland

CONTENTS

I. INTRODUCTION

Many problems in kinetic theory allow a rigorous formulation in terms of a Liouville equation which can then be reduced to equations for distribution functions involving small numbers of particles. Although the reduction can be effected rigorously, a strict solution is usually unavailable since the equation for the single particle distribution function contains the two particle distribution function, that for the two particle distribution function contains the three particle distribution function, and so forth. To arrive at an approximate solution, one must postulate factorization properties, so that, for example, the two-particle distribution function can be written as a product of single-particle distribution functions, or the three-particle function can be written in terms of single- and double-particle distribution functions. This procedure is implicit in a derivation of the Boltzmann equation for dilute gases from the BBGKY hierarchy. A more sophisticated approach to the problem of decoupling kinetic equations was initiated by Boguliubov,[1] who postulated that the n particle distribution functions could be represented as time-independent functionals of the single-particle distribution function after an initial time interval larger than the average duration of intermolecular collisions, but smaller than the mean free time between collisions. Further work on this general problem was done by Green[2,3] and Picirelli.[4] Kac[5] has discussed a similar problem for his "reduced" master equation, but only gave results on factorization properties in systems in which the initial distribution function is factorized.

It is the purpose of this article to review some recent work on some many-body models which can be solved exactly, making it possible to study factorization properties in some detail. Three models will be considered. The first is a set of random walkers on an infinite lattice, whose initial positions are correlated.[6] The subsequent motion of each random walker is independent of the others. The second model is a chain of harmonic oscillators in which the initial distribution of momenta is Gaussian but contains correlations.[7] This model stands in contrast to the random walk model in that it allows interactions between particles, albeit of a very simple form. The third model, first studied by Glauber,[8] is a one-dimensional Ising model with prescribed transition rates for spin reversals. This model is also one in which interparticle interactions can be taken into account in an exact way. There are further models[9,10] which allow the study of the same questions, so that this article is by no means a complete review of the problem area. Furthermore, even in the two models with interactions we have not considered the most general classes of initial conditions, so that we have bypassed the problem of whether there are special sets of initial conditions for which our conclusions about the decay of correlations do not hold.[11] Nevertheless, we are able to demonstrate that the Boguliubov hypothesis is valid for some simple systems, and to give an account of the time dependent behavior involved.

II. THE INDEPENDENT RANDOM WALK MODEL

The simplest of these models which permits a detailed discussion of the decay of correlations is a random walk model in which a set of random walkers whose positions are initially correlated is allowed to diffuse; the motion of any single random walker being independent of any other member of the set. Let us assume that there are r particles in the set and motion occurs on a discrete lattice. The state of the system is, therefore, completely specified by the probabilities $\{P_r(n_1, n_2, \ldots, n_r; t)\}$, $(n_j = \cdots -1, 0, 1, 2, \ldots)$ in which $P_r(n; t)$ is the joint probability that particle 1 is at n_1, particle 2 is at n_2, etc., at time t. We will also use the notation $N_j(t)$ for the random variable that is the position of random walker j at time t. Reduced probability distributions can be defined in terms of the $P_r(n; t)$ by summation. We will use the notation $P_j(n_{i_1}, n_{i_2}, \ldots, n_{i_j}; t)$ to denote the distribution of random walkers $i_1, i_2, \ldots, i_j$ at time t. We define

$P_j(n_{i_1}, \ldots, n_{i_j}; t)$ to be the joint probability that $N_{i_1}(t) = n_{i_1}$, $N_{i_2}(t) = n_{i_2}$, and so forth. This function is related to the complete distribution P_r by

$$P_j(n_{i_1}, n_{i_2}, \ldots, n_{i_j}; t) = \sum_{C(n_{i_1}, \ldots, n_{i_j})} P_r(\mathbf{n}; t) \qquad (1)$$

where the sum is to be taken over the set of n's complementary to $(n_{i_1}, n_{i_2}, \ldots, n_{i_j})$. In order to study properties related to correlation we require a functional of the P's which vanishes when the particles are uncorrelated. The most convenient set of functionals with this property is the set of Ursell functions

$$U_1(n; t) = P_1(n; t)$$
$$U_2(n_1, n_2; t) = P_2(n_1, n_2; t) - P_1(n_1; t)P_1(n_2; t)$$
$$U_3(n_1, n_2, n_3; t) = P_3(n_1, n_2, n_3; t) - P_2(n_1, n_2; t)P_1(n_3; t) \qquad (2)$$
$$- P_2(n_1, n_3; t)P_1(n_2; t) - P_2(n_2, n_3; t)P_1(n_1; t)$$
$$+ 2P_1(n_1; t)P_1(n_2; t)P_1(n_3; t)$$
$$\vdots$$

Successive terms in this sequence can be obtained from a type of cumulant generating function. If, in the expansion of

$$\ln \varphi(s_1, s_2, \ldots, s_r) = \ln \langle \exp [i(s_1 N_{i_1} + s_2 N_{i_2} + \cdots + s_r N_{i_r})] \rangle \qquad (3)$$

we replace terms of the form $\langle N_{i_1}, N_{i_2}, \ldots, N_{i_k} \rangle$ by $P_k(n_{i_1}, n_{i_2}, \ldots n_{i_k}; t)$ then the coefficient of $(-1)^k s_{i_1}, s_{i_2}, \ldots, s_{i_k}$ is just $U_k(n_{i_1}, \ldots, n_i; t)$. It is evident that if the N's are uncorrelated so that $\langle N_{i_1}, N_{i_2}, \ldots, N_{i_R} \rangle = \langle N_{i_1} \rangle \langle N_{i_2} \rangle \cdots \langle N_{i_k} \rangle$ then the U's with the exception of U_1 will all be equal to zero. It is also not difficult to show that

$$\sum_{n_j} U_s(\mathbf{n}; t) = 0 \qquad \text{for } s = 2, 3, \ldots \qquad (4)$$
$$j = 1, 2, \ldots, r$$

We now consider the development of $P_r(n; t)$ in time, making the assumption that the stochastic process can be described by a master equation

$$\dot{P}_r(\mathbf{n}; t) = \sum_{\mathbf{m}} A_r(\mathbf{n}, \mathbf{m})P_r(\mathbf{m}; t) \qquad (5)$$

in which $A_r(\mathbf{n}, \mathbf{m})$ is the transition rate (assumed independent of time) from state $\mathbf{m}$ to $\mathbf{n}$. Our assumption of independence of transitions made by the separate random walkers can be expressed as a condition on the transition probability $W_r(n, t \mid m, 0)$ (that is, the probability that the system is in state n at time t conditional on its being in state m at time 0. This condition is

$$W_r(\mathbf{n}, t \mid \mathbf{m}, 0) = \prod_{j=1}^{r} W_1(n_j, t \mid m_j, 0) \qquad (6)$$

Since, by definition

$$P_r(\mathbf{n}; t) = \sum_{\mathbf{m}} W_r(\mathbf{n}, t \mid \mathbf{m}, 0) P_r(\mathbf{m}; 0) \qquad (7)$$

it follows from Eq. (2) that

$$U_r(\mathbf{n}; t) = \sum_{\mathbf{m}} \left\{ \prod_{i=1}^{r} W(n_i, t \mid m_i, 0) \right\} U_r(\mathbf{m}; 0) \qquad (8)$$

Furthermore, the Markov assumption implies that the W_1 satisfy

$$\frac{\partial W(n, t \mid m, 0)}{\partial t} = \sum_{m'} A_1(n, m') W(m', t \mid m, 0) \qquad (9)$$

It is now possible to derive rather general results on the relaxation of all of the Ursell functions for the particular model just outlined. Let us decompose $W(n, t \mid m, 0)$ in the following form

$$W(n, t \mid m, 0) = P_1(n; \infty) + \varepsilon_{nm}(t) \qquad (10)$$

where $P_1(n; \infty)$ is the equilibrium distribution and $\lim_{t \to \infty} \varepsilon_{nm}(t) = 0$. We substitute this last relation into Eq. (7) and consider the resulting expressions for $P_2(n; t)$ and $U_2(n; t)$. These are

$$P_2(\mathbf{n}; t) = P_1(n_1; \infty) P_1(n_2; \infty) + P_1(n_1; \infty) \sum_{m_2} \varepsilon_{n_2 m_2} P_1(m_2; 0)$$

$$+ P_1(n_2; \infty) \sum_{m_1} \varepsilon_{n_1 m_1} P_1(m_1; 0) + \sum_{\mathbf{m}} \varepsilon_{n_1 m_1} \varepsilon_{n_2 m_2} P_2(\mathbf{m}; 0) \qquad (11a)$$

$$U_2(\mathbf{n}; t) = P_1(n_1; \infty) P_1(n_2; \infty) \sum_{\mathbf{m}} U_2(\mathbf{m}; 0) + P_1(n_1; \infty) \sum_{\mathbf{m}} \varepsilon_{n_2 m_2} U_2(\mathbf{m}; 0)$$

$$+ P_1(n_2; \infty) \sum_{\mathbf{m}} \varepsilon_{n_1 m_1} U_2(\mathbf{m}; 0) + \sum_{\mathbf{m}} \varepsilon_{n_1 m_1} \varepsilon_{n_2 m_2} U_2(\mathbf{m}; 0). \qquad (11b)$$

When the equilibrium singlet distribution is not equal to zero it is possible to infer from these equations that $U_2(n; t)$ goes to zero at a faster rate than $P_2(n; t)$ goes to its equilibrium value. From Eq. (10) we see that

$$P_2(\mathbf{n}; t) - P_1(n_1; \infty) P_1(n_2; \infty) \sim P_1(n_1; \infty) \sum_{m_2} \varepsilon_{n_2 m_2} P_1(m_2; 0)$$

$$+ P_1(n_2; \infty) \sum_{m_1} \varepsilon_{n_1 m_1} P_1(m_1; 0) = 0(\varepsilon) \qquad (12)$$

at sufficiently large values of t. On the other hand, the first three terms on the right-hand side of Eq. (11b) are identically zero according to the sum rules given in Eq. (4). Thus

$$U_2(\mathbf{n}; t) = \sum_{\mathbf{m}} \varepsilon_{n_1 m_1} \varepsilon_{n_2 m_2} U_2(\mathbf{m}; 0) = 0(\varepsilon^2) \tag{13}$$

at sufficiently long times. This argument can be extended trivially to show that

$$P_r(\mathbf{n}; t) - \prod_{i=1}^{r} P_1(n_i; \infty) = 0(\varepsilon); \qquad U_r(\mathbf{n}; t) = 0(\varepsilon^r) \tag{14}$$

for any $r \geq 1$.

Slightly different results apply when the $P_1(n; \infty) = 0$. Then, in several special cases that we have examined the $\varepsilon_{nm}(t)$ appearing in Eq. (10) can be decomposed as

$$\varepsilon_{nm}(t) = a_n(t) + b_{nm}(t) \tag{15}$$

where

$$\lim_{t \to \infty} \frac{b_{nm}(t)}{a_n(t)} = 0 \tag{16}$$

Substitution of Eq. (15) into Eq. (11a) leads to

$$P_2(\mathbf{n}; t) \sim a_{n_1}(t) a_{n_2}(t) = 0(a^2) \tag{17}$$

for large t while $U_2(n; t)$ goes as

$$U_2(\mathbf{n}; t) = \sum_{\mathbf{m}} b_{n_1 m_1}(t) b_{n_2 m_2}(t) U_2(\mathbf{m}; 0) = 0(b^2) \tag{18}$$

Thus when the decomposition of Eq. (15) is valid together with the limit properties of Eq. (16), U_2 goes to zero faster than P_1 or P_2.

The properties relating to decay of correlations have so far been discussed only in terms of Ursell functions, or functions generated from a cumulant expansion. This is obviously not a unique choice. Although there has been no systematic exploration of possible alternative families with, perhaps, better separation of rates of convergence than that expressed in Eqs. (12) and (13), or (17) and (18), it is of some interest to examine the Kirkwood[12] approximation form

$$K_3(\mathbf{n}; t) = P_3(\mathbf{n}; t) - \frac{P_2(n_1, n_2; t) P_2(n_1, n_3; t) P_2(n_2, n_3; t)}{P_1(n_1; t) P_1(n_2; t) P_1(n_3; t)} \tag{19}$$

When an analysis similar to that given for U_3 is carried out it is found that asymptotically $K_3 = 0(\varepsilon^3)$, i.e., the relaxation goes at the same rate as U_3.

Two special cases of the theory illustrate the important features. The first is the relaxation of an ensemble of noninteracting harmonic oscillators in contact with a heat bath, and subject to nearest neighbor transitions in the discrete translational energy space. The master equations which describe the evolution of the ensemble can be written[13]

$$\dot{P}_n = ne^{-\theta}P_{n-1} + (n+1)P_{n+1} - [n + (n+1)e^{-\theta}]P_n \qquad n = 0, 1, 2, \ldots \tag{20}$$

where $P_n(\tau)$ is the fraction of oscillators in energy state n at dimensionless time τ, $\theta = h\nu/(kT)$ where ν is the fundamental frequency of the oscillators, T is the temperature of the heat bath, and $\tau = \Lambda t$ where Λ is a rate constant. At sufficiently large τ the transition probability $W(n, \tau \mid m, 0)$ takes the form[14]

$$W(n, \tau \mid m, 0) \sim e^{-n\theta}(1 - e^{-\theta})\{1 + e^{-\tau}[4nm \sinh^2 \theta + e^{-\theta}$$
$$- (m+n)(1 - e^{-\theta})] + 0(e^{-2\tau})\} = P_1(n; \infty) + F_{nm} e^{-\tau} \tag{21}$$

Hence, the relaxation properties of the P's and U's are summarized by

$$P_r(\mathbf{n}; \tau) - \prod_{i=1}^{r} P_1(n_i; \infty) \sim c_r e^{-\tau}$$
$$U_r(\mathbf{n}; \tau) \sim d_r e^{-r\tau} \tag{22}$$

where c_r and d_r are constants depending on the initial values. A second example is that of an ensemble of random walkers on a lattice in which the rate of transitions from any site n to $n \pm j$ is $\Lambda\alpha_j$ where Λ is a rate constant and the α_j's are probabilities. If we let $\tau = \Lambda t$ and

$$\sigma^2 = \sum_{j=1}^{\infty} j^2 \alpha_j < \infty; \qquad \rho^4 = \sum_{j=1}^{\infty} j^4 \alpha_j < \infty \tag{23}$$

then the transition probability W can be shown to have the asymptotic form[6]

$$W(n, \tau \mid m, 0) \sim \frac{1}{\sigma(2\pi\tau)^{1/2}}\left\{1 + \frac{1}{\tau}\left[\frac{\rho^4}{8\sigma^2} - \frac{(m-n)^2}{2\sigma^2}\right] + o\left(\frac{1}{\tau}\right)\right\} \tag{24}$$

Thus, the function $\varepsilon_{nm}(\tau)$ can be decomposed as shown in Eq. (15), and it follows that asymptotically

$$P_r(\mathbf{n}; \tau) \sim A_r \tau^{-r/2}$$
$$U_r(\mathbf{n}; \tau) \sim B_r \tau^{-3r/2} \tag{25}$$

where A_r and B_r are constants.

III. HARMONIC OSCILLATOR MODELS

The simple class of models just discussed is of interest because it is possible to characterize the decay of correlations rather completely. However, these models are rather far from reality since they take no account of interparticle forces. A next step in our examination of the decay of initial correlations is to find an interacting system of comparable simplicity whose dynamics permit us to calculate at least some of the quantities that were calculated for the noninteracting systems. One model for which reasonably complete results can be derived is that of an infinite chain of harmonic oscillators in which initial correlations in momentum are imposed. Since the dynamics of the system can be calculated exactly, one can, in principle, study the decay of correlations due solely to internal interactions (as opposed to interactions with an external heat bath). We will not discuss the most general form of initial correlations but restrict our attention to those in which the initial positions and momenta have a Gaussian distribution so that two-particle correlations characterize the initial distribution completely. Let the displacement of oscillator j from its equilibrium position be denoted by q_j and let the momentum of oscillator j be p_j. On the assumption that the mass of each oscillator is equal to 1, the momentum is related to displacement by $p_j = \dot{q}_j$. We shall study the relaxation properties of the correlation function

$$\mu_{rs}(t) = \langle p_r(t)p_s(t) \rangle \tag{26}$$

Notice that this problem differs from one analyzed by Mazur and Montroll[16] since they were interested in the time relaxed momentum correlation functions $\langle p_r(0)p_s(t) \rangle$. In an equilibrium ensemble it is known that both the q_j and the p_j have a Gaussian distribution,[15] and the distribution of momenta is characterized by

$$\langle p_r(t) \rangle = 0, \langle p_r(t)p_s(t) \rangle = kT \delta_{rs} \tag{27}$$

where T is the temperature of the system and δ_{rs} is a Kronecker delta. Furthermore, since the distribution is Gaussian, knowledge of the mean and covariance matrix is sufficient to specify the distribution, i.e., all of the higher order moments and correlation functions can be written in terms of the $\langle p_j \rangle$ and the $\langle p_r p_s \rangle$.

The problem to be discussed contains the assumption of an initial Gaussian distribution of momenta in which

$$\langle p_r(0) \rangle = 0, \qquad \langle p_r(0)p_s(0) \rangle = kT\rho_{rs}(0) \tag{28}$$

We will assume that $\rho_{rr}(0) = 1$, for all r, as would be characteristic of contact with a heat bath at temperature T at $t = 0$. The new feature of the present model is in the examination of the effect of initially correlated momenta. Some specification of the initial position distribution is required for a complete description of the model. This is also taken as a Gaussian distribution, and the probability density is assumed to be characteristic of a chain of harmonic oscillators in equilibrium with a heat bath at temperature T; that is

$$P(\mathbf{q}(0)) = \exp(-\beta V)/\int_{-\infty}^{\infty} \cdots \int \exp(-\beta V)\, d\mathbf{q} \qquad (29)$$

where $\beta = (kT)^{-1}$ and V is the potential energy. A further hypothesis is that positions and momenta are initially uncorrelated, or

$$\langle p_r(0)q_s(0)\rangle = 0 \qquad (30)$$

The equations of motion for the system can be written

$$\begin{aligned}
\dot{q}_r &= p_r \\
\dot{p}_r &= \sum_s \gamma_{r-s}(q_s - q_r)
\end{aligned} \qquad (31)$$

where the γ_j are force constants relating force to displacement of oscillators j lattice points apart, and where $\gamma_j = \gamma_{-j}$. These equations, being linear, have solutions which depend linearly on the initial values of the $p_r(0)$ and $q_r(0)$, that is to say, on a set of Gaussian random variables. Hence, the $p_r(t)$ and $q_r(t)$ have a Gaussian distribution for all values of t, which is completely characterized by the correlation functions $\langle q_r(t)q_s(t)\rangle$, $\langle p_r(t)q_s(t)\rangle$, and $\langle p_r(t)p_s(t)\rangle$, since $\langle p_r(t)\rangle = \langle q_r(t)\rangle = 0$.

We will be interested only in the probability density for momentum which implies that we need only calculate the quantity $\langle p_r(t)p_s(t)\rangle = \mu_{rs}(t)$. More complete results can be obtained if desired, but these do not lead to more information and needlessly complicate the analysis. A calculation of $\mu_{rs}(t)$ is considerably simplified by introducing the normal coordinates (for an infinite lattice):

$$P(\theta, t) = \sum_{r=-\infty}^{\infty} p_r(t)e^{-ir\theta}, \qquad Q(\theta, t) = \sum_{r=-\infty}^{\infty} q_r(t)e^{-ir\theta} \qquad (32)$$

together with the inverse relations

$$p_r(t) = \frac{1}{2\pi}\int_{-\pi}^{\pi} P(\theta, t)e^{ir\theta}\, d\theta, \qquad q_r(t) = \frac{1}{2\pi}\int_{-\pi}^{\pi} Q(\theta, t)e^{ir\theta}\, d\theta \qquad (33)$$

Since $\dot{q}_r = p_r$, $P(\theta, t)$ and $Q(\theta, t)$ are related by $P = \partial Q/\partial t$.

We shall be interested in properties of

$$\mu_{rs}(t) = \frac{1}{4\pi^2} \int_{-\pi}^{\pi} \int_{-\pi}^{\pi} \langle P(\theta, t)P(\theta', t)\rangle \exp\left[i(r\theta + s\theta')\right] d\theta\, d\theta' \qquad (34)$$

where $P(\theta, t)$ is the solution to $\ddot{P} + \omega^2(\theta)P = 0$, and

$$\omega^2(\theta) = 2\sum_{r=1}^{\infty} \gamma_r(1 - \cos r\theta) \qquad (35)$$

The value of $\langle P(\theta, t)P(\theta', t)\rangle$ to be inserted into Eq. (34) can be written in terms of initial values of correlation functions as

$$
\begin{aligned}
\langle P(\theta, t)P(\theta', t)\rangle = {} & \langle P(\theta, 0)P(\theta', 0)\rangle \cos \omega(\theta)t \cos \omega(\theta')t \\
& + \langle Q(\theta, 0)Q(\theta', 0)\rangle\omega(\theta)\omega(\theta') \sin \omega(\theta)t \sin \omega(\theta')t \\
& - \langle P(\theta, 0)Q(\theta', 0)\rangle\omega(\theta') \sin \omega(\theta')t \cos \omega(\theta)t \\
& - \langle P(\theta', 0)Q(\theta, 0)\rangle\omega(\theta) \sin \omega(\theta)t \cos \omega(\theta')t
\end{aligned}
\qquad (36)
$$

By hypothesis $\langle P(\theta, 0)Q(\theta', 0)\rangle = 0$, and $\langle Q(\theta, 0)Q(\theta', 0)\rangle$ is easily shown to be[16]

$$\langle Q(\theta, 0)Q(\theta', 0)\rangle = \frac{kT}{\omega^2(\theta)}\, \delta(\theta + \theta') \qquad (37)$$

An expression for $\langle P(\theta, 0)P(\theta', 0)\rangle$ can be derived from the initial conditions given in Eq. (28), and is

$$
\begin{aligned}
\langle P(\theta, 0)P(\theta', 0)\rangle = {} & kT \sum_{r} \sum_{\substack{s \\ r \neq s}} \rho_{rs}(0) \exp\left[-i(r\theta + s\theta')\right] \\
& + kT \sum_{r} \exp\left[-ir(\theta + \theta')\right] \\
= {} & 2\pi kT\, \delta(\theta + \theta') + kT \sum_{r} \sum_{\substack{s \\ r \neq s}} \rho_{rs}(0) \\
& \times \exp\left[-i(r\theta + s\theta')\right]
\end{aligned}
\qquad (38)
$$

Substituting this into Eq. (36), and using the expression for

$$\langle Q(\theta, 0)\, Q(\theta', 0)\rangle$$

given in Eq. (37), we find that $\mu_{rs}(t)$ is given by

$$
\begin{aligned}
\mu_{rs}(t) &= kT\, \delta_{rs} + kT \sum_{m} \sum_{\substack{n \\ m \neq n}} \rho_{mn}(0)A_{r-m}(t)A_{s-n}(t) \\
&= kT\, \delta_{rs} + kT\rho_{rs}(t)
\end{aligned}
\qquad (39)
$$

in which

$$A_s(t) = \frac{1}{2\pi} \int_0^{2\pi} \cos \omega(\theta)t \cos s\theta \, d\theta \qquad (40)$$

and $\rho_{jk}(t)$ is defined by the sum in Eq. (39).

It is easily verified that $|A_s(t)| \leq 1$ and that $\lim_{t \to \infty} A_s(t) = 0$. Hence, if the sum $\displaystyle\sum_r \sum_s \rho_{rs}(0)$ converges then
$$_{r \neq s}$$

$$\lim_{t \to \infty} \mu_{js}(t) = kT \, \delta_{js} \qquad (41)$$

as is required by equipartition of energy. When the lattice is finite, the sum defining $\rho_{jk}(t)$ is always a finite sum and we can always infer that $\rho_{jk}(t)$ approaches 0 for times t that satisfy $\omega_L^{-1} \ll t \ll t_p$ where ω_L is the maximal normal mode of the lattice, and where t_p is the Poincaré cycle time for recurrences associated with dynamic properties of the lattice. It is possible that the sum defining $\rho_{jk}(t)$ does not approach 0 for sufficiently large times on an infinite lattice model. This apparent difficulty can be traced to taking the limit $N = \infty$ *before* taking the limit $t = \infty$. When the two limits are interchanged the difficulty disappears.

We now turn our attention to functions that are of more direct interest; the probability densities that describe the momenta of specified sets of particles. It will prove advantageous to work with characteristic functions rather than probability densities. We consider a specified set of r particles labelled $(i_1, i_2, \ldots, i_r)$ in which the particles are not necessarily related as nearest neighbors. Let $P_r(p_{i_1}, p_{i_2}, \ldots, p_{i_r}; t)$ be the probability density for the set of momenta $(p_{i_1}, \ldots, p_{i_r})$ at time t, and let the characteristic function $\varphi_r(\omega_{i_1}, \omega_{i2}, \ldots, \omega_{i_r}; t)$ be defined by

$$\varphi_r(\omega; t) = \int_{-\infty}^{\infty} \cdots \int P_r(\mathbf{p}; t) e^{i\omega \cdot \mathbf{p}} \, d^r \mathbf{p} \qquad (42)$$

together with the reciprocal relation

$$P_r(\mathbf{p}; t) = \frac{1}{(2\pi)^r} \int_{-\infty}^{\infty} \cdots \int \varphi_r(\omega; t) e^{-i\omega \cdot \mathbf{p}} \, d^r \omega \qquad (43)$$

Since the joint probability density of the complete set of positions and momenta is Gaussian, the distribution of any subset must also be Gaussian. But the characteristic function corresponding to a Gaussian density takes a simple form, and in the present case is

$$\varphi_r(\omega; t) = \exp \left[-\frac{1}{2} \sum_{j=1}^r \sum_{k=1}^r \omega_{i_j} \omega_{i_k} \mu_{i_j i_k}(t) \right] \qquad (44)$$

The expression given in this equation is easier to analyze than the equivalent one for P_r, since it involves the momentum correlation function directly rather than the inverse of the correlation matrix. It is a simple matter now to extract information related to the decay of correlations starting from Eq. (44). We note, first of all, that the functions $\mu_{rs}(t)$ can be expressed in terms of the $A_r(t)$, and these have the property $\lim_{t \to \infty} A_r(t) = 0$. Let us also set

$$\mu_{rs}(t) = kT[\delta_{rs} + \rho_{rs}(t)] \tag{45}$$

in which $\lim_{t \to \infty} \rho_{rs}(t) = 0$.

As a measure of the relaxation of the single particle distribution function we define a function $\Delta_1(\omega; t)$ by

$$\Delta_1(\omega_j; t) = \varphi_1(\omega_j; t) - \varphi_1(\omega_j; \infty) \tag{46}$$

For sufficiently large values of t the term $\rho_{jj}(t)$ is small so that to first order

$$\Delta_1(\omega_j; t) \sim -\frac{kT}{2} \omega_j{}^2 \rho_{jj}(t) \exp\left[-\frac{kT}{2} \omega_j{}^2\right] + 0(\rho^2) \tag{47}$$

This result can be transformed back into momentum space by making use of Eq. (43), and leads to the result

$$P_1(p_j; t) - P_1(p_j; \infty) \sim \frac{\beta}{2} \rho_{jj}(t)(\beta p_j{}^2 - 1) P_1(p_j; \infty) + 0(\rho^2) \tag{48}$$

In similar fashion, the relaxation of the two-particle characteristic function can be described in terms of a function $\Delta_2(\omega_r, \omega_s; t)$:

$$\Delta_2(\omega_r, \omega_s; t) = \varphi_2(\omega_r, \omega_s; t) - \varphi_1(\omega_r; t)\varphi_1(\omega_s; t)$$
$$\sim -kT\omega_r\omega_s \rho_{rs}(t)\varphi_1(\omega_r; \infty)\varphi_1(\omega_s; \infty) + 0(\rho^2) \tag{49}$$

from which it follows that in momentum space, at sufficiently large values of t

$$P_2(p_r, p_s; t) - P_1(p_r; t)P_1(p_s; t) = U_2(p_r, p_s; t)$$
$$\sim \beta^2 p_r p_s \rho_{rs}(t) P_1(p_r; \infty) P_1(p_s; \infty) + 0(\rho^2) \tag{50}$$

This function is the analogue of U_2 introduced in the study of independent particle dynamics. The significance of Eqs. (48) and (50) is that the relaxation goes as a first order of ρ for both the single and two-particle density functions. In contrast, in the independent particle dynamics case the two-particle distribution function went to zero at a faster rate than did the single-particle distribution. A further, and more detailed comparison of the two types of dynamics must, therefore, be made in terms of three and higher order density functions. For the three-particle density functions both of the forms

$$U_3(p_i, p_j, p_k; t) = P_3(p_i, p_j, p_k; t) - P_2(p_i, p_j; t)P_1(p_k; t)$$
$$- P_2(p_j, p_k; t)P_1(p_i; t) - P_2(p_i, p_k; t)P_1(p_j; t) \qquad (51)$$
$$+ 2P_1(p_i; t)P_1(p_j; t)P_1(p_k; t)$$

and $K_3(p_{i_1}, p_{i_2}, p_{i_3}; t)$ (cf. Eq. (19)) go to zero as $0(\rho^2)$. Thus, as in the case of independent-particle dynamics, U_3 goes to zero at a faster rate than U_2 or U_1. It can be shown that in the present model, the U_n go to zero as $O(\rho^{n-1})$; analogous to the random walk model.[7]

It is possible to discuss the asymptotic time dependence of the $A_r(t)$ in some generality, basing it on the critical point analysis of van Hove.[17, 15]. In this brief survey, we shall just cite the analysis for the one-dimensional infinite chain with nearest-neighbor interactions only, that is, $\gamma_1 = \gamma$, $\gamma_2 = \gamma_3 = \cdots = 0$. For this case

$$\omega^2(\theta) = 2\gamma(1 - \cos\theta) = \omega_L{}^2 \sin^2 \frac{\theta}{2}, \qquad \omega_L{}^2 = 4\gamma \qquad (52)$$

and $A_r(t)$ can be written in terms of the dimensionless time $\tau = \omega_L t$ as

$$A_r(\tau) = \frac{1}{2\pi} \int_{-\pi}^{\pi} \cos\left(\tau \sin\frac{\theta}{2}\right) \cos r\theta \, d\theta = J_{2r}(\tau) \qquad (53)$$

where $J_{2r}(\tau)$ is a Bessel function of the first kind of order $2r$. This expression for $A_r(\tau)$ can be substituted into Eq. (39) to yield an explicit formula for $\rho_{rs}(\tau)$. Let us consider a special example in which two particles, one at m and one at n, have a correlation $\rho_{mn}(0) \neq 0$ and $\rho_{jk}(0) = 0$ for $(j, k) \neq (m, n)$. For large τ and m, n, r, and s satisfying $\tau \gg |m - r|$, $|m - s|$, $|n - r|$, $|n - s|$, the asymptotic form of $\rho_{rs}(\tau)$ is

$$\rho_{rs}(\tau) \sim (-1)^{r+s+m+n} \frac{4}{\pi\tau} \rho_{mn}(0) \cos\left(\tau - \frac{\pi}{4}\right) \qquad (54)$$

If, instead of analyzing the infinite lattice, we had studied a finite lattice with periodic boundary conditions the functions $A_r(\tau)$ would be

$$A_r(\tau) = \frac{1}{N} \sum_{s=0}^{N-1} \cos\left[\tau\omega\left(\frac{2\pi s}{N}\right)\right] \cos\frac{2\pi rs}{N} \qquad (55)$$

where N is the number of oscillators. This expression replaces the integral form given in Eq. (40). In such a case the function $\rho_{rs}(\tau)$ is an almost periodic function and the initial correlations must recur at least approximately. However, the analysis given for the infinite lattice is valid for values of τ satisfying $1 \ll \tau \ll \tau_p$ where τ_p is the Poincaré cycle for the lattice.

A further refinement of the harmonic oscillator model is possible, in which the lattice is put into contact with a heat bath at temperature T and remains in contact with the heat bath, so that the initial correlations decay not only through mutual interactions but also through random collisions with an external fluctuating field. Although it might appear that such a case would contain features of both the independent particle case and the harmonic oscillator model just analyzed, the resulting formalism is much closer to that required for the latter, and the results differ only in detail. The model to be discussed is specified by the equations of motion

$$\ddot{q}_r + \zeta \dot{q}_r + \sum_{s(\neq r)} \gamma_{r-s} q_s = \varepsilon_r(t) \tag{56}$$

where ζ is a friction constant, the γ_j are force constants, and the $\varepsilon_r(t)$ describe Gaussian processes with correlation properties

$$\langle \varepsilon_r(t) \rangle = 0$$

$$\langle \varepsilon_r(t) \varepsilon_s(t') \rangle = kT\zeta \, \delta_{rs} \, \delta(t - t') \tag{57}$$

We shall assume the initial correlation properties specified in Eq. (28), and, as before, make the assumption that $\langle p_r(0)q_s(0) \rangle = 0$ for all r and s. In order to solve Eq. (56) we introduce the normal coordinates of Eq. (32) together with an additional function

$$\varepsilon(\theta, t) = \sum_{r=-\infty}^{\infty} \varepsilon_r(t) e^{ir\theta} \tag{58}$$

This function is described by the moment properties

$$\langle \varepsilon(\theta, t) \rangle = 0$$
$$\langle \varepsilon(\theta_1, t) \varepsilon(\theta', t') \rangle = kT\zeta \, \delta(\theta + \theta') \, \delta(t - t') \tag{59}$$

Since the $\varepsilon_r(t)$ are Gaussian, $\varepsilon(\theta, t)$ will also be Gaussian in t with mean equal to zero so that only second order moments and correlation functions will be required for the analysis.

The normal coordinate $Q(\theta, t)$ is the solution to

$$\ddot{Q} + \zeta \dot{Q} + \omega^2(\theta)Q = \varepsilon(\theta, t) \tag{60}$$

and from the solution to this equation $P(\theta, t)$ can be found as the time derivative of $Q(\theta, t)$. A formal solution for $P(\theta, t)$ can be written

$$P(\theta, t) = P(\theta, 0)R(\theta, t) - Q(\theta, 0)\omega^2(\theta)S(\theta, t) + \int_0^t R(\theta, t - \tau)\varepsilon(\theta, \tau) \, d\tau \tag{61}$$

where the functions $R(\theta, t)$ and $S(\theta, t)$ are

$$R(\theta, t) = e^{-\zeta t/2}\left[\cosh \eta(\theta)t - \frac{\zeta}{2\eta(\theta)} \sinh \eta(\theta)t\right]$$

$$S(\theta, t) = e^{-\zeta t/2} \frac{\sinh \eta(\theta)t}{\eta(\theta)}$$

(62)

with $\eta(\theta) = (\zeta^2/4 - \omega^2(\theta))^{1/2}$. Since $\varepsilon(\theta, t)$ is Gaussian in t, $P(\theta, t)$ is Gaussian in t, and the $p_r(t)$ are all Gaussian random variables, all with mean value equal to zero. Equation (34) can be used to determine $\mu_{rs}(t)$ from a knowledge of $\langle P(\theta, t)P(\theta', t)\rangle$. If the indicated multiplications and subsequent averages are carried out, it is found that $\mu_{rs}(t)$ is given by the expression in Eq. (39) where, in the present case

$$A_j(t) = \frac{1}{2\pi} \int_{-\pi}^{\pi} R(\theta, t) \cos j\theta \, d\theta$$

(63)

Therefore, the general argument which led from the representation of $\mu_{rs}(t)$ in Eq. (39) to the relaxation of the functions $\Delta_1(\omega; t)$ (Eq. (47)) and $\Delta_2(\omega_1, \omega_2; t)$ (Eq. (49)) apply in the present case, and the multiple particle density functions decouple in the same qualitative way as is indicated in Eqs. (48), (50), and (51). The only difference introduced by the presence of heat bath is in having the form of $A_j(t)$ given in Eq. (63) in the functions $\rho_{jk}(t)$.

IV. THE ONE-DIMENSIONAL ISING MODEL

Another model which includes interaction and for which partial results are available on the decay of initial correlations is that of the one dimensional time-dependent Ising model. This model was first suggested by Glauber,[18] and analyzed by him for one-dimensional Ising lattices. Let us consider a one-dimensional lattice, each of whose sites contain a spin. The spin on site j will be denoted by $s_j(t)$ where $s_j(t)$ can take on values ± 1, and transitions are made randomly between the two states due to interactions with an external heat reservoir. The state of the system is specified by the spin vector $\mathbf{s}(t) = (\dots, s_{-1}(t), s_0(t), s_1(t), \dots)$. A full description of the system is provided by the probability $P(\mathbf{s}; t)$, but of more immediate interest are the reduced probabilities

$$P_r(s_{i_1}, s_{i_2}, \dots, s_{i_r}; t) = \sum_{C(i_1, \dots, i_r)} P(\mathbf{s}; t)$$

(64)

where the summation is over the values ± 1 for all spins in the complement set to $(i_1, i_2, \dots, i_r)$. The principal assumption in Glauber's model is that the changes in spin can be described as a temporally homogeneous process, such that in an infinitesimal time interval $(t, t + dt)$ no more than a single spin can change sign. If we let $w_r(\mathbf{s})$ be the transition rate for changes in spin $s_r(t)$, then $P(\mathbf{s}; t)$ satisfies a master equation

$$\dot{P}(\mathbf{s}; t) = \sum_r w_r(\ldots, s_{r-1}, -s_r, s_{r+1}, \ldots)P(\ldots, s_{r-1}, -s_r, s_{r+1}, \ldots, t)$$
$$- P(\mathbf{s}; t) \sum_r w_r(\mathbf{s}) \qquad (65)$$

The further analysis of this equation proceeds by choosing a sufficiently simple form for the transition rates. In particular, Glauber's choice was

$$w_r(\mathbf{s}) = \frac{\alpha}{2} \left\{ 1 - \frac{\gamma}{2} s_r(s_{r+1} + s_{r-1}) \right\} \qquad (66)$$

where α and γ are positive constants, and $\gamma < 1$. This choice of transition rate has the property that the most stable configuration of three consecutive spins (the configuration with the least tendency to change) is one in which a middle spin is lined up with two nearest-neighbor parallel spins. The most unstable configuration occurs when a middle spin is opposite in direction to its two neighbors.

Properties of the distribution function are mostly easily derived by means of an identity given by Glauber which expresses the distribution function in terms of moments. We define moments by

$$\mu(j_1, r_1; j_2, r_2; \ldots, j_k, r_k; t) = \langle s_{j_1}^{r_1}(t)s_{j_2}^{r_2}(t) \cdots s_{j_k}^{r_k}(t) \rangle$$
$$= \sum_{\{s\}} s_{j_1}^{r_1}s_{j_2}^{r_2} \cdots s_{j_k}^{r_k}P(\mathbf{s}; t)$$
$$= \sum_{s_{j_1}} \cdots \sum_{s_{ik}} P_k(s_{j_1}, \ldots, s_{j_k}; t)s_{j_1}^{r_1} \cdots s_{j_k}^{r_k}$$
$$(67)$$

in which the sum runs over all values of $\mathbf{s}$. Then for any value of r,

$$P_r(s_{i_1}, s_{i_2}, \ldots, s_{i_r}; t) = 2^{-r} \sum_{\{s'\}} (1 + s_{i_1}s_{i_1}')(1 + s_{i_2}s_{i_2}') \cdots (1 + s_{i_r}s_{i_r}')$$
$$\times P_r(s_{i_1}', s_{i_2}', \ldots, s_{i_r}'; t) \qquad (68)$$

If this expansion is carried out for successive values of r, one finds that

$$P_1(s_j; t) = 2^{-1}[1 + s_j\mu(j, 1; t)]$$
$$P_2(s_j, s_k; t) = 2^{-2}[1 + s_j\mu(j, 1; t) + s_k\mu(k, 1; t)$$
$$+ s_js_k\mu(j, 1; k, 1; t)], \text{ etc.} \qquad (69)$$

Differential equations for the μ's can now be derived by multiplying the master equation by the relevant spin variables and summing over all s.

The first moment $\mu(j; 1; t)$, for simplicity to be denoted μ_j, satisfies

$$\frac{d\mu_j}{d\tau} = -\mu_j + \frac{\gamma}{2}(\mu_{j+1} + \mu_{j-1}) \tag{70}$$

where $\tau = \alpha t$. The correlation function $\mu(j, 1; k, 1; t) = v_{jk}(\tau)$ satisfies

$$v_{jk} = -2v_{jk} + \frac{\gamma}{2}(v_{j+1,k} + v_{j-1,k} + v_{j,k+1} + v_{j,k-1}) \tag{71}$$

for $j \neq k$ and $v_{jj}(\tau) = 1$ for all j. Similar equations can be derived for higher moments but they look progressively more complicated because of the identity $s_i^2 = s_i^4 = \cdots = 1$ which must always be taken into account. The first two equations can, however, be solved with no great difficulty. If an infinite lattice is assumed, Eq. (71) can be solved through the introduction of a generating function

$$\mu(\theta; \tau) = \sum_{j=-\infty}^{\infty} \mu_j \exp(ij\theta) \tag{72}$$

which satisfies

$$\frac{\partial\mu}{\partial\tau} = (-1 + \gamma \cos\theta)\mu \tag{73}$$

with the solution

$$\mu(\theta, \tau) = \mu(\theta, 0)\exp(-1 + \gamma \cos\theta)\tau \tag{74}$$

As an example of the form of the result for $\mu_j(\tau)$, let us suppose that all of the spin expectations vanish except for the spin located at the origin which is equal to 1. This implies that $\mu(\theta, 0) = 1$. The inversion formula

$$\mu_j(\tau) = \frac{1}{2\pi}\int_{-\pi}^{\pi} \mu(\theta, \tau)\exp(-ij\theta)\,d\theta \tag{75}$$

then implies that

$$u_j(\tau) = \exp(-\tau)I_j(\gamma\tau) \tag{76}$$

For the solution of the equation for $v_{jk}(\tau)$ we introduce the double generating function

$$v(\theta, \varphi; \tau) = \sum_{j,k} v_{jk}(\tau)\exp[i(j\theta + k\varphi)] \tag{77}$$

which satisfies

$$\frac{\partial v}{\partial\tau} = [-2 + \gamma(\cos\theta + \cos\varphi)]v + 2\pi[2 - \gamma(\cos\theta + \cos\varphi)]\delta(\theta + \varphi) \tag{78}$$

with the solution

$$v(\theta, \varphi; \tau) = v(\theta, \varphi; 0) \exp [-\lambda(\theta, \varphi)\tau]$$
$$+ 2\pi \, \delta(\theta + \varphi)[1 - \exp (-\lambda(\theta, \varphi)\tau)] \quad (79)$$

where $\lambda(\theta, \varphi) = 2 - \lambda(\cos \theta + \cos \varphi)$. The inversion formula for the generating function given in Eq. (80) is

$$v_{jk}(\tau) = \frac{1}{4\pi^2} \int_{-\pi}^{\pi} \int v(\theta, \varphi; \tau) \exp [-i(j\theta + k\varphi)] \, d\theta \, d\varphi \quad (80)$$

Let us suppose that initially $v_{jk}(0) = 0$ for $j \neq k$ except for special values m and n for which $v_{mn}(0) = 1$. Then, the application of this equation to the resulting expression for $v(\theta, \varphi; \tau)$ yields

$$v_{jk}(\tau) = \delta_{j,k} + e^{-2\tau} I_{m-j}(\gamma\tau)I_{n-k}(\gamma\tau) \quad (81)$$

We can now calculate the rate of decay of initial correlations by making use of Eq. (69). The single-particle distribution function has the asymptotic behavior.

$$P_1(s_j; \tau) - P_1(s_j; \infty) = \frac{s_j}{2} \mu_j(\tau) \quad (82)$$

and

$$P_2(s_j, s_k; \tau) - P_1(s_j; \tau)P_1(s_k; \tau) = (1/4)s_j s_k v_{jk}(\tau) \quad (83)$$

etc. The asymptotic behavior of these functions can readily be determined for a large class of initial conditions. One can see from the representation in Eqs. (75) and (80) that for sufficiently large τ the only contribution to the integral will come from values of θ where $\cos \theta$ is a maximum, i.e., at $\theta = 0$. In this vicinity we can write

$$\mu_j(\tau) = \frac{1}{2\pi} \int_{-\pi}^{\pi} \mu(\theta; 0) \exp \left[-\tau + \gamma\tau \left(1 - \frac{\theta^2}{2} + \cdots \right) - ij\theta \right] d\theta$$
$$\sim \frac{1}{2\pi} \exp [-(1 - \gamma)\tau] \int_{-\infty}^{\infty} \mu(\theta; 0) \exp \left(-\frac{\gamma\tau\theta^2}{2} - ij\theta \right) d\theta \quad (84)$$

But at $\tau = 0$ we also have

$$\mu(\theta; 0) \sim \sum_j \mu_j(0) \left[1 + ij\theta - j^2 \frac{\theta^2}{2} + \cdots \right]$$
$$= \rho_0 + i\rho_1\theta - \frac{\rho_2 \theta^2}{2} + \cdots \quad (85)$$

where

$$\rho_j = \sum_r r^j \mu_r(0). \tag{86}$$

Substituting Eq. (85) into Eq. (84), and performing the resulting integrations we find that for large τ

$$\mu_j(\tau) \sim \frac{\rho_0 \exp\left[-(1-\gamma)\tau\right]}{(2\pi\gamma\tau)^{1/2}} \exp\left(-\frac{j^2}{2\gamma\tau}\right)\left[1 + 0\left(\frac{1}{\tau}\right)\right] \sim \frac{\rho_0 \exp\left(-(1-\gamma)\tau\right)}{(2\pi\gamma\tau)^{1/2}} \tag{87}$$

for $\rho_0 \neq 0$, $v\tau \gg |j|$ and ρ_0 assumed finite. This form of asymptotic behavior can be verified in detail for the expression in Eq. (76). Higher order terms can be calculated by using further terms in the expansion of Eq. (85).

One can evaluate the asymptotic behavior of $v(\theta, \varphi; \tau)$ in much the same way, and finds that

$$v(\theta, \varphi; \tau) = 2\pi\, \delta(\theta + \varphi) + \eta(\theta, \varphi; 0) \exp\left[-\lambda(\theta, \varphi)\tau\right] \tag{88}$$

in which

$$\eta(\theta, \varphi; 0) = \sum_j \sum_{\substack{k \\ j \neq k}} v_{jk}(0) \exp\left[i(j\theta + k\varphi)\right] \tag{89}$$

Hence, if we set

$$\rho_{00} = \sum_j \sum_{\substack{k \\ j \neq k}} v_{jk}(0) \tag{90}$$

on the assumption that this constant is neither 0 nor infinite in value, we arrive at the asymptotic formula

$$v_{jk} \sim \delta_{j,k} + \frac{\rho_{00} \exp\left[-2(1-\gamma)\tau\right]}{(2\pi\gamma\tau)} \exp\left(-\frac{j^2 + k^2}{2\gamma\tau}\right)\left[1 + 0\left(\frac{1}{\tau}\right)\right]$$

$$\sim \delta_{j,k} + \frac{\rho_{00} \exp\left[-2(1-\gamma)\tau\right]}{2\pi\gamma\tau} \tag{91}$$

Since the only values of v_{jk} of interest are those for which $j \neq k$, we see that

$$v_{jk} \sim A\mu_j\mu_k \tag{92}$$

for large τ. This conclusion is valid under the assumptions that ρ_0 and ρ_{00} are both finite and neither is equal to zero. When these conditions are violated different relations can be obtained for the relaxation rates indicating that there can be initial conditions that are pathologic from this point of view. The calculation of the third order decomposition, symbolically denoted by $P_3 - 3P_2P_1 + 2P_1{}^3$ yields

$$P_3 - 3P_2 P_1 + 2P_1{}^3 \sim \frac{\rho_{000}\, e^{\,-3(1-\gamma)\tau}}{(2\pi\gamma\tau)^{3/2}} \qquad (93)$$

for three spins s_j, s_k, s_l, with $j \neq k \neq l$, and with

$$\rho_{000} = \sum_j \sum_k \sum_l{}' v_{jkl}(0) \qquad (94)$$

where the sum is carried out with no two indices equal. Again it must be assumed that ρ_{000} is neither 0 nor ∞ for Eq. (93) to be valid asymptotically. We see that this Ising model mimics the earlier random walk model, insofar as we have carried out the detailed calculations. Thus, it is not true that internal coupling necessarily disrupts a quicker relaxation of higher order distribution functions *vis-à-vis* lower order ones. It is also interesting to note that the character of the relaxation changes at $T \to \infty$. Glauber has shown that γ can be identified as $\tanh(2J/kT)$ so that $\gamma \to 1$ in that limit. The essentially exponential relaxation then changes to one which goes like $\tau^{-1/2}$ for large τ. However, the relation between the relaxation behavior of various orders of cumulants remains unchanged.

As a final comment on this model, we note that the asymptotic results here are somewhat more general than we have stated, since similar results can be proved for the class of transition rates (replacing Eq. (66))

$$w_j(\mathbf{s}) = \frac{\alpha}{2}\left\{1 - \frac{s_j}{2}\sum_{r=1}^{\infty}\gamma_r(s_{j+r} + s_{j-r})\right\} \qquad (95)$$

provided that the sum $\sum \gamma_r$ converges and is less than 1. In this case the exponent appearing in Eqs. (87), (91), and (94) will have γ replaced by

$$\bar{\gamma} = \sum_{j=1}^{\infty} \gamma_j \qquad (96)$$

and in the denominators of these equations γ is to be replaced by

$$\gamma_m = \sum_{j=1}^{\infty} j^2 \gamma_j \qquad (97)$$

provided that this sum converges.

In summary, we have examined several models both with and without internal coupling, in order to get some insight into the possible form that might be taken by the decoupling of initial correlations. We have shown that decoupling occurs in some form for all of these models. Since the possible forms of decomposition that we have studied (i.e., the cumulant form and the Kirkwood form) constitute a fairly restricted class, we have not touched on the possibly more interesting questions of whether one can choose a different type of decomposition to achieve a quicker decay of initial correlations, or how one would terminate the kinetic equations in more realistic physical problems. Certainly, the analysis given by Boguliubov[1] leads to fairly difficult mathematics. The models discussed here would seem to give hope that simple forms for the decoupling functions lead to reasonably satisfactory results.

References

1. N. N. Boguliubov, *J. Phys. (USSR)*, **10**, 256, 265 (1946) [English translation in *Studies in Statistical Mechanics*, Vol. 1, J. de Boer and G. E. Uhlenbeck, Eds. Interscience, New York, 1962.]
2. M. S. Green, *J. Chem. Phys.*, **25**, 836 (1956).
3. M. S. Green, *Physica*, **24**, 393 (1958).
4. M. S. Green and R. A. Picirelli, *Phys. Rev.*, **132**, 1388 (1963).
5. M. Kac, in *Proceedings of the Third Berkeley Symposium on Mathematical Statistics and Probability*, Vol. III, J. Neyman, Ed., University of California Press, Berkeley, 1956.
6. I. Oppenheim, K. E. Shuler, and G. H. Weiss, *J. Chem. Phys.*, **46**, 4100 (1967).
7. I. Oppenheim, K. E. Shuler, and G. H. Weiss, *J. Chem. Phys.* (to appear).
8. R. J. Glauber, *J. Math. Phys.*, **4**, 294 (1963).
9. M. Kac, *Bull. Roy. Soc. Belg.*, **42**, 356 (1956).
10. M. Dresden, in *Studies in Statistical Mechanics*, Vol. 1, J. de Boer and G. E. Uhlenbeck, Eds., Interscience, New York, 1962.
11. R. Brout, *Physica*, **22**, 509 (1956).
12. J. G. Kirkwood, *J. Chem. Phys.*, **3**, 300 (1935).
13. L. Landau and E. Teller, *J. Phys. (USSR)*, (1936).
14. E. W. Montroll and K. E. Shuler, *J. Chem. Phys.*, **26**, 454 (1957).
15. P. Mazur and E. W. Montroll, *J. Math. Phys.*, **1**, 70 (1960).
16. M. Born and K. Huang, *Dynamical Theory of Crystal Lattices*, Cambridge Univ. Press, Cambridge, 1954.
17. L. van Hove, *Phys. Rev.*, **89**, 1189 (1953).
18. R. Glauber, *J. Math. Phys.*, **4**, 294 (1963).

VIBRATIONAL RELAXATION OF A GAS OF DIATOMIC MOLECULES

THOR A. BAK and

PREBEN GRAAE SØRENSEN

*H. C. Ørsted Institute, University of Copenhagen,
Copenhagen, Denmark*

CONTENTS

I. INTRODUCTION

In 1958 Montroll and Shuler[1] analyzed in great detail the "master equation" for a harmonic oscillator interacting with a gas of particles which only have translational energy and which are in equilibrium. The interaction was assumed to lead to transition between neighboring levels only, and in this approximation the master equation is

$$\frac{dx_n}{dt} = \kappa\{ne^{-\theta}x_{n-1} - [n + (n + 1)e^{-\theta}]x_n + (n + 1)x_{n+1}\} \quad (1)$$

in which $x_n(t)$ is the population of the nth level at time t, $\theta = \beta\hbar\omega$, and κ is a parameter expressing the strength of the interaction with the heat bath, essentially equal to the number of collisions which the oscillator experiences per second times the transition probability per collision. This equation can be considered as the quantum analog of the Kramers equation,[2]

$$\frac{\partial f(\xi, t)}{\partial t} = \eta \frac{\partial}{\partial \xi} \xi\left(1 + \frac{\partial}{\partial \xi}\right)f(\xi, t) \quad (2)$$

219

in which $f(\xi, t)\, d\xi$ is the probability that the harmonic oscillator has energy between $\xi\beta^{-1}$ and $(\xi + d\xi)\beta^{-1}$ at time t and the so-called friction coefficient η is the limit of $\theta\kappa$ as $\beta\hbar\omega \to 0$. An equation similar to that of Montroll and Shuler has also been considered by Nikitin.[3]

As shown by Montroll and Shuler, Eq. (1) can be used to make a stochastic model for the dissociation of a diatomic molecule, but it is quite clear that this model will never be very realistic since the transition probabilities are too restrictive and the true intermolecular potential is quite different from a cutoff harmonic potential. A large number of papers which claim to improve the model with respect to these two deficiencies have been published,[4] but we shall not be concerned with those here.

The Montroll-Shuler equation can also predict how fast a molecule which is created in a highly excited vibrational state will decay to the equilibrium state. This is of interest in connection with chemiluminescence phenomena. In certain cases one finds experimentally that this relaxation is much faster than what one would expect from the master equation of Montroll and Shuler and improved versions of this equation. One possible mechanism for this fast relaxation is that although most of the collisions in which the diatomic molecule participates are between the diatomic molecule and an inert gas atom, there will also be some collisions between diatomic molecules. In the latter case we have the situation where two diatomic molecules in quantum state n collide producing, with fairly high probability, molecules in quantum states $n - 1$ and $n + 1$, respectively. The number of such collisions is, of course quite small compared to the number of collisions of the first kind, but since they are so extremely efficient they may still be of importance. This mechanism, we believe, was first suggested in connection with chemiluminescence by Norrish in a Faraday Society discussion.[5] The equations describing this relaxation had, however, been discussed several years earlier by Shuler[6] and Osipov.[7]

In this paper we investigate the consequences of this addition to the original Montroll-Shuler equation. To keep it simple we retain the harmonic oscillator potential and the simple dipole-transition probabilities in the linear part of the equation and in the nonlinear part we restrict ourselves to the simple resonance transition

$$(n + 1) + (n - 1) \rightleftharpoons 2n \tag{3}$$

The reason for this is primarily that even in this case we have only been able to solve the equations numerically and by sticking to the simple example, the number of parameters which we have to vary is kept at a minimum. In this way we hope to make the importance of this nonlinear term more apparent. More realistic examples have been considered by

Fisher and Kummler[8] and by Treanor.[9] It is clear that if one considers anharmonic oscillators and strongly nonadiabatic collisions with the heat bath then the relative importance of the nonlinear term will diminish. The case we consider, therefore, is the case where one may expect the largest contribution to the relaxation from the nonlinear part of the equation.

II. THE MASTER EQUATION

The rate of the reaction $(n + 1) + (n - 1) \rightleftharpoons 2(n)$ is given by

$$\frac{dx_n}{dt} = 2w x_{n+1} x_{n-1} \tag{4}$$

where x_n is the fraction of the diatomic molecules which are in vibrational state n and w is a rate constant which for simplicity we take to be independent of n. Roughly speaking we have

$$w = a_2 \bar{v}_2 P_2 c \tag{5}$$

where a_2 is a hard sphere cross-sectional area for collisions between diatomic molecules, $\bar{v}_2$ an average relative velocity, P_2 a probability of reaction during collisions, and c the concentration of diatomic molecules.

Denoting the right hand side of Eq. (1) by $\kappa F(x_{n-1}, x_n, x_{n+1})$ we have

$$\frac{dx_n}{dt} = \kappa F(x_{n-1}, x_n, x_{n+1})$$
$$+ w[x_{n-1}^2 + 2x_{n-1}x_{n+1} + x_{n+1}^2 - x_{n-2}x_n - 2x_n^2 - x_n x_{n+2}] \tag{6}$$

For the coefficient κ we can write an approximate expression similar to that of Eq. (5), namely,

$$\kappa = a_1 \bar{v}_1 P_1 C \tag{7}$$

where a_1 is the hard sphere cross-sectional area for collision between gas atoms and diatomic molecules, $\bar{v}_1$ is the average relative velocity, P_1 is the probability of vibrational excitation in an encounter, and C is the con- concentration of the gas atoms which serve as thermostat for the diatomic molecules. Since the cross sections and the average velocities are approximately equal, the ratio w/κ, which is the natural expansion parameter, is

$$\frac{w}{\kappa} \approx \frac{c}{C} \frac{P_2}{P_1} \tag{8}$$

In an experiment designed to study the behavior of single diatomic molecules the ratio c/C will be kept as small as possible, i.e., anywhere between 10^{-3} and 10^{-1} depending on the experimental technique one wants to use. The ratio P_2/P_1 may have values ranging from 10 to 10^4 and the ratio w/κ may thus have values ranging from 10^{-2} to 10^3 and typically it is of the order unity.

In the continuous approximation, i.e., for $\beta\hbar\omega \to 0$ Eq. (6) becomes

$$\frac{\partial f}{\partial t} = \eta \frac{\partial}{\partial \xi} \, \xi \left(1 + \frac{\partial}{\partial \xi}\right) f - \mu \left[f \frac{\partial^4 f}{\partial \xi^4} - \left(\frac{\partial^2 f}{\partial \xi^2}\right)^2 \right]$$

$$\overset{\text{def}}{=} \eta L f - \mu N[f] \tag{9}$$

where the coefficient μ is

$$\mu = \lim_{\beta\hbar\omega \to 0} (\beta\hbar\omega)^4 w$$

$$= \lim_{\beta\hbar\omega \to 0} (\beta\hbar\omega)^3 \frac{w}{\kappa} \overset{\text{def}}{=} \eta\gamma \tag{10}$$

Using the dimensionless time $\tau = \eta t$, we therefore have

$$\frac{\partial f}{\partial \tau} = L f - \lambda N[f]$$

and in realistic cases the dimensionless parameter λ is probably not a small number.

The nonlinear functional $N[f]$ can also be written as

$$N[f] = \frac{\partial^2}{\partial \xi^2} f^2 \frac{\partial^2}{\partial \xi^2} \ln f \tag{11}$$

and this shows immediately that f vanishes not only for the equilibrium distribution $\exp(-\xi)$, but also for instance for $\exp(-\alpha\xi)$ where α may be a function of τ. A distribution relaxing through a sequence of Boltzmann distributions, only with temperatures different from that of the thermostat, will thus in a sense be unaffected by the nonlinear term, but as we shall see later such a reduction is only asymptotically correct in the limit $\lambda \to \infty$.

III. THE LINEAR EQUATION

We shall briefly recapitulate some of the properties of the linear equation. Defining the moments as

$$\mathscr{M}_n(\tau) = \int_0^\infty \xi^n f(\xi, \tau) \, d\xi \tag{12}$$

and

$$M_n(t) = \sum_{v=0}^{\infty} v^n x_v(t) \tag{13}$$

we have for the continuous case, by partial integration

$$\frac{d}{d\tau} \mathcal{M}_n(\tau) + n \mathcal{M}_n(\tau) = n^2 \mathcal{M}_{n-1}(\tau) \tag{14}$$

and from this recursive equation all moments can be expressed in terms of $\mathcal{M}_n(0)$, i.e., in terms of the distribution at $\tau = 0$. In particular we have

$$\mathcal{M}_1(\tau) = 1 + (\mathcal{M}_1(0) - 1)e^{-\tau} \tag{15}$$

and

$$\mathcal{M}_n(\tau \to \infty) = \mathcal{M}_n^{eq} = n! \tag{16}$$

For the discrete case it is slightly more complicated, but here also we can set up a recursive relationship leading to

$$M_1(t) = \frac{e^{-\theta}}{1 - e^{-\theta}} + \left(M_1(0) - \frac{e^{-\theta}}{1 - e^{-\theta}} \right) \exp\left[-(1 - e^{-\theta})\kappa t \right] \tag{17}$$

$$M_2(t) = \frac{e^{-\theta}(1 + 3e^{-\theta})}{2(1 - e^{-\theta})^2} + \left[\frac{1 + 3e^{-\theta}}{1 - e^{-\theta}} M_1(0) - \frac{e^{-\theta}(1 + 3e^{-\theta})}{(1 - e^{-\theta})^2} \right]$$
$$\times \exp\left[-(1 - e^{-0})\kappa t \right]$$
$$+ \left[M_2(0) - \frac{1 + 3e^{-\theta}}{1 - e^{-\theta}} M_1(0) + \frac{e^{-\theta}(1 + 3e^{-\theta})}{2(1 - e^{-\theta})^2} \right] \tag{18}$$

The central moments which are of greater interest are

$$m_1(t) = M_1(t)$$

$$m_2(t) = M_2(t) - [m_1(t)]^2$$

$$= \frac{e^{-\theta}(1 + e^{-\theta})}{2(1 - e^{-\theta})^2} + \left(\frac{1 + e^{-\theta}}{1 - e^{-\theta}} M_1(0) - \frac{e^{-\theta}(1 + e^{-\theta})}{(1 - e^{-\theta})^2} \right)$$
$$\times \exp\left[-(1 - e^{-\theta})\kappa t \right]$$
$$+ \left(M_2(0) - M_1(0)^2 - \frac{1 + e^{-\theta}}{1 - e^{\theta}} M_1(0) + \frac{e^{-\theta}(1 + e^{-\theta})}{2(1 - e^{-\theta})^2} \right)$$
$$\times \exp\left[-2(1 - e^{-\theta})\kappa t \right] \tag{19}$$

In the Monte Carlo calculations described below we have checked the accuracy of the calculation by comparing the calculated first and second central moments for the linear equation with these exact expressions.

IV. QUALITATIVE FEATURES OF THE NONLINEAR EQUATION

A simple calculation shows that the first moment for the nonlinear equation is identical with that of the linear equation. Since the first moment is the average energy and the processes which give rise to the nonlinear term conserve energy, this is also intuitively obvious. Furthermore, it can be seen from the form of the nonlinear term that one can find convex functions for which the nonlinear term is zero locally, even in fairly large domains. Finally, as mentioned above for equilibrium-like distributions such as $\exp(-\alpha\xi)$ (and the discrete equivalent) the nonlinear term vanishes identically. All this indicates that it may play a less important role than originally believed.

The most interesting initial distribution is a narrow distribution around a fairly high average energy, corresponding for instance to a molecule which by a chemical reaction is created in a vibrationally excited state. One would expect that for such a strongly localized distribution the nonlinear term would be very important in the spreading out of the initial distribution, but once this has happened, the term will be of almost negligible importance since it is proportional to products of two populations which rapidly become smaller than one.

In the limit $\lambda \to \infty$ a Boltzmann distribution (with a nonequilibrium temperature) is established almost instantaneously and we can use an approach based on two time scales. Assuming that under these circumstances the solution to the differential equation is $\alpha(\tau)\exp(-\alpha(\tau)\xi)$ we get, using the known form of $\mathcal{M}_1(\tau)$

$$\alpha(\tau) = [1 + (\mathcal{M}_1(0) - 1)e^{-\tau}]^{-1} \tag{20}$$

and in the discrete case we get, setting $x_n(t) = (1 - e^{-\alpha})\exp[-n\alpha(t)]$

$$\alpha(t) = \ln\left[\frac{1}{e^{-\theta}/(1-e^{-\theta}) + [M_1(0) - e^{-\theta}/(1-e^{-\theta})]\exp{-(1-e^{-\theta})\kappa t}} - 1\right] \tag{21}$$

V. THE MONTE CARLO PROCESS

To solve the equation by simulation, we replace the discrete equation by the following Markov process. A number of particles is distributed in states which are denoted by the non-negative integers 0, 1, 2, ..., N. The particles can be moved from one state to another by processes which are identical to those which give rise to Eq. (6). Each of these processes occurs with the probability given by the number of particles in the states and the chosen rate constants, i.e., the process $(n + 1) + (n - 1) \rightarrow 2n$ occurs with probability $w x_{n-1} x_{n+1}$ and when it occurs one particle is moved from state $n - 1$ to state n and one particle from state $n + 1$ to state n.

The actual procedure is as follows: For a given distribution the probability of each reaction is calculated and a process is chosen at random, subject to the given probability distribution. Particles are moved according to the chosen reaction, a new distribution is calculated, and the process starts all over again. The number of random choices is the time parameter and the fraction of the total number of particles in a state n is x_n.

In the calculations the result of which are given below we used 10^4 particles and as the initial distribution we used $x_4 = 1$. In most cases the number of states was taken to be 10, but in the case of a strongly nonlinear equation (i.e., $w/\kappa \sim 100$) it was necessary to use a larger number of states in order to reduce overflow. In no cases reported here did we find an overflow larger than one out of 10^4 particles. The value of $\theta = \beta\hbar\omega$ was chosen as 1 in all cases.

VI. DISCUSSION

Figure 1 shows how an initially sharp distribution is spread out as a function of w/κ. There is no doubt that if one wanted to observe the initial population for instance by chemiluminescence the spreading out which is found for high values of w/κ would reduce the possibilities of succeeding quite significantly. Figure 2 shows how the second reduced moment behaves as function of time for various values of w/κ. The increase in the height of the maximum again shows the rapid spreading out of the initial sharp distribution and the curves also show that for large times the behavior of the nonlinear equation is almost identical to that of the linear equation.

It should be stressed that the above calculations refer to a perhaps overly simplified model. When anharmonicities in the oscillator potential and processes like $(n + m) + (n - m) \rightleftharpoons 2n$ with $m \neq 1$ are taken into account, both the linear and the nonlinear term in the equation changes drastically. For this case one can, however, still obtain a simple analytical expression for the steady-state distribution, as discussed by Treanor[9] and Fisher and Kummler.[8] Our main concern here has been the dynamic

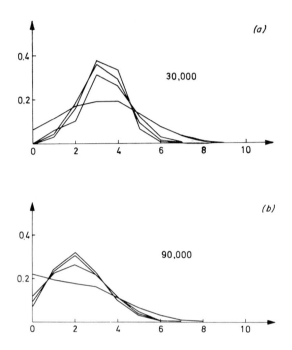

Fig. 1. Distributions for $w/\kappa = 0, 1, 2.5$, and 100 (a) at $t = 30{,}000$ and (b) at $t = 90{,}000$. Initial distribution $x_4 = 1$.

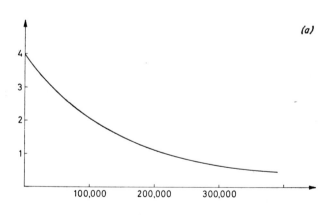

Fig. 2. (a) The first reduced moment $m_1(t)$ as function of time.

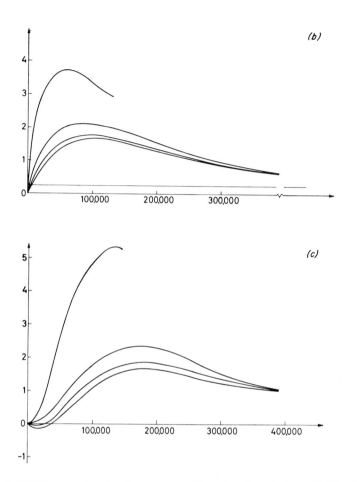

FIG. 2. (b) The second reduced moment $m_2(t)$ as function of time, (c) The third reduced moment $m_3(t)$ as function of time.

behavior and for this we will suggest that the nonlinear relaxation mechanism has been somewhat overestimated in the past except in connection with the short time behavior of very sharp initial distributions. For this case it explains for instance why chemiluminescence may sometimes be absent. When chemiluminescence occurs (and decays exponentially, as is always observed) we believe the nonlinear mechanism to be only of minor importance.

References

1. E. W. Montroll and K. E. Shuler, in *Advances in Chemical Physics*, Vol. I, I. Prigogine, Ed., Interscience, New York, 1958, pp. 361–399.
2. H. A. Kramers, *Physica*, **7**, 284 (1940).
3. E. E. Nikitin, *Dokl. Akad. Nauk. SSSR*, **121**, 991 (1958); *Soviet Phys. Dokl.* (English transl.), **3**, 701 (1958).
4. See, for instance, S. K. Kim, *J. Chem. Phys.*, **28**, 1057 (1958).
5. R. G. W. Norrish, *Discussions Faraday Soc.*, **33**, 273 (1962).
6. K. E. Shuler, *J. Chem. Phys.*, **32**, 1692 (1960).
7. A. I. Osipov, *Dokl. Akad. Nauk SSSR*, **130**, 523 (1960).
8. E. R. Fisher and R. H. Kummler, Rept. R 67SD15 from General Electric Space Science Laboratory (1967).
9. C. E. Treanor, CAL Rept. No. AF-2184-A-1 (1966).

SELF-AVOIDING WALKS ON LATTICES*

CYRIL DOMB

*Belfer Graduate School of Science,
Yeshiva University,† New York*

CONTENTS

I. INTRODUCTION

A self-avoiding walk on a lattice is a random walk subject to the condition that no lattice site may be visited more than once in the walk. Self-avoiding walks were first introduced as models of polymer chains which took into account in a realistic manner the "excluded volume" effect[1] (i.e., the fact that no element of space can be occupied more than once by the polymer chain). Although the mathematical problem of

* Research supported by AFSOR Grant No. 68-1416 and the U.S. Atomic Energy Commission.

† Part of this work was done while the author was a summer visitor at Department of Applied Mathematics, Brookhaven National Laboratory, Upton, L.I., New York. Permanent Address: King's College, London, England.

229

calculating the properties of self-avoiding walks is formidable, the model is well suited to computer enumerations, and has been the subject of many investigations.

Interest has also centered on the correspondence between self-avoiding walks and the Ising model. The partition function for the Ising model can be expanded in a high temperature series whose nth coefficient is obtained by enumerating certain configurations of n lines on the crystal lattice. The similarity between the Ising and self-avoiding walk enumerations has attracted attention and comment for several years, but only recently has the precise relationship between the two problems been clarified.

Despite the shortage of rigorous analytical results, information has been accumulating regarding various properties of self-avoiding walks, and it now seems possible to put forward a coherent pattern of general behavior. This is the aim of the present paper. No attempt will be made to provide complete references to the extensive literature, but a sufficient number of key papers will be cited to enable anyone interested to do so for himself.

II. RANDOM WALKS, RESTRICTED WALKS, AND SELF-AVOIDING WALKS

We shall start by recalling some well known properties of ordinary random walks on lattices. Consider a random walk on a lattice of co-ordination number q. When any new step has to be taken there are q independent choices; hence the total number of walks of n steps is equal to q^n.

To study the distribution of end points of these walks it is convenient to make use of the method of generating functions.[2] We shall take a three-dimensional example, the generalization to any other dimension being immediately evident. Let $P_n(t_1, t_2, t_3)$ be the number of walks that are at (t_1, t_2, t_3) after n steps. The generating function for n step walks is defined as

$$\varphi_n(x, y, z) = \sum_{t_1, t_2, t_3} P_n(t_1, t_2, t_3)x^{t_1}y^{t_2}z^{t_3} \tag{1}$$

and it is easy to show that for simple Bravais lattices $\varphi_n(x, y, z)$ is equal to $[\varphi(x, y, z)]^n$, where $\varphi(x, y, z)$ is a simple polynomial. To give an example, $\varphi(x, y, z)$ for the simple cubic (sc) lattice is equal to $(x^{-1} + x + y^{-1} + y + z^{-1} + z)$. Hence, it is possible to express $P_n(t_1, t_2, t_3)$ as a contour integral,

$$P_n(t_1, t_2, t_3) = \frac{1}{2\pi i} \iiint \frac{\varphi^n \, dx \, dy \, dz}{x^{t_1+1}y^{t_2+1}z^{t_3+1}} \tag{2}$$

and to derive properties of the three-dimensional probability distribution.

We shall pay particular attention to three properties. The number of walks which are at the starting point after n steps is asymptotically equal to $q^n/n^{d/2}$ in d dimensions. This is closely related to the Polya theorem[3] that the probability of ultimate return is 1 in one and two dimensions and less than 1 in three or more dimensions. The mean square length of walks of n steps is equal to n for all lattices in all dimensions. We shall shortly give a general proof of this result. For any individual lattice it can readily be derived from the generating function, since

$$\sum_{t_1 t_2 t_3} (t_1^2 + t_2^2 + t_3^2) P_n(t_1, t_2, t_3)$$

$$= \left[\left(x \frac{\partial}{\partial x} \right)^2 + \left(y \frac{\partial}{\partial y} \right)^2 + \left(z \frac{\partial}{\partial z} \right)^2 \right] \varphi(x, y, z)_{(1, 1, 1)} \qquad (3)$$

The distribution of any coordinate of the end point of a walk approaches a Gaussian value asymptotically for all lattices in all dimensions,

$$f_{On}(x)\, dx \sim \frac{1}{(2\pi n)^{1/2}} \exp\left(-\frac{x^2}{2n} \right) \qquad (4)$$

Also the distributions of different rectangular coordinates of the end point are independent; hence, the distribution of the end point in space is spherically symmetrical.

A useful alternative approach starts from the consideration of a random walk on a lattice as a sequence of n uncorrelated unit steps $\mathbf{u}_{io}(i = 1, 2, \ldots, n)$ the end point $\mathbf{R}_{no}$ being given by

$$\mathbf{R}_{no} = \mathbf{u}_{10} + \mathbf{u}_{20} + \cdots \mathbf{u}_{no} \qquad (5)$$

(The suffix O is introduced to differentiate a random walk from a restricted walk which will be defined shortly.) Thus

$$\langle \mathbf{R}_{no}^2 \rangle = \sum_{i=1}^{n} \langle \mathbf{u}_{io}^2 \rangle + 2 \sum_{i<j} \langle \mathbf{u}_{io} \mathbf{u}_{jo} \rangle \qquad (6)$$

But

$$\langle \mathbf{u}_{io}^2 \rangle = 1, \qquad \langle \mathbf{u}_{io} \mathbf{u}_{jo} \rangle = 0; \qquad \text{hence } \langle \mathbf{R}_{no}^2 \rangle = n$$

An important quantity characterizing the shapes of polymer chains is the radius of gyration. To define this precisely we must associate a suitable mass with each step of the walk, and it is convenient to take a model with $n + 1$ equal masses one placed at the end of each step of the walk and one at the beginning. The center of mass, G_O, is then defined by

$$G_O = \frac{1}{(n+1)} \sum_{i=1}^{n} R_{iO} \tag{7}$$

and the radius of gyration is given by

$$(n+1)S_{nO}^2 = \left(\sum_{i=1}^{n} R_{iO}^2\right) - G_O^2 \tag{8}$$

Using the reversal symmetry of random walks Eq. (8) can be transformed into

$$\langle S_{nO}^2 \rangle = \frac{n(n+2)}{6(n+1)} + \frac{2}{(n+1)^2} \sum_{i<j} i(n-j+1)\langle u_{iO} u_{jO}\rangle \tag{9}$$

Because of the independence of $u_{iO} \cdot u_{jO}$ the second term is zero, and $\langle S_{nO}^2 \rangle / \langle R_{nO}^2 \rangle$ tends asymptotically to $\frac{1}{6}$.

We now restrict the walks successively as follows: first, we exclude immediate reversals, we then further exclude all triangular closures, then all quadrilateral closures, and so on. We describe the stage which excludes r-gons as a restricted walk of order r. The properties of this walk are governed by a Markovian transition matrix[4] which increases rapidly in size as r increases. (It is roughly of order q^r.) For no-reversal walks the matrix is relatively simple and the properties of the walks have been calculated in detail.[5] For higher order walks one must resort to the general theory of Markov processes.

In fact as long as r remains finite most of the important general properties are the same as for the unrestricted walk. The total number of walks is

$$c_{nr} = A_{1r}\lambda_{1r}^n + A_{2r}\lambda_{2r}^n + \cdots A_{Nr}\lambda_{Nr}^n \tag{10}$$

where the λ_{ir} are the eigenvalues of the stochastic matrix. As n increases the largest eigenvalue dominates, and Eq. (10) reduces to $A_{1r}\lambda_{1r}^n$; this is similar in asymptotic behavior to unrestricted walks, q being replaced by λ_{1r}. The number of walks which are at the original after n steps has the same asymptotic behavior in d dimensions as for unrestricted walks,

$$u_{nr} \sim B_{1r}\lambda_{1r}^n/n^{d/2} \tag{11}$$

The mean square length acquires an expansion factor which is independent of n, and end-correction terms of order less than n, so that

$$\langle R_{nr}^2 \rangle \sim C_r n \tag{12}$$

Finally the distribution of any coordinate of the end point remains Gaussian

$$f_{rn}(x)\,dx \sim \frac{1}{\sigma_r(2\pi)^{1/2}} \exp - \left(\frac{x^2}{2\sigma_r^2}\right) dx \tag{13}$$

Individual steps of restricted walks are no longer independent, since the restriction introduces a correlation. However, this correlation is "short range" in character and falls off exponentially with increasing separation of steps. The short range correlation is insufficient to change the characteristic features of the walk from those of a simple random walk.

A self-avoiding walk corresponds to the limit of a restricted walk as $r \to \infty$. Such a walk is no longer Markovian, and no general analytical methods have been found for determining its properties. However, evidence has been accumulating to indicate that the basic characteristics differ in an essential manner from those of restricted walks. We now proceed to discuss this evidence in further detail.

III. METHODS OF INVESTIGATING SELF-AVOIDING WALKS

Four independent approaches have been used to investigate the properties of self-avoiding walks.

A. Rigorous Analysis

This is due mainly to Hammersley[6] and Kesten,[7] who have been concerned with the total number of walks, C_n, and the number, u_n, which return to the origin at the nth step. They have established the existence of a number μ for each lattice (which Hammersley terms the "connective constant") such that

$$\left. \begin{array}{l} C_n \sim \mu^n f_1(n) \\ u_n \sim \mu^n f_2(n) \end{array} \right\} \tag{14}$$

where

$$\lim_{n \to \infty} [f_1(n)]^{1/n} = \lim_{n \to \infty} [f_2(n)]^{1/n} = 1$$

Certain bounds have also been established for μ and $f_1(n)$, (e.g., $1 \leqq f_1(n) \leqq \exp[\alpha n^{1/2}]$) but these are far short of what is required for numerical calculation. It has also been proved[7] for an sc lattice that the ratios C_{n+2}/C_n and u_{n+2}/u_n tend to μ^2 as $n \to \infty$. In numerical work the ratios C_{n+1}/C_n and u_{n+1}/u_n are more useful than $C_n^{1/n}$, $u_n^{1/n}$.

B. Monte Carlo

The aim is to generate on a computer a sufficiently large number of self-avoiding walks to provide a representative sample. The constant μ is estimated from the rate of attrition; the behavior of other properties with increasing length of walk (e.g., mean square end-to-end distance or radius of gyration) is determined from the sample. A digital computer is particularly well suited to generating self-avoiding walks; the great difficulty is to overcome the high attrition rate, and ensure that enough long walks survive. The Monte Carlo method was suggested initially by G. W. King and developed largely by F. T. Wall and his collaborators,[8] and considerable ingenuity has been exercised in devising efficient computer programs and overcoming attrition.[9]

C. Exact Enumeration

For sufficiently short chains it is possible to calculate C_n, u_n, and all other features of interest exactly. Such enumerations were initiated independently because of their application to the statistical mechanics of interacting systems on crystal lattices,[10] and a variety of analytical and computational methods (including the use of digital computers) has been employed to extend the enumerations to as large a value of n as practicable. These exact results are then used to conjecture the pattern of asymptotic behavior.

It is of great importance to assess whether the enumerations have been carried far enough for such conjectures to be reliable. The numerical analysis of successive terms usually provides a fairly clear indication, but parallel work on the Ising model in two dimensions is an excellent guide since exact analytical results are available.

Most of this development has been due to the Theoretical Physics Group at King's College, in collaboration with the National Physics Laboratory.[11-13]

D. Transition Matrix

In the previous section we considered the approach to a self-avoiding walk by means of a restricted walk of order r, governed by a Markovian transition matrix. Although the size of this matrix increases rapidly, it is possible to calculate the distribution of its eigenvalues for small r in the hope of detecting a general pattern of behavior as r increases and tends to infinity. This approach has been used by Domb and Hioe[14] and more recently by Mazur.[15] It is difficult to draw direct conclusions from the method but confirmatory evidence can be provided for a type of behavior suggested by other methods, and useful insight can be obtained on the nature of the change from a restricted to a self-avoiding walk.

The methods described above should be regarded as complementary rather than alternative. In the absence of adequate exact knowledge it is useful to derive evidence from as many sources as possible, and the pattern of behavior of self-avoiding walks proposed in the next section is the result of a synthesis of the information provided by the different methods.

IV. PROPERTIES OF SELF-AVOIDING WALKS

One of the important general conclusions to emerge from a study of cooperative phenomena is the existence of "long-range" properties which depend only on dimension and not on particular lattice structure within a given dimension.[10] Other properties of a "local" character are dependent on lattice structure, and the simultaneous study of several lattices in a given dimension is of particular help in differentiating between long range and local properties. The properties of ordinary random walks described in Section II can be separated in this manner. For example, the coordination number of the lattice is a local property, whereas the mean-square length $\langle R_n^2 \rangle$, the ratio $\langle S_n^2 \rangle / \langle R_n^2 \rangle$, and the probability distribution of any coordinate of the endpoint are long-range properties.

A. Number of Walks of n Steps, C_n

Table I (taken from Martin, Sykes, and Hioe[16]) contains the most recent exact enumerations of C_n for the triangular and fcc lattices. Similar enumerations for other lattices have been given elsewhere[10, 11]; numerical analysis indicates that the close packed lattices lead to most rapid convergence, and these were therefore selected for an extensive enumeration project. It should be noted that C_{12} for the fcc lattice is of order 1.8×10^{12}. Using a direct enumeration procedure on a digital computer, the machine time required would be quite prohibitive. It is only by the way of sophisticated counting theorems[17] and skilled programming that these numbers could be obtained.

Equations (14) tell us the asymptotic form of C_n, and a natural initial choice for $f_1(n)$ is n^g. We should then expect that

$$C_n/C_{n-1} \sim \mu[1 + g/n] \tag{15}$$

Then if we plot C_n/C_{n-1} against $1/n$, once the region of asymptotic validity has been attained we should obtain a straight line whose slope determines g and whose intercept on the axis $1/n = 0$ determines μ. In fact reference to Figures 1a and 2a indicates that the region of linearity is attained quite rapidly, and detailed numerical analysis confirms this view. The value of g is close to $\frac{1}{3}$ for all two-dimensional lattices, and to $\frac{1}{6}$ for all three-dimensional lattices; it is reasonable to conjecture that the values are given exactly by these fractions. Improved methods of convergence[18] can then be used to calculate μ, and estimates are available for all common two- and three-dimensional lattices with an error thought to be about 1 part in 10^4. These are also in good agreement with Monte Carlo[8, 9, 11, 12] estimates.

Martin, Sykes, and Hioe[16] found it more convenient and accurate to represent C_n in the form

$$A\binom{j}{n}\mu^n \qquad (j = -g - 1) \qquad (16)$$

TABLE I

Tables of C_n and u_n for the triangular and fcc lattices
(From Martin, Sykes, and Hioe.[16])

| n | Triangular | | Face-centered cubic | |
	C_n	u_n	C_n	u_n
1	6		12	
2	30		132	
3	138	12	1 404	48
4	618	24	14 700	264
5	2 730	60	152 532	1 680
6	11 946	180	1 573 716	11 640
7	51 882	588	16 172 148	86 352
8	224 130	1 968	165 697 044	673 104
9	964 134	6 840	1 693 773 924	5 424 768
10	4 133 166	24 240	17 281 929 564	44 828 400
11	17 668 938	87 252	176 064 704 412	377 810 928
12	75 355 206	318 360	1 791 455 071 068	3 235 366 752
13	320 734 686	1 173 744		28 074 857 616
14	1 362 791 250	4 366 740		
15	5 781 765 582	16 370 700		
16	24 497 321 682	61 780 320		
17	103 673 881 482	234 505 140		

where $j = -\frac{4}{3}$ in two dimensions and $j = -\frac{7}{6}$ in three dimensions. The value of A varies from one lattice to another and corresponds to a local property; j is long range.

B. Number of Polygonal Closures of n Steps, u_n

Table I also gives the value of u_n for the triangular and fcc lattices. These behave less regularly than C_n, and take longer to settle down to asymptotic form (Figs. 1a and 2a). However, a useful check is provided by the equality of the value of μ derived from u_n with that derived from C_n. (In fact this equality was conjectured[18] from such a numerical analysis before it had been proved rigorously.[6])

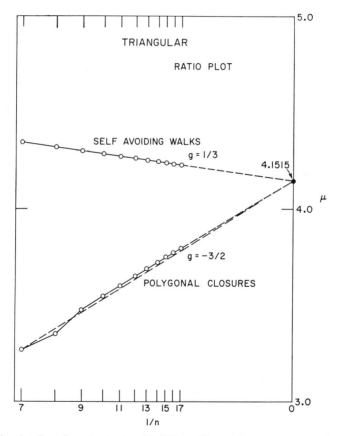

Fig. 1. Ratio plot for triangular lattice. (a) Self-avoiding walks u_n/u_{n-1} and C_n/C_{n-1} vs. $1/n$

The values of u_n also fit an asymptotic formula of form of Eq. (16) with $j = \frac{1}{2}$ in two dimensions $(u_n \sim \mu^n n^{-3/2})$, and $j = \frac{3}{4}$ in three dimensions $(u_n \sim \mu^n n^{-7/4})$. The probability of ring closure, u_n/C_n, is thus proportional to $n^{-11/6}$ in two dimensions, and $n^{-23/12}$ in three dimensions. For a simple or restricted walk the corresponding values are those of Polya, n^{-1} and $n^{-3/2}$, respectively. Hence, the volume exclusion reduces the probability of return by $n^{5/6}$ and $n^{5/12}$, respectively.

The behavior of u_n is more difficult to estimate by Monte Carlo methods since a return to the origin is a relatively rare event. Wall and co-workers[8,9] suggested that $u_n/C_n \sim n^{-2}$ independently of lattice and dimension and this is not too far from the values quoted above.

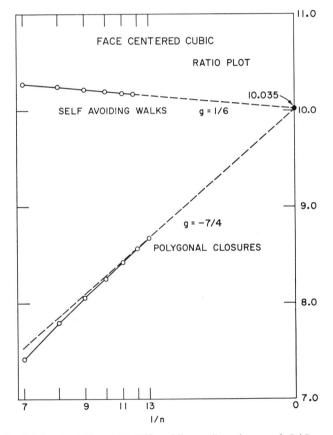

Fig. 2. Ratio plot for fcc lattice. (a) Self-avoiding walks u_n/u_{n-1} and C_n/C_{n-1} vs. $1/n$ (b) Ising coefficients $na_n/(n-1)a_{n-1}$ and d_n/d_{n-1} vs. $1/n$.

C. Mean Square Length $\langle R_n^2 \rangle$

The majority of attention in earlier discussions of self-avoiding walks was focused on the behavior of mean square length with increasing n, and on the question whether $\langle R_n^2 \rangle / n$ converges to a limit, as for restricted walks, or increases indefinitely. Monte Carlo investigation gave strong

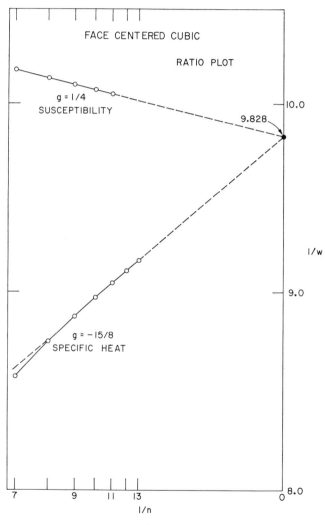

FACE CENTERED CUBIC

RATIO PLOT

$g = 1/4$
SUSCEPTIBILITY

9.828

$g = -15/8$
SPECIFIC HEAT

1/w

10.0

9.0

8.0

7   9   11   13

1/n

FIG. 2. (b)

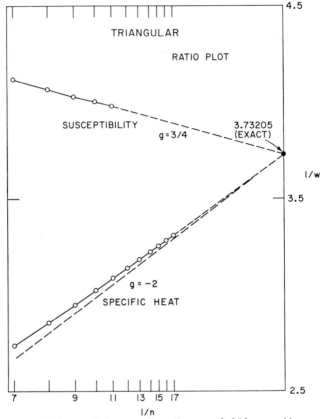

FIG. 1. (*b*) Ising coefficients $na_n/(n-1)a_{n-1}$ and d_n/d_{n-1} vs. $1/n$.

indications[8,9] that $\langle R_n^2 \rangle/n$ diverges; the data could be well fitted by a relation of the form

$$\langle R_n^2 \rangle = Cn^\theta \tag{17}$$

typical values of θ being 1.50 for a two-dimensional model and 1.18 for a three-dimensional model. (1.47 and 1.22 were corresponding figures for shorter chains.)

Exact enumerations were subsequently undertaken for a number of lattices in two and three dimensions.[13] Since $\langle R_n^2 \rangle$ is equal to n for a random walk, and n^2 for a completely stiff walk the form of Eq. (17) provides a reasonable interpolation between these extreme bounds. We should then expect

$$\langle R_{n+1}^2 \rangle/\langle R_n^2 \rangle \simeq 1 + \theta/n \tag{18}$$

and if we calculate successive values of

$$\theta_n = n[\langle R_{n+1}^2 \rangle/\langle R_n^2 \rangle - 1] \tag{19}$$

we will be furnished with a series of approximations to θ. For the fcc lattice these approximations behave smoothly and regularly. For the other lattices an odd–even alternation is present, and it is convenient to average out the effect partially by tabulating $\frac{1}{2}(\theta_n + \theta_{n+1})$.

The results are plotted graphically as a function of $1/n$ in Figure 3, and they suggest that $\theta = \frac{6}{5}$ for all lattices in three dimensions. Corresponding enumerations in two dimensions suggest $\theta = \frac{3}{2}$.

If these conjectures are accepted the quantity $\langle R_n^2 \rangle / n^\theta$ should tend to a limit as $n \to \infty$, and an estimate of this limit can be derived from the exact enumerations. Consequently an asymptotic formula can be put forward for the behavior of $\langle R_n^2 \rangle$ as a function of n, and this can be compared with Monte Carlo values for much longer walks. Such a comparison with walks of up to 600 steps on the tetrahedral and square lattices is reproduced in Table II, and the percentage deviations are recorded. An error of order 2% or 3% seems reasonable for a sample of about 1000 walks and the constanty of sign of eror may well be due to the "enrichment"[9] procedure introduced by Wall and Erpenbeck so as to overcome attrition.

It is striking that for walks of 600 steps on the tetrahedral lattice, more than 40 times the length of the walks from which the asymptotic formula is derived, the deviation is less than $2\frac{1}{2}\%$. This gives confidence that the asymptotic formula has a sound basis (criticism of the method by Flory and Fisk[31] will be considered in the next section). There are serious deviations in two dimensions for walks above 500 steps but it is possible that

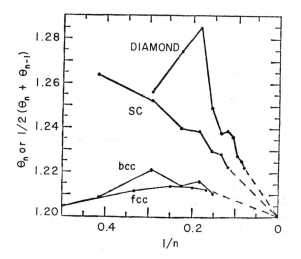

Fig. 3. θ_n as a function of $1/n$ [$\frac{1}{2}(\theta_n + \theta_{n-1})$ for loose-packed lattices]. After initial irregularities, θ_n apparently tends steadily to $\frac{6}{5}$ for all lattices. (From Domb.[13])

C. DOMB

TABLE II

Comparison between asymptotic formulas based on direct enumeration and Monte Carlo estimates. Tetrahedral and square lattices. (Wall and Erpenbeck[9]).

n	Calculated	Monte Carlo	% Deviation	n	Calculated	Monte Carlo	% Deviation
				20	72.3	68.7	−5.0
40	107.4	108.1	+0.7	40	200.6	195.5	−2.5
				60	391.3	354.6	−9.4
80	247.2	243.5	−1.5	80	559.4	545.8	−2.4
				100	779.0	768.7	−1.3
120	402.2	409.7	+1.9	120	1 021	1 013	−0.8
				140	1 284	1 307	+1.8
160	568.2	570.8	+0.5	160	1 566	1 616	+3.2
				180	1 866	1 955	+4.8
200	742.7	726.0	−2.2	200	2 183	2 226	+2.0
				220	2 516	2 557	+1.6
240	924.5	879.9	−4.8	240	2 865	2 798	−2.3
				260	3 228	3 211	−0.5
280	1 112	1 074	−3.5	280	3 600	3 531	−2.0
				300	3 995	3 865	−3.2
320	1 306	1 256	−3.8	320	4 399	4 345	−1.2
				340	4 815	4 688	−3.0
360	1 504	1 456	−3.2	360	5 243	5 006	−4.5
				380	5 684	5 470	−3.8
400	1 707	1 646	−3.5	440	6 136	6 037	−1.6
				420	6 599	6 553	−0.7
440	1 914	1 885	−1.5	440	7 074	6 923	−2.1
				460	7 559	7 488	−0.9
480	2 124	2 057	−3.2	480	8 055	8 004	−0.6
				500	8 561	8 749	+2.2
520	2 338	2 264	−3.2	520	9 077	8 709	−4.0
				540	9 604	9 390	−2.2
560	2 556	2 501	−2.1	560	10 140	9 233	−8.9
				580	10 685	9 934	−7.0
600	2 777	2 709	−2.4	600	11 240	9 732	−13.4

these last figures are unreliable (the enrichment procedure plays a greater role in two dimensions because of the higher attrition).

Monte Carlo evidence confirming the $\frac{6}{5}$ power was provided subsequently by Gans,[9] who introduced a new technique for overcoming attrition and generating long walks. As a result of a statistical analysis of a quarter of a million self-avoiding random walks on the diamond lattice, which varied in length from 40 to 1700 steps, Gans concluded that the exponent θ did not deviate from $\frac{6}{5}$ by more than statistical error.

Some recent computations by Mazur[15] and McCrackin on self-avoiding walks with nearest neighbor interactions have incidentally provided supporting evidence for asymptotic conjectures based on exact enumeration. Mazur did not use the enrichment procedure because of uncertainty regarding its precise statistical effects. He generated walks of up to 100 steps on the sc lattice, and new samples were run off for each length, the number in each sample being from 10,000 to 50,000. The results are shown in Table III and compared directly with the asymptotic formula derived from exact enumeration.[13] It will be seen that the deviations are not significantly greater than might be expected from statistical error. The greater persistence of negative deviations may mean that the correction term from Eq. (17) derived from exact enumerations is of the wrong form; more extensive runs would be required to test this in detail.

D. Probability Distribution of the End Points, $f_n(x)\ dx$

Monte Carlo runs[9] and earlier exact enumerations[12] suggested that the distribution of end points of self-avoiding walks might not be Gaussian. A more detailed analysis, which fitted histogram plots resulting from exact enumerations for the square and sc lattices, was undertaken by Domb, Gillis, and Wilmers.[19] Figure 4 shows this plot in two dimensions, the broken curve corresponding to a Gaussian distribution. It strongly indicates that the distribution of a coordinate of the end point of a self-avoiding walk is non-Gaussian; the full curve represented by $\exp -(x/\sigma)^4$

TABLE III

Comparison between asymptotic formulas based on direct enumeration and Monte Carlo estimates. Simple cubic lattices. (Mazur and McCrackin[15])

		Monte Carlo					Monte Carlo
n	Calculated	10,000 %	20,000 %	20,000 %	n	Calculated	50,000 %
19	36.436	36.098(−1.2)	36.627(+0.6)	36.357(−0.2)	23	45.849	45.846(0.0)
29	60.582	60.293(−0.5)	60.646(+0.1)	59.929(−1.0)	35	75.942	75.913(0.0)
39	86.485	86.662(+0.2)	86.869(+0.5)	86.109(−0.4)	47	108.212	108.04(−0.2)
49	113.765	115.43(+1.5)	113.35(−0.4)	113.19(−0.5)	59	142.189	140.95(−0.9)
59	142.189	143.41(+0.8)	140.13(−1.5)	140.83(−1.0)	71	177.587	175.81(−1.0)
69	171.598	169.64(−0.7)	169.48(−1.2)	170.36(−0.7)	83	214.206	213.53(−0.3)
79	201.874	199.53(−1.2)	203.50(+0.8)	199.89(−1.0)	95	251.904	249.52(−1.0)
89	232.928	231.66(−0.8)	233.27(+0.2)	231.87(−0.4)	107	290.568	288.58(−0.7)

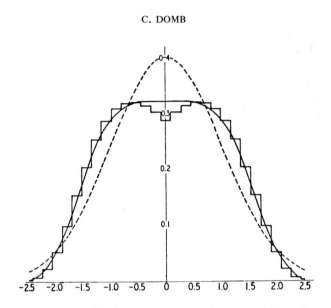

Fig. 4. Histogram plot of rectangular coordinate for self-avoiding walks on the SQ lattice ($N = 18$). The broken curve corresponds to a Gaussian distribution, and the full curve to $\delta = 4$ in Section IV-D. (From Domb, Gillis, and Wilmers.[19])

provides an adequate fit to the data (the slight dip near the origin arises from the restriction of no returns to the origin and is probably a "small number" effect). In three dimensions the deviation from Gaussian is less marked (Fig. 5), and the corresponding fit is obtained by using the function $\exp\left(-|x|/\sigma^{5/2}\right)$.

It is more difficult to use the Monte Carlo method to estimate the form of the probability distribution since the tails of the distribution correspond to rare events. Mazur[20] attempted to fit the three-dimensional end-to-end distribution by an expression of the form

$$p_n(\mathbf{r}) \simeq C_n r^{\varepsilon} \exp\left[-(r/R_n)^{\delta}\right] \qquad (20)$$

using the first few moments to determine ε and δ. Although the best fit to the data corresponded to $\delta = 3.2$, $\varepsilon = 2$, the moments were insensitive to δ and ε and an adequate fit could be obtained from $\delta = \varepsilon = 2.58$. The Monte Carlo calculations by Mazur and McCrackin mentioned previously[15] have also provided support for the values of reduced moments $\langle R_n^4\rangle/\langle R_n^2\rangle^2$, $\langle R_n^6\rangle/\langle R_n^2\rangle^3 \cdots$ estimated by exact enumeration.

The tentative conclusions described above regarding the form of $\langle R_n^2\rangle$ and $f_n(x)\,dx$ for self-avoiding walks were substantially strengthened by a relation formulated by Fisher.[21] Strong numerical evidence had been adduced by Domb, Gillis, and Wilmers[19] to indicate that the distributions

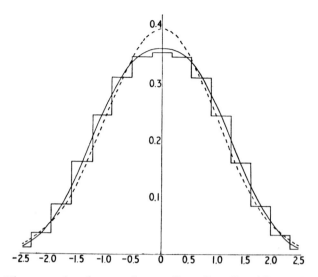

Fig. 5. Histogram plot of rectangular coordinate for self-avoiding walks on the SC lattice ($N = 13$). The broken curve corresponds to a Gaussian distribution and the full curve to $\delta = \frac{5}{2}$ in Section IV-D. (From Domb, Gillis, and Wilmers.[19])

in space of self-avoiding walks become spherically (or circularly) symmetrical for large n. Defining

$$P(\theta, \mathbf{r}) = \sum_{n=1}^{\infty} p_n(\mathbf{r}) \exp(-n\theta) \qquad (21)$$

Fisher established two rigorous bounds which suggest that the decay of $P(\theta, \mathbf{r})$ with r is of the form $\exp[-K(\theta)r]$. In order to obtain this form with a function of type (20) and $\langle R_n^2 \rangle$ given by Eq. (17) it was necessary that the following consistency condition be satisfied:

$$\theta/2 + 1/\delta = 1 \qquad (22)$$

This relation is satisfied by the two-dimensional conjectures ($\theta = \frac{3}{2}$, $\delta = 4$), the three-dimensional conjectures ($\theta = \frac{6}{5}$, $\delta = \frac{5}{2}$), as well as standard Gaussian values ($\theta = 1$, $\delta = 2$). Its significance in relation to the Ising model will be considered in the next section.

E. Mean Square Radius of Gyration $\langle S_n^2 \rangle$

From Eq. (9) we deduced that for a simple random walk the ratio $\langle S_{no}^2 \rangle / \langle R_{no}^2 \rangle$ tends asymptotically to $\frac{1}{6}$ as $n \to \infty$. The same relation holds for $\langle S_{nr}^2 \rangle / \langle R_{nr}^2 \rangle$ for a restricted walk; the correlations $\langle \mathbf{u}_{ir} \mathbf{u}_{jr} \rangle$

fall off exponentially with increasing distance $(i - j)$, and it can readily be shown that the expansion factor in $\langle \mathbf{R}_{nr}^2 \rangle$ arising from the correlations (analogue of Eq. (6)) is exactly matched by a corresponding expansion in $\langle S_{nr}^2 \rangle$.

However, for a self-avoiding walk the longer range correlations change the ratio from $\frac{1}{6}$ (for a completely stiff rod the ratio would be $\frac{1}{12}$). Monte Carlo calculations by Wall and Erpenbeck[9] estimated a value of 0.157 for the diamond lattice in three dimensions, and 0.145 for the square lattice in two dimensions. Recently Domb and Hioe[14] have used the method of exact enumeration for the square and triangular lattices in two dimensions, and for the diamond, sc, bcc, and fcc lattices in three dimensions. The ratio $\langle S_n^2 \rangle / \langle R_n^2 \rangle$ is calculated as a function of $1/n$ and extrapolated to $1/n = 0$. The individual lattice structure does not significantly affect the limiting ratio, so this property seems to be long range as for simple and restricted walks. The three-dimensional estimates converge smoothly to a value 0.155 ± 0.001; the two-dimensional estimates are more erratic, and the suggested limit is 0.140 ± 0.002. The agreement between Monte Carlo and exact enumeration is thus quite satisfactory.

F. Correlation Between Steps, $\langle \mathbf{u}_i \mathbf{u}_j \rangle_n$

Let us examine the analog of Eq. (6) for a self-avoiding walk,

$$\langle R_n^2 \rangle = n + 2 \sum_{i<j} \langle \mathbf{u}_i \mathbf{u}_j \rangle_n \tag{23}$$

If a relation of the form of Eq. (17) is satisfied, the first term in Eq. (23) will be negligible asymptotically in comparison with the second, and we should expect that $\langle \mathbf{u}_i \mathbf{u}_j \rangle_n$ will fall off as $1/(j - i)^k$ where k is chosen so as to yield Eq. (17). Assuming the correlations tend to a limiting form as the walk assumes a limiting shape, we can write

$$\langle \mathbf{u}_i \mathbf{u}_j \rangle_n \sim A\psi(s, t)/n^k \qquad s = i/n, \qquad t = (n - j)/n \tag{24}$$

We find that [14]

$$2 \sum_{i<j} \langle \mathbf{u}_i \mathbf{u}_j \rangle_n \to 2An^{2-k} \int_0^1 ds \int_0^{1-s} \psi(s, t)\, dt \tag{25}$$

Thus

$$\theta = 2 - k \tag{26}$$

and $k = \frac{1}{2}$ in two dimensions and $\frac{4}{5}$ in three dimensions.

The function $\psi(s, t)$ can conveniently be normalized in the form

$$\int_0^1 \int_0^{1-s} \psi(s, t)\, ds\, dt = 1 \tag{27}$$

The radius of gyration is then given by the moment m_{11} of $\psi(s, t)$

$$\langle S_n^2 \rangle / \langle R_n^2 \rangle = \int_0^1 \int_0^{1-s} st\psi(s, t) \, ds \, dt \tag{28}$$

and higher moments can be found by direct enumeration in a similar manner to $\langle S_n^2 \rangle$. Since $\langle \mathbf{u}_i \mathbf{u}_{i+1} \rangle_n$ remains nonzero as $n \to \infty$ it can be shown that the function $\psi(s, t)$ must be singular on $s + t = 1$, the singularity being of the form

$$1/[1 - (s + t)]^k \tag{29}$$

Hence, if we assume

$$\psi(s, t) = \chi(s, t)/[1 - (s + t)]^k \tag{30}$$

$\chi(s, t)$ is slowly varying and can be fitted by moments.

Knowledge of $\chi(s, t)$ enables us to calculate $\langle R_{ij}^2 \rangle_n$ between any two points of the walk; we have the relation

$$\frac{\langle R_{an, bn}^2 \rangle}{\langle R_n^2 \rangle} = \int_a^b \int_{1-b}^{1-s} \psi(s, t) \, ds \, dt \tag{31}$$

$\langle R_{an, bn}^2 \rangle$ had been estimated independently by Monte Carlo methods[9] for a number of values of a and b, and a comparison could be made. The agreement was within the limits of the standard errors of the Monte Carlo estimates.

We may finally note that calculations for different lattices did not produce significant differences in the function $\psi(s, t)$, and it seems likely that this is also a long range property.

G. Passage from a Restricted to a Self-Avoiding Walk

We may now inquire how the fundamental change in properties takes place in passing from a restricted to a self-avoiding walk as $r \to \infty$. For example, taking the simplest property, the total number of walks, how do we pass from the complex formula (10) for restricted walks to the simple formula (16) for self-avoiding walks, and what is the significance of the factor n^g in Eq. (16)?

Numerical studies[14] of the distribution of eigenvalues of the transition matrix for a number of two- and three-dimensional lattices (e.g., $r = 1$ to 7 for the triangular lattice, $r = 1$ to 5 for the fcc lattice) indicate a fairly simple pattern of behavior with increasing r. The largest eigenvalue λ_{1r} is real and positive and well separated from the other eigenvalues which seem roughly to lie on a circle centered at the origin in the complex plane; this is shown diagrammatically in Figure 6. A mutual cancellation is found

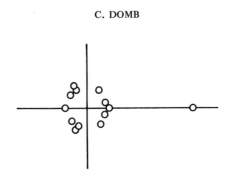

Fig. 6. A typical distribution of eigenvalues of the transition matrix.

in the contribution of all eigenvalues other than the largest to C_{nr}. For example, taking $r = 7$ for the triangular lattice and ignoring all but the largest eigenvalue produces an error of 0.11% in C_{77}. For $r = 5$ and the fcc lattice the error in C_{55} is 0.015%. It seems reasonable, therefore, to confine attention to the largest eigenvalue and its dependence on r.

The λ_{1r} are found to satisfy the approximate relation

$$\lambda_{1r} \simeq \mu\left(1 + \frac{g}{r}\right) \tag{32}$$

and this automatically recalls the parallel relation (15). Upon further reflection, however, we should not be surprised at this analogy. For the first r steps C_n is identical with C_{nr}, and the freedom to take a new step at the $(n - 1)$th stage of a self-avoiding walk is precisely equal to the freedom to take a new step at the corresponding stage of a restricted walk of order n. A self-avoiding walk does not establish its true character until the limit $n \to \infty$. Equations (15) and (32) represent an "end effect" at the $(n - 1)$th stage and it is the combination of all these end effects,

$$C_n = (C_n/C_{n-1})(C_{n-1}/C_{n-2})(C_{n-2}/C_{n-3}) \cdots (C_2/C_1)$$

$$\simeq \mu^n \prod_{r=1}^{n} (1 + g/r) \tag{33}$$

which give rise to the factor n^g.

Regarding the probability of return at the $(n + 1)$th stage of a restricted walk of order n we must use Eqs. (10) and (11) to calculate u_{n+1n}/C_{n+1n}, and it is no longer the behavior of λ_{1r} but of B_{1n}/A_{1n} which is relevant (provided that other eigenvalues can still be neglected). The calculations are now much more involved since the spatial distribution of walks must be taken into account, and not merely their total number, and this results in the disappearance of certain simplifying symmetries. Preliminary investigations have been undertaken but have not yet reached a conclusive stage; however, one can see qualitatively that if B_{1n}/A_{1n} is of order $1/n^c$ with a suitable value of c the reduction factor described above in Section B can be achieved.

For $\langle R_n^2 \rangle$ Eq. (12) suggests that the behavior of C_r as a function of r should be studied. Again this involves the spatial distribution of walks, and has not been adequately investigated. Equation (17) and the conclusions of Section C lead us to expect that $(C_r - C_{r-1})$ is of order $r^{-1/2}$ in two dimensions and $r^{-4/5}$ in three dimensions.

In higher dimensions once the dependence on r is of order $r^{-1-\eta}$ or less, the sum converges to a constant factor independent of n and the numerical values quoted above for two and three dimensions indicate that this should already be true in four dimensions. However this does not necessarily mean that $g = 1$ in Eq. (15), and numerical evidence points to the contrary.[22] Similarly, one cannot conclude that u_n has reached the Polya $n^{-d/2}$ dependence.

V. ANALOGY WITH THE ISING MODEL*

The Ising model has been the subject of numerous investigations, and the past few years have seen substantial progress in unravelling its behavior.[23, 24] By means of a suitable transformation, the partition function for the Ising model for a given lattice can be expanded in a high temperature series whose nth coefficient is given by the number of configurations of specified types which can be constructed from n bonds of the lattice. The analogy between these Ising configurations and self-avoiding walks was noted some years ago by Temperley[25] and Fisher and Sykes.[11] These authors were concerned largely with the relation between the self-avoiding walk limit, μ, and the Ising critical point $w_c[w = \tanh (J/kT), J = \text{inter-action of two parallel spins}]$. They noted the small numerical difference between μ and $1/w_c$, and Fisher and Sykes[11] were able to show that this difference is about 10% in two dimensions and $2\frac{1}{2}\%$ in three dimensions.

To obtain a clearer insight into the relationship between the Ising and self-avoiding walk enumerations, it is better to pass to the logarithm of the partition function, $\ln Z$, since this eliminates the need to consider disjoint graphs. We can then find a property of the Ising model which corresponds to each of $C_n, u_n, \langle R_n^2 \rangle, f_n(x)\, dx$. The Ising enumerations are much more

---

* The contents of this section formed part of an invited lecture at the Nordita Conference on Statistical Physics, Trondheim, June 1967. A more complete account is in the course of preparation.

complex than those of self-avoiding walks, but in certain particular cases in two dimensions cancellations occur which enable an exact analytic solution to be found. This is extremely important since we can examine the numerical behavior of coefficients in series expansions for these cases, and use them as guides to the more frequent and general cases in which no analytic solution is available.

Let us first consider $\ln Z$ in zero field. This can be expanded in the form

$$\ln Z = \sum_{n=0}^{\infty} a_n w^n \tag{34}$$

where the nth coefficient a_n is made up of contributions from graphs constructed with n or fewer bonds of the lattice

$$a_n = \sum_{l \leq n} P_{lx} g_{lx} \tag{35}$$

Here l denotes the number of bonds in the graph, and x is a classification symbol to differentiate between types of graph. P_{lx} represents the number of graphs of type x (per lattice site) which can be constructed from l bonds of the lattice (usually termed the lattice constant); g_{lx} is a weighting factor of order unity.

In fact, for the Ising model of spin $\frac{1}{2}$ with which we are here concerned, only multiply connected graphs contribute to the sum (35), and these have been conveniently classified in terms of cyclomatic number.[26] (For a graph of p points and l lines this is defined as $C = l - p + 1$.) The graph corresponding to cyclomatic number 1 is a polygon, and it is easy to see that its lattice constant P_l is related to number of self-avoiding polygons u_l by

$$u_l = 2l P_l \tag{36}$$

Numerical analysis now indicates that for the terms which have been evaluated so far P_l provides the dominant contribution to a_l. This is illustrated in Table IV by the breakdown of a_{11} into contributions from graphs having $C = 1$–5 (the data were supplied by M. F. Sykes). Hence we are tempted to investigate an approximation in which only the polygon is taken into account, and all other types with $C > 1$ are ignored. We shall call this the self-avoiding walk approximation to the specific heat C_H (second derivative with respect to W of $\ln Z$) and its behavior in the critical region is characterized by the function

$$\sum_n n u_n w^n \tag{37}$$

TABLE IV

Breakdown of contributions to coefficient a_{11}
for specific heat series of Ising mode, fcc lattice
(Data of M. F. Sykes.)

Cyclomatic Number	Contribution		
1	17	173	224
	−2	226	456
3	−1272	528	
4	−151896		
5	−2016		
Total	13	520	328

Using the numerical results of Section IV-B the critical point is given by $w_c = 1/\mu$, and the behavior in its neighborhood by

$$C_H = (1 - w/w_c)^{-1/2} \qquad \text{in two dimensions}$$
$$= (1 - w/w_c)^{-1/4} \qquad \text{in three dimensions} \tag{38}$$

The error in this approximation to the Ising model is known rigorously in two dimensions, and from extensive numerical studies in three dimensions[27] (which also have the support of "scaling laws")

$$C_H = \ln\left(1 - \frac{w}{w_c}\right) \qquad \text{in two dimensions}$$
$$= (1 - w/w_c)^{-1/8} \qquad \text{in three dimensions} \tag{39}$$

The error in the value of w_c was noted previously. It is possible to take account systematically of the graphs which have been neglected in such a manner as to improve the approximation.[28] However we need not concern ourselves with the details of this aspect, but with the observation that these graphs do not change the basic character and behavior of the coefficients of w^n.

The magnetic susceptibility in zero field, x_0, can likewise be expressed as a high temperature expansion

$$\frac{kT\chi_0}{m^2} = \sum_{n=0}^{\infty} d_n w^n \qquad (m = \text{magnetic moment of single spin}) \tag{40}$$

where the d_n are given by Eq. (35); however to P_{lx} must now be added a new set of graphs which include those obtained by removing part or all of a single bond of a multiply connected graph. Numerical analysis of the contributions to d_n now shows that the dominant contribution comes from simple chains. If we take only such chains into account we have a self-avoiding walk approximation in which the behavior of the susceptibility in the critical region is characterized by the function

$$\sum_n C_n w^n \qquad (41)$$

Using the numerical results of Section IV-A the critical point is given by $w_c = 1/\mu$, and the behavior in its neighborhood by

$$\begin{aligned} \chi_0 &\simeq (1 - w/w_c)^{-4/3} &&\text{in two dimensions} \\ &\simeq (1 - w/w_c)^{-7/6} &&\text{in three dimensions} \end{aligned} \qquad (42)$$

The error in this approximation is again known rigorously in two dimensions,[29] and from numerical studies in three dimensions

$$\begin{aligned} \chi_0 &\simeq (1 - w/w_c)^{-7/4} &&\text{in two dimensions} \\ &\simeq (1 - w/w_c)^{-5/4} &&\text{in three dimensions} \end{aligned} \qquad (43)$$

To illustrate more directly the analogy between the Ising coefficients and self-avoiding walks, ratio plots of C_n/C_{n-1} and u_n/u_{n-1} are drawn in Figures 1a, 2a to compare with d_n/d_{n-1} and $na_n/(n-1)a_{n-1}$ in Figures 1b, 2b. The limit and slopes in Figure 1b are exact; but the general pattern of behavior of the other plots is sufficiently similar to give us confidence in the conclusions. (The convergence in three dimensions is more rapid since excluded volume plays a smaller part. Similarly the self-avoiding walk approximation provides a closer fit to the correct behavior of the Ising model.)

Coming now to the mean square length of self-avoiding walks, the corresponding Ising model property is the mean square correlation range L^2, and the analog of the end to end distribution is the spin pair correlation function $\Gamma(\mathbf{R}) = \langle S_0 S_{\mathbf{R}} \rangle$. These properties have been discussed comprehensively by Fisher and Burford,[30] and although they formulated their high temperature expansions in terms of disjoint graphs, a parallel development can be given which uses only connected graphs. We then have

$$L^2 \simeq \sum_{n=0}^{\infty} f_n w^n \Big/ \sum_{n=0}^{\infty} d_n w^n \qquad (44)$$

where

$$f_n = \sum_{l \leq n} P_{lx} g_{lx} \langle R_{lx}^2 \rangle \qquad (45)$$

The graphs in Eq. (45) are the same as occur in the susceptibility coefficients d_n, but each graph is now multiplied by a mean-square length factor. Taking for the self-avoiding walk approximation simple chains C_n, and using the results of Section IV-C we find

$$L^2 \simeq (1 - w/w_c)^{-3/2} \qquad \text{in two dimensions}$$
$$\simeq (1 - w/w_c)^{-6/5} \qquad \text{in three dimensions} \tag{46}$$

The correct values are known rigorously in two dimensions, and from numerical studies in three dimensions

$$L^2 \simeq (1 - w/w_c)^{-2} \qquad \text{in two dimensions}$$
$$\simeq (1 - w/w_c)^{-1 \cdot 29} \qquad \text{in three dimensions} \tag{47}$$

Again the approximation is greatly improved in three dimensions.

Finally the spin pair correlation function is given by

$$\Gamma(R) = \sum h_n(\mathbf{R}) w^n \tag{48}$$

where

$$h_n(\mathbf{R}) = \sum_{l \leq n} P_{lx}(\mathbf{R}) g_{lx} \tag{49}$$

and the P_{lx} refer to graphs used for the susceptibility whose end points are at $(0, \mathbf{R})$. For the self-avoiding walk approximation we confine $P_{lx}(\mathbf{R})$ to chains $C_n(\mathbf{R})$ and use the results of Section IVD. We obtain an expression of the form

$$\Gamma(\mathbf{R}) = \sum_n \frac{w^n \mu^n}{n^a} \exp\left(-\frac{R}{\sigma}\right)^{\delta} (\sigma^2 \sim n^\theta) \tag{50}$$

$$= \sum \frac{1}{n^a} \exp\left[n \ln (\mu W) - R^\delta n^{-\delta\theta/2}\right] \tag{51}$$

Evaluating Eq. (51) by the method of steepest descents for large R, δ, n, we find that the saddle point n^* is given by

$$\ln (\mu W) + \left(\frac{\theta\delta}{2}\right) R^\delta n^{*-\delta\theta/2-1} = 0 \tag{52}$$

Because of Fisher's relation (22) this reduces to

$$n^* \sim R(1 - T_c/T)^{-1/\delta}\left(\frac{\theta\delta}{2}\right)^{1/\delta} \tag{53}$$

and hence, for large R

$$\Gamma(\mathbf{R}) \sim \exp -[R(1 - T_c/T)^{\theta/2}] \tag{54}$$

This is of correct form but the exponent contains the same error as in Eq. (46). [The form of the correlation function for small R, and when $T_c = T$ needs a more refined analysis.]

We now turn to recent criticism by Flory and Fisk[31] of conclusions drawn from the method of direct enumeration. Developing an approach introduced a number of years ago by Flory[32] for calculating $\langle R_n^2 \rangle$, these authors suggest that although $\langle R_n^2 \rangle$ is asymptotically of the form $n^{6/5}$ in three dimensions, the asymptotic limit is attained only for extremely long chains ($n > 10^6$). Hence they regard the agreement between the results of direct enumeration and the earlier predictions of Flory[32] as fortuitous.

The most effective reply to this criticism is a reference to the two-dimensional Ising model for which an analytic solution is available, and coefficients can be computed for all values of n. Taking the triangular lattice, for example, predictions based on values of n up to 15 are quite adequate to represent the asymptotic behavior of the coefficients relating to thermodynamic and correlation properties to a high degree of accuracy.

It is true that important physical problems can be found in which the convergence to asymptotic behavior is extremely slow.[33] When attractive interacting forces are introduced into a self-avoiding chain tightly bound configurations play a major part, and far more extensive enumerations would be required. An Ising analog is provided by the coefficients in the expansion for the partition function in powers of $\lambda [= \exp(-\beta m H)]$ below the Curie temperature. The "droplet model"[34] indicates that a large number of terms would be required to determine the critical behavior correctly.

However, for the enumerations considered in the present paper no such complications arise and it is reasonable to rely on the results of extrapolations. The suggestion made by Flory and Fisk[31] that the exact enumerations in the range $n = 1$ to 14 are dominated by immediate reversals is incorrect. The discussion of Section IV-G indicates that the nth step in the enumeration eliminates the effect of polygons of order n, and the contribution of the nth stage is of order $1/n^c$. Thus the exact enumeration procedure is equivalent to assessing the asymptotic behavior of $\sum_1^n 1/n^c$ from the first 14 terms.

VI. CONTINUUM MODELS

Although this survey is concerned primarily with lattice models, we shall refer briefly in this section to the investigation of continuum models which take account of excluded volume. By analogy with random walks and restricted walks, we might expect the long range properties to be identical for lattice and continuum models.

It is remarkable that the asymptotic value $\theta = \frac{6}{5}$ in three dimensions (and correspondingly $\theta = \frac{3}{2}$ in two dimensions) was suggested many years ago by Flory.[32] Using a mean field type of argument, and denoting by α the expansion factor over a chain with no excluded volume, Flory derived the equation (in three dimensions)

$$\alpha^5 - \alpha^3 = Dn^{1/2} \tag{55}$$

where D depends on the magnitude of the excluded volume but is independent of n. The difficulty with this treatment is that approximations are introduced whose precise effect is difficult to assess. Attempts to improve the approximation have subsequently led to a different value of the exponent θ.[35]

Recently a new analytic approach has been initiated by Edwards[36] using a self-consistent field treatment similar to that of Hartree for atomic wave functions. (Edwards also gives a more rigorous justification in terms of functional integration.) The resulting formula for mean square end-to-end distance is

$$\langle R_n^2 \rangle = l^2 (v/l^3)^{2/5} n^{6/5} \tag{56}$$

Here l is the length of an individual step and v is the excluded volume. Edwards derives a correction term to Eq. (56) from which he deduces that the formula is valid as long as

$$n \gg l^6/v^2 \tag{57}$$

Applying this criterion to a lattice model, v corresponds roughly to the volume of a unit cell, and l to a lattice spacing. Hence the values of $n \sim 10$ for exact enumeration quoted in Section IV seem quite reasonable. Certainly there is no support for the claim by Flory and Fisk[31] that the 6/5 power law is attained only for $n > 10.^6$

Regarding the probability of return to the origin, Edwards[36] suggests that it is proportional to $n^{-9/5}$. In fact such a relationship can be deduced from the assumption that the walk tends to a limiting shape.[37] However, for a self-avoiding walk on a lattice we have seen that $u_n/C_n \sim n^{-23/12}$ and Domb, Gillis, and Wilmers[19] noted that the behavior at the origin is anomalous, and is not truly representative of the region $\langle R_n^2 \rangle^{1/2}$ enclosing it. For the total number of configurations Edwards gives $C_n \sim n^{1/5}$ whereas the lattice estimate is $\sim n^{1/6}$. Finally Edwards does not find any evidence of non-Gaussian behavior and this is a little difficult to reconcile

TABLE V

Passage from a random to a self-avoiding walk and Ising analogs

	Normal random walks	Restricted walks (order r)	Self-avoiding walks		Ising analog
			Two dimensions	Three dimensions	
Number of walks of n steps	$c_{nO} = q^n$	$c_{nr} = A_{1r}\lambda_{1r}^n + \cdots A_{Nr}\lambda_{Nr}^n$	$c_n \sim A\mu^n n^{1/3}$	$A\mu^n n^{1/6}$	Magnetic susceptibility
Number at origin after n steps	$u_{nO} \sim B_{1O}q^n/n^{d/2}$	$u_{nr} \sim B_{1r}\lambda_{1r}^n/n^{d/2}$	$u_n \sim B\mu^n n^{-3/2}$	$B\mu^n n^{-3/4}$	Specific heat (zero field)
Fraction at origin after n steps	$u_{nO}/c_{nO} \sim B_{1O}/n^{d/2}$	$u_{nr}/c_{nr} \sim B_{1r}/A_{1r}n^{d/2}$	$u_n/c_n \sim n^{-11/6}$	$n^{-23/12}$	
Mean square length	$\langle R_{nO}^2 \rangle = n$	$\langle R_{nr}^2 \rangle \sim C_{Or}n$	$\langle R_n^2 \rangle \sim Cn^{3/2}$	$Cn^{6/5}$	Mean square correlation range
Probability distribution of x coord. of end point	$f_{On}(x) \sim \dfrac{1}{\sqrt{2\pi n}}\exp\left(-\dfrac{x^2}{2n}\right)$	$f_{rn}(x) \sim \dfrac{1}{\sigma_r\sqrt{2\pi}}\exp\left(-\dfrac{x^2}{2\sigma_r^2}\right)$	$f_n(x) \sim \exp -\left(\dfrac{x}{l}\right)^4$	$\exp -\left(\dfrac{x}{\sigma}\right)^{5/2}$	Spin pair correlation function

with Section IV-D. A recent attempt by Reiss[38] to use a variational treatment for the problem leads in first approximation to a non-Gaussian distribution of the form $\exp(-A/r + Br^2)$. However, the $\langle R_n^2 \rangle$ dependence is now changed to $n^{4/3}$.

Although Monte Carlo runs are more difficult to set up for continuum models, such calculations have been undertaken[39] and a number of suggestions have been advanced as a result; that a higher power than $n^{6/5}$ is required to represent the data, and that the $n^{6/5}$ dependence is valid only for a sufficiently large excluded volume. However, some caution is required before accepting such conclusions since it is not clear that asymptotic behavior has yet been achieved, and log–log plots are insensitive. It is more significant, perhaps, that the ratio $\langle S_n^2 \rangle / R_n^2 \rangle$ found by Windwer[39] is 0.158, and this is close enough to the value for lattice systems (Section IV-E) to support the assumption that they are identical.

VII. CONCLUSIONS

During the early history of the excluded volume problem there were conflicting claims in the literature regarding asymptotic behavior, and it was difficult to find suitable criteria to decide between these claims. The same was true of the early history of the Ising model. However, exact solutions in two dimensions and exact series expansions in three dimensions have done a great deal to clarify the situation for the Ising model. By drawing on the analogy with the Ising model it is hoped that a similar clarification can be achieved with the properties of self-avoiding walks. A summary of the main suggestions put forward in this paper is presented in Table V.

Acknowledgment

I am grateful to Dr. M. F. Sykes and Dr. D. L. Hunter for providing data on which the plots in Figures 1 and 2 are based, and to Dr. J. Mazur for communicating his Monte Carlo data prior to publication.

References

1. For previous reviews on this topic see, for example, F. T. Wall and L. A. Hiller, *Ann. Rev. Phys. Chem.*, **5**, 267 (1954); J. J. Hermans, **8**, 179 (1957); E. F. Cassassa, **11**, 477 (1960); W. H. Stockmayer, *Makromol. Chem.*, **35**, 54 (1960).
2. C. Domb, *Proc. Camb. Phil. Soc.*, **50**, 586 (1954); E. W. Montroll and G. H. Weiss, *J. Math. Phys.*, **6**, 167 (1965).
3. G. Polya, *Math. Ann.*, **84**, 149 (1921); see also E. W. Montroll, *J. Soc. Ind. Appl. Math.*, **4**, 241 (1956).
4. W. Feller, *An Introduction to Probability Theory and Applications*, Wiley, New York, 1951; E. W. Montroll, *Ann. Math. Stat.*, **18**, 18 (1947).

258   C. DOMB

5. C. Domb and M. E. Fisher, *Proc. Camb. Phil. Soc.*, **54**, 48 (1958); J. Gillis, *Proc. Camb. Phil. Soc.*, **51**, 639 (1955).
6. J. M. Hammersley and K. W. Morton, *J. Roy. Stat. Soc.*, **16**, 23 (1954); J. M. Hammersley, *Proc. Camb. Phil. Soc.*, **53**, 642 (1957); **57**, 516 (1961); *Quart. J. Math. Oxford*, **12**, 250 (1961); *Sankha*, **A25**, 269 (1963); J. M. Hammersley and D. J. A. Welsh, *Quart. J. Math. Oxford*, **13**, 108 (1962). Hammersley was the first to introduce the term "self-avoiding walk."
7. H. Kesten, *J. Math. Phys.*, **4**, 960 (1963); **5**, 1128 (1964).
8. E.g., F. T. Wall, L. A. Hiller, Jr., and D. J. Wheeler, *J. Chem. Phys.*, **22**, 1036 (1954); F. T. Wall, L. A. Hiller, Jr., and W. F. Atchison, *J. Chem. Phys.*, **23**, 913 (1955); **26**, 1742 (1957).
9. E.g., F. T. Wall and J. J. Erpenbeck, *J. Chem. Phys.*, **30**, 634, 637 (1958); F. T. Wall, S. Windwer, and P. J. Gans, in *Methods in Computational Physics*, Vol. 1, Academic, New York, 1963; P. J. Gans, *J. Chem. Phys.*, **42**, 4159 (1965). The last paper provides a good reference list to the rest of the literature.
10. C. Domb, *Advan. Phys.*, **9**, 149, 245 (1960).
11. M. E. Fisher and M. F. Sykes, *Phys. Rev.*, **114**, 45 (1959).
12. E.g., B. J. Hiley and M. F. Sykes, *J. Chem. Phys.*, **34**, 1531 (1961); M. E. Fisher and B. J. Hiley, *J. Chem. Phys.*, **34**, 1253 (1961); M. F. Sykes, *J. Chem. Phys.*, **39**, 410 (1963); see also, G. S. Rushbrooke and J. Eve, *J. Chem. Phys.*, **31**, 1333 (1959).
13. J. L. Martin, *Proc. Camb. Phil. Soc.*, **58**, 92 (1962); C. Domb, *J. Chem. Phys.*, **38**, 2957 (1963).
14. C. Domb and F. T. Hioe, to be published *J. Chem. Phys.* (in press); F. T. Hioe "Self-Avoiding Walk Model of a Polymer Chain," Thesis, University of London, 1967.
15. J. Mazur, private communication; J. Mazur and F. McCrackin, *J. Chem. Phys.*, **49**, 648 (1968) and also unpublished results.
16. J. L. Martin, M. F. Sykes, and F. T. Hioe, *J. Chem. Phys.*, **46**, 3478 (1967).
17. M. F. Sykes, *J. Math. Phys.*, **2**, 52 (1961).
18. C. Domb and M. F. Sykes, *J. Math. Phys.*, **2**, 63 (1961). (See also, more recently A. J. Guttmann, B. W. Ninham, and C. J. Thompson, *Physics Letters*, **26A**, 180 (1968)).
19. C. Domb, J. Gillis, and G. Wilmers, *Proc. Phys. Soc.*, **85**, 625 (1965); **86**, 426 (1965).
20. J. Mazur, *J. Res. Natl. Bur. Std.*, **69A**, 355 (1965); *J. Chem. Phys.*, **43**, 4354 (1965).
21. M. E. Fisher, *J. Chem. Phys.*, **44**, 616 (1966).
22. M. E. Fisher and D. S. Gaunt, *Phys. Rev.*, **133A**, 224 (1964).
23. C. Domb, *J. Roy. Stat. Soc., London*, **B26**, 373 (1964); "Critical Phenomena" (National Bureau of Standards, Washington, D.C., 1965). Misc. Publ. 273, p. 29.
24. M. E. Fisher, *J. Math. Phys.*, **5**, 944 (1964); *Rept. Progr. Phys.*, **30**, 615 (1967).
25. H. N. V. Temperley, *Phys. Rev.*, **103**, 1 (1956).
26. M. F. Sykes, J. W. Essam, B. R. Heap, and B. J. Hiley, *J. Math. Phys.*, **7**, 1557 (1966).
27. M. F. Sykes, J. L. Martin, and D. L. Hunter, *Proc. Phys. Soc.*, **91**, 671 (1967). For a popular exposition, see C. Domb, *Phys. Today*, **21**, 23 (1968).
28. C. Domb, *J. Appl. Phys.*, **39**, 614 (1968) gives a brief preliminary discussion.
29. M. E. Fisher, *Physica*, **25**, 521 (1959); L. P. Kadanoff, *Nuovo Cimento*, **44**, 276 (1966); T. T. Wu, *Phys. Rev.*, **149**, 380 (1966); G. V. Ryazanov, *Soviet Phys.* JETP, **22**, 789 (1966). Historically this was first conjectured from numerical analysis by C. Domb and M. F. Sykes, *Proc. Roy. Soc.* (*London*), Ser. A, **240**, 214 (1957).
30. M. E. Fisher and R. J. Burford, *Phys. Rev.*, **156**, 583 (1967).

31. P. J. Flory and S. Fisk, *J. Chem. Phys.*, **44**, 2243 (1966).
32. P. J. Flory, *J. Chem. Phys.*, **17**, 303 (1949).
33. C. Domb, N. W. Dalton, G. S. Joyce, and D. W. Wood, *Proc. International Conference on Magnetism, London*; Institute of Physics and Physical Society, p. 85 (1964).
34. M. E. Fisher, *Physics*, **3**, 255 (1967).
35. M. Kurata and W. H. Stockmayer, *Fortschr. Hochpolymer Forsch.*, **3**, 196 (1963); M. Fixman, *J. Chem. Phys.*, **36**, 3132 (1962); Z. Alexandrowicz, *J. Chem. Phys.*, **46**, 3789 (1967).
36. S. F. Edwards, *Proc. Phys. Soc.*, **85**, 613 (1965); "Critical Phenomena" Natl. Bur. Std., Washington, D.C., Misc. Publ. 273, p. 225 (1965).
37. M. E. Fisher, *Discussions Faraday Soc.*, **25**, p. 200 (1958).
38. H. Reiss, *J. Chem. Phys.*, **47**, 186 (1967); See also H. Yamakawa preprint "On the Asymptotic Solution of the Excluded Volume Problem in a Linear Polymer Chain."
39. S. Windwer, *J. Chem. Phys.*, **43**, 115 (1965); R. J. Fleming, *Proc. Phys. Soc.*, **90**, 1003 (1967).

NON-SELF-INTERSECTING
RANDOM WALKS IN LATTICES WITH
NEAREST-NEIGHBOR INTERACTIONS

JACOB MAZUR

Institute for Materials Research,
National Bureau of Standards, Washington, D.C.

CONTENTS

I. INTRODUCTION

In his paper Domb presents a detailed analysis of the statistical properties of self-avoiding walks on lattices.[1] These walks serve as models for linear polymer chains with hard-core intramolecular interactions associated with the exclusion of multiple occupancies of the lattice sites by the chain; so-called chains with excluded volume.

In our paper we are concerned with a potential energy function which is somewhat more realistic than one implied by the excluded volume effects. This potential function allows indirectly bonded chain elements which occupy adjacent lattice sites to interact with a finite energy ε. We call these interactions nearest-neighbor interactions, which should not be confused with interactions between near-neighbor pairs along the chain.

Self-avoiding walks with nearest-neighbor interactions of attraction (corresponding to negative values of ε), are of particular interest to us. As a consequence of the presence of the forces of attraction there is a possibility of configurational transition in the chain of the kind encountered

261

in the helix–coil transition, and which can be associated with a transformation of a chain from a coil-like configuration to a chain which is packed into a collapsed, ball-like configuration. Another consequence of the presence of the forces of attraction in the self-avoiding chain is the existence of the ideal or theta point. At this point, the dependence of the configurational chain partition function on the number of chain elements is of the same functional form as if the chain were simulated by an equivalent Markov-chain model.[2]

Domb[1] discusses four independent approaches that have been used to investigate statistical properties of self-avoiding walks. Those are: (1) rigorous analysis, (2) exact chain enumeration, (3) Monte Carlo methods and (4) transition matrix method. Of these four methods, only the last two will be discussed in connection with the investigations of statistical properties of self-avoiding chains with nearest-neighbor interactions. Both these methods of investigating, the Monte Carlo calculations and the transition matrix method, deal directly with finite-length chain. Therefore, the statistical properties of an infinitely long chain which are essential in connection with the investigation of the configurational transitions in the chain and the existence of the theta point, can be assessed only through some kind of extrapolation of the results obtained for finite-length chains. However, these two methods of investigation are so different in the models they employ and in the handling of the resulting statistical informations, that they can be described as being complementary, rather than alternative.[1] It is, therefore, our hope that the conclusions made on the statistical and thermodynamic properties of infinitely long chain, which are based on the existing Monte Carlo computations, could be reexamined on the basis of the information obtained from the transition matrix method. In the present paper, we will develop the transition matrix method by describing the generation of a chain as a stochastic process of dependent events.

The organization of this paper is as follows: First, we will present some of the evidences which point to the existence of the chain theta point and to the possibility of the configurational transition, based on the recently conducted Monte Carlo studies by McCrackin and Mazur.[2] Next, we will describe the chain as a stochastic process of dependent events. This stochastic process will serve as a basis for the formulation of the chain partition function. The chain partition function will be subsequently expanded in terms of the eigenvalues of the transition matrix. We will also present a general outline showing how the study of the distribution of the eigenvalues of the transition matrix could be employed in conjunction with the Monte Carlo calculations in order to study the thermodynamic properties of the self-avoiding chains with nearest-neighbor interactions. At the end of the paper, some preliminary calculations, based on the method of stochastic matrices will be presented and discussed.

II. THERMODYNAMIC PROPERTIES OF SELF-INTERACTING CHAINS FROM THE MONTE CARLO COMPUTATIONS

We will now present some of the results of the recent Monte Carlo computations of the chain partition function and the related thermo-dynamic functions for some three-dimensional lattices performed recently by McCrackin and Mazur.[2]

An expression for the chain partition function which is employed in these computations is proposed on the basis of the following considerations[2]:

Let $C_{n,z}$ be the number of the generated non-self-intersecting chains of n steps with z nearest-neighbor contacts, and let C_n be the total number of the generated non-self-intersecting chains with n chain elements and C_n^0 be the number of generated random chains with no self-reversals. The configurational partition function employed in connection with Monte Carlo computations is defined here as[2]

$$Q_n(x) = \frac{1}{C_n^0} \sum_{z=0} C_{n,z}\, e^{zx} \tag{1}$$

$$\sum_{z=0} C_{n,z} = C_n$$

The summation in Eq. (1) is carried over all possible values of z. The quantity $x = -\varepsilon/kT$, is the nearest-neighbor interaction parameter. Equation (1) serves as a basis for the direct numerical calculation of the chain partition function $Q_n(x)$.

It was proposed, on the basis of the exact chain enumeration, that C_n, the total number of distinct chains of n steps, varies with n according to Eq. (2).[4]

$$C_n \cong A\mu^n n^\alpha \tag{2}$$

where μ is the effective coordination number and is defined as $\lim_{n\to\infty} c_n^{1/n}$. A is a constant, which is independent of n and α is a numerical parameter. This parameter was shown on the basis of existing numerical computations to be independent of the lattice, and to depend only on dimensionality.[5] Because of this, and because of the fact that $\alpha = 0$ for chains which possess only finite range of interactions,[1] the parameter α is also designated as a long-range interaction parameter.[2]

In Monte Carlo computations, we do not calculate c_n but C_n/C_n^0. Since, in the limit of large C_n^0, $C_n/C_n^0 = c_n/\sigma^n$, where σ is the number of choices for the equivalent unrestricted chain with no self-reversals, the following expression is given for C_n:

$$C_n \cong B(\mu/\sigma)^n n^\alpha \tag{2a}$$

where μ/σ is the effective reduced coordination number and B is another proportionality constant.

Fisher and Hiley,[3] and Mazur and McCrackin[2] suggested that the dependence of $Q_n(x)$ on n is of a form which is similar to the way C_n depends on n. The proposed expression for $Q_n(x)$ is

$$Q_n(x) \cong D(x)n^{\alpha(x)}\left[\frac{\mu(x)}{\sigma}\right]^n \tag{3}$$

with $\mu(x)/\sigma$ defined as $\lim_{n\to\infty}[Q_n(x)^{1/n}]$ and $D(x)$ independent of n. We have found that Eq. (3) holds reasonably well for $\sigma x < 2.5$.[2] For $\sigma x > 2.5$, the large scatter of the data precludes us from making a reasonable assumption on the dependence of $Q_n(x)$ on n.

Equation (3) serves as a basis for computing α and μ as functions of the nearest-neighbor interaction parameter x. The results of these computations are shown in Figures 1 and 2.

In Figure 1, α is plotted vs. σx for a face-centered lattice (a close-packed lattice) and for a simple cubic lattice (a loose-packed lattice). We notice that (1) the dependence of α on σx can be regarded as being practically the same for both lattices and that, (2) α undergoes a rapid change around $x = x_c$, which is the point at which $\alpha = 0$ (Fig. 1). However, μ/σ does not attain the value it would have for the case of the unrestricted random walk model at $x = x_c$, since at this point, $\mu/\sigma > 1$ (Fig. 2), while for unrestricted chain $\mu/\sigma = 1$. Moreover, the dependence of μ/σ on σx is not the same for the two lattices while α as a function of σx is practically independent of the lattice.

The thermodynamic properties of the chain can be obtained in the standard way by differentiating the logarithm of the partition function with respect to x. Thus, if

$$\langle z \rangle = d\log Q_n(x)/dx \tag{4}$$

and

$$\langle z^2 \rangle = d^2 \log Q_n(x)/dx^2 \tag{5}$$

are the mean number of nearest-neighbor contacts and the mean square

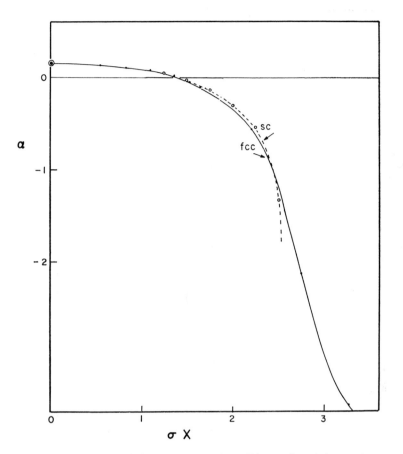

Fig. 1. Configurational index α versus σx for self-interacting chains on face centered and simple cubic lattices.

number of these contacts in the chain, then the internal energy is given by

$$\Delta E = -kT\langle z\rangle x \tag{6}$$

The specific heat is

$$\Delta C_n = k(\langle z^2\rangle - \langle z\rangle^2)x^2 \tag{7}$$

and the excess entropy $\Delta S = S - S_0$ is

$$\Delta S = k\left[\log\frac{Q_n(x)}{Q_n(0)} + \langle z\rangle x\right] \tag{8}$$

where

$$S_0 = k \log Q_n(0)$$

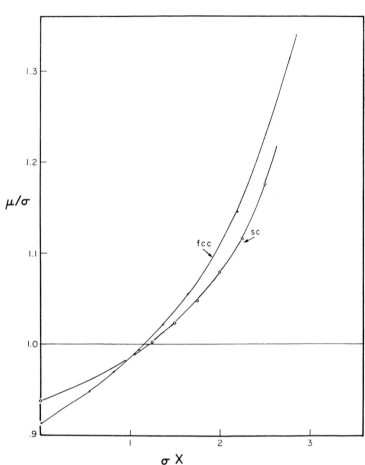

Fig. 2. The reduced effective coordination number, μ/σ, versus σx for the face-centered and simple cubic lattices.

In Figure 3, the mean number of contacts per chain element, $\langle z \rangle/n$ is plotted versus x for a chain in the face-centered lattice. In Figure 4, the dispersion of $\langle z \rangle$ per chain element, $(\langle z^2 \rangle - \langle z^2 \rangle)n^{-1}$ is plotted versus x for the same lattice and in Figure 5, the excess entropy per chain element is plotted versus x. We notice in Figures 3–5, that there exists a region of x in which the thermodynamic properties of the chain undergo a rapid change. This change is in the vicinity of $x = 0.2$ for walks on the face-centered lattice. We also notice that an infinitely long chain displays a more rapid change in the values of the thermodynamic functions than a finite-length chain.

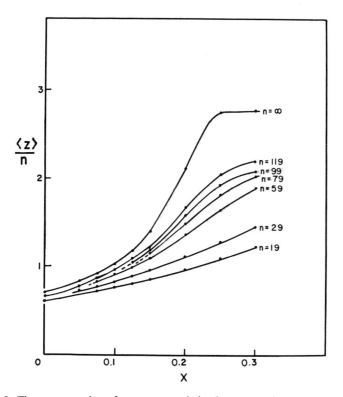

Fig. 3. The mean number of contacts per chain element, $\langle z \rangle / n$, versus x for the face-centered lattice.

The dependence of the dispersion of $\langle z \rangle$ per chain element, on x is especially interesting (Fig. 4). Not only the infinitely long chain shows a maximum dispersion at $x = 0.2$, but also the finite-length chains with $n > 50$ show a maximum at this point. Shorter chains do not display this maximum.

Our calculations do not as yet prove an existence of the configurational phase transition in the infinitely long chain. Our results for $n = \infty$ (Figs. 3–5) are based on an assumption that Eq. (3) is valid in the entire region of x in which the calculations were performed, and on the accuracy of the extrapolation of the Monte Carlo computations for finite chains toward infinitely long chains. Thus, it is always possible that a more accurate procedure for handling Monte Carlo calculations could lead to more positive evidence on the possibility of configurational transition in the infinitely long chain.

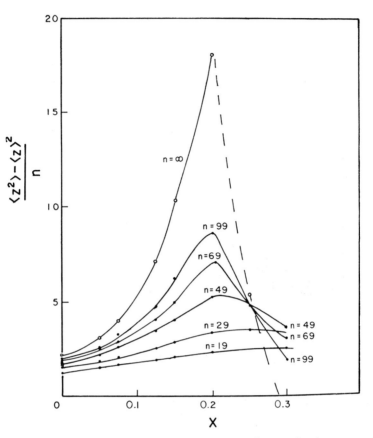

Fig. 4. The dispersion of z per chain element, $(\langle z^2 \rangle - \langle z \rangle^2)n^{-1}$, versus x for the face-centered lattice. The broken line for $n = \infty$ and $x > 0.2$ indicates uncertainty in the data. (See Ref. 2.)

III. STOCHASTIC MODEL FOR RESTRICTED SELF-AVOIDING CHAINS WITH NEAREST-NEIGHBOR INTERACTIONS

A. General Considerations

Domb[6] has originally suggested the use of the method of stochastic matrices to study problems which are related to the presence of long-range interactions in the self-avoiding chains. We introduce this method in order to study these interactions in self-avoiding chains with the nearest-neighbor interactions. Specifically, we would like to determine whether this method

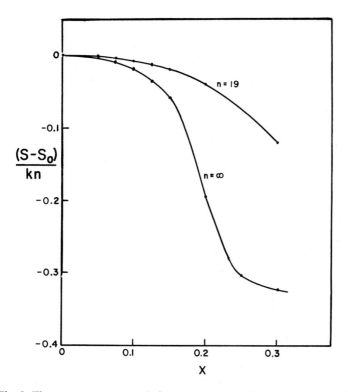

Fig. 5. The excess entropy per chain element versus x for the face-centered lattice.

will confirm our proposition that the Monte Carlo computations presented in the preceding chapter might indicate the possibility of configurational transition in an infinitely long chain. In addition, we would like to find whether the stochastic matrix method will confirm the Monte Carlo computations which demonstrate the existence of the ideal, or theta point in the infinitely long chain.

Consider a restricted random walk, defined as a walk in which one eliminates only self-intersections in the chain which involve a finite number of steps, say t, in a chain of n steps, with $n \gg t$. In other words, formations of polygons or closures with more than t steps are allowed. The properties of this walk are governed by a Markovian transition matrix. This restricted chain model precludes any existence of phase transition since the largest eigenvalue of the transition matrix will always remain positive and nondegenerate. However, as t approaches n and n becomes infinitely large, the largest eigenvalue, under certain conditions, could become degenerate, which is a condition for the existence of a phase transition.[7]

We might expect that even in restricted chains, the investigation of the other eigenvalues and eigenvectors, besides the largest eigenvalue and its accompanying eigenvectors, would throw light on the way the long range interactions extend in finite chains and which could be responsible for the rather abrupt changes in the thermodynamic properties of the chain, as shown in Figures 3–5.

The procedure employed is similar to the one described by Domb in his paper.[1] We consider a restricted chain in which all closures, or polygons, formed with t or fewer steps, are excluded. Thus, the intrachain interactions are confined to those chain elements which are separated by no more than t chain elements. Our procedure calls for gradually increasing the size of the largest excluded polygon, starting with the lowest-order polygon which can be formed in the particular lattice model. The order of the matrices of transition probabilities increases rapidly as the size of the largest excluded polygon is increased.

We investigate the partition function derived from those matrices, the distribution of eigenvalues and the structure of the eigenvectors and their dependence on both the range of interactions (determined by the size of the largest excluded polygon) and on the energy per nearest-neighbor contact ε. This work is now in progress. In the present paper some preliminary results based on these investigations will be presented. However we would like to formulate in more detail the derivation of the matrix of transition probabilities and of the chain partition function by treating this problem as a stochastic process.

B. Derivation of the Chain Partition Function

We consider the generation of a restricted chain of n steps on a lattice.[4] In this restricted chain model, we eliminate closed polygons of the lowest order. Thus, for example, in a square lattice, squares are eliminated but hexagons and higher-order polygons are permitted. We also assume that n sufficiently exceeds the size of the eliminated polygon, so that the chain-end effects may be neglected. We describe the generation of this chain by considering it as a sequence of consecutive events. Let these events be $E_1, \ldots, E_n$. Each event represents an addition of a single step to the chain. We define an outcome of each event E_k by $q^{(l)}$, where l is the minimum number of steps that are needed to form the lowest order polygon from the kth step of the generated chain. If the size of the excluded polygon is t, then there are $\nu = t - 1$ possible outcomes of these events, and therefore $l = 1, 2, \ldots, \nu$.

In order to better illustrate our model of the generated chain as a sequence of events, let us consider an example of the restricted walk on a square lattice. In this lattice, $v = 3$ and $q^{(1)}$, $q^{(2)}$, and $q^{(3)}$ denote configurations $\leftharpoondown$, $\uparrow$, and $\longrightarrow$, respectively. In the following illustration

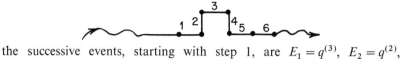

the successive events, starting with step 1, are $E_1 = q^{(3)}$, $E_2 = q^{(2)}$, $E_3 = q^{(2)}$, $E_4 = q^{(1)}$, etc.

We denote the probability that the event E_k will result in the configuration $q^{(l)}$ by $P(E_k = q^{(l)})$. Our particular model for the restricted chain implies that the probability of the event E_{k+1} leading to the outcome $q^{(l)}$ depends only on the probability of the previous event E_k leading to the outcome $q^{(m)}$, $m = 1, 2, \ldots, v$. Therefore, the probability of a consecutive sequence of events $P_n(E_1, \ldots, E_n)$ is[8]:

$$P_n = Prob\{E_1 = q^{[l(1)]}, \ldots, E_n = q^{[l(n)]}\}$$

$$= \prod_{k=1}^{n-1} P\{E_{k+1} = q^{[l(k+1)]} \mid E_k = q^{[l(k)]}\} \qquad (9)$$

when $P(E_{k+1} = q^{(l)} \mid E_k = q^{(m)})$ are the transition probabilities and are denoted by $p_k(l, m)$. In our example of the restricted chain on a square lattice, $p_k(1, 1)$ denotes the probability that, upon adding a step to a configuration of k steps, and ending with a hook $\leftharpoondown$, another three-step hook will be obtained. Of course, $p_k(1, 1) = 0$.

The probabilities $p_k(l, m)$ with all possible l and m for fixed k form a $v \times v$ matrix of transition probabilities $\mathbf{P}_k$. This matrix is a column stochastic one, since $\sum_{l=1} p_k(l, m) = 1$ and $p_k(l, m) \geqq 0$. In what follows, the subscript k will be dropped, since the elements of the matrices of transition probabilities are independent of k.

Direct evaluation of $p(l, m)$ is not immediate. For example, in the restricted random walk on a square lattice in which squares are eliminated, the transition $p(2, 2)$ is smaller than the transition $p(3, 2)$. However, in an unrestricted random walk on a square lattice with no self reversals, $p(2, 2) = p(3, 2) = \frac{1}{3}$.

The following procedure for evaluation of the elements of the stochastic matrix of transition probabilities is employed. Let $p_0(l, m)$ denote the probabilities

$$p_0(l, m) = P_0\{E_{k+1} = q^{(l)} \mid E_k = q^{(m)}\} \qquad (10)$$

for an unrestricted random walk model for the configurations denoted by

$q^{(l)}$. The probabilities $p_0(l, m)$ form a matrix of transition probabilities $\mathbf{Q}$. This matrix is not stochastic, since $\sum_{l+1}^{v} p_0(l, 1) < 1$ (see Reference 9). The elements of $\mathbf{Q}$ can be readily calculated on the basis of an unrestricted random walk model for the configurations denoted by $q^{(l)}$. For example, for a three-choice square lattice,

$$\mathbf{Q} = \begin{pmatrix} 0 & \frac{1}{3} & 0 \\ \frac{1}{3} & \frac{1}{3} & \frac{2}{3} \\ \frac{1}{3} & \frac{1}{3} & \frac{1}{3} \end{pmatrix}$$

The matrix $\mathbf{Q}$ can now be transformed into a stochastic matrix, which will be descriptive of the restricted random walks rather than of their generation employing probabilities based on unrestricted walk models. The transformation is performed as follows: Let λ_1 be the largest eigenvalue of the matrix $\mathbf{Q}$, and let $\mathbf{s}_1$ be the corresponding left-hand side eigenvector (defined by $\mathbf{s}_1\mathbf{Q} = \lambda_1\mathbf{s}_1$). Let $\mathbf{A}$ be a diagonal matrix with elements $a(i, j) = s_1(i)\,\delta(i, j)$, $\mathbf{s}_1 = [s_1(1), s_1(2), \ldots, s_1(v)]$ and $\delta(i, j)$ is the Kronecker delta. Then the transformation

$$\mathbf{P} = \lambda_1^{-1}\mathbf{A}^{-1}\mathbf{Q}\mathbf{A} \tag{11}$$

defines a stochastic matrix $\mathbf{P}$. The elements of this matrix are given by

$$p(i, j) = \lambda_1^{-1}q(i, j)s_1(i)/s_1(j) \tag{12}$$

In our example of a three-choice square lattice, the matrix $\mathbf{Q}$ is transformed into the following stochastic matrix $\mathbf{P}$.

$$\mathbf{P} = \begin{pmatrix} 0 & 0.262 & 0 \\ 0.477 & 0.353 & 0.647 \\ 0.523 & 0.385 & 0.353 \end{pmatrix}$$

We now introduce nearest-neighbor interactions in the restricted chain models. In our particular model these interactions are nonzero only for those nearest-neighbor contacts which can lead to excluded configurations upon addition of a single step. Thus for example, in a square lattice, nonzero interactions involve only contacts created by the three-step chain configuration denoted by $q^{(1)}$. The new transition probabilities are

$$P_x\{E_{k+1} = q^{(l)} \mid E_k = q^{(m)}\} = p(l, m)\exp[x\,\delta_{l,1}] \tag{13}$$

with $x = -\varepsilon/kT$. From (13), we obtain a new matrix of transition probabilities $\mathbf{P}_x$ with elements $p_x(l, m)$, which are related to the elements of the matrix $\mathbf{P}$ by

$$p_x(l, m) = p(l, m)\exp(x\,\delta_{l,1}) \tag{14}$$

The partition function, $Z_n(x)$, for the non-self-intersecting chain with nearest-neighbor interactions is[10]

$$Z_n(x) = \sum_{l(1)} \cdots \sum_{l(n)} \prod_{k=1}^{n-1} P_x\{E_{k+1} = q^{[l(k+1)]} \mid E_k = q^{[l(k)]}\}$$

$$l(1) = 1, \ldots, v; \ldots; l(n) = 1, \ldots, v. \quad (15)$$

Since the matrix $\mathbf{P}$ is a stochastic matrix, one can show that $Z_n(0) = 1$. The summation in Eq. (12) extends over all possible values of each E_k. The partition function is equivalently given by the sum of the elements of the matrix $\mathbf{P}_x$, raised to the power n.[10] Therefore, another way of writing the chain partition function is

$$Z_n(x) = \sum_{i=1}^{v} \lambda_i^n (\mathbf{s}_i \cdot \mathbf{1})(\mathbf{1} \cdot \mathbf{r}_i) \quad (16)$$

Each eigenvalue λ_1 has associated with it a column, or right-hand eigenvector $\mathbf{r}_i$ and a row, or left-hand eigenvector $\mathbf{s}_i$. The λ_i are given by the roots of the equation: $|\mathbf{P}_x - \lambda \mathbf{I}| = 0$ ($\mathbf{I}$ is the unit matrix).

For large n, Eq. (16) is approximated by Eq. (17),

$$Z_n(x) = \lambda_1^n (\mathbf{s}_1 \cdot \mathbf{1})(\mathbf{1} \cdot \mathbf{r}_1) \quad (17)$$

where λ_i is the largest eigenvalue of the matrix $\mathbf{P}_x$, and is always simple and positive.

The thermodynamic properties of the system are obtained from $\log Z_n(x)$ and its first and second derivatives with respect to x.

So far, the effects of the chain ends were neglected in our stochastic model for the restricted chain. Therefore, n must be much larger than the number of steps needed to form the largest excluded polygon. The partition function, which incorporates the chain-end effects and which could be also employed for exact statistical description of short non-self-intersecting chains can be obtained as follows: Assume, as before, that we eliminate only lowest-order polygons of t steps. Therefore, the first $t - 1$ steps in the chain are described as a sequence of independent events. Eq (9), then, will be replaced by

$$P_n = P(E_{\{k=t-1\}} = q^{[l(t-1)]}) \prod_{k=t-1}^{n-1} P\{E_{k+1} = q^{[l(k+1)]} \mid E_k = q^{[l(k)]}\} \quad (18)$$

$E_{\{k=t-1\}}$ represents the cumulative events of the first $t - 1$ steps in the chain. The probability distribution of $P(E_{\{k=t-1\}} = q^{(l)})$, $l = 1, 2, \ldots$, v is called the initial distribution of the events $q^{(l)}$. These probabilities can be represented as components of a v-vector $\mathbf{p}$.

$$\mathbf{p} = \{p(0), \ldots, p(v)\}$$

Thus, $P[E_{\{k=t-1\}} = q^{(l)}] = p(l)$

In the presence of nearest-neighbor interactions, we have a new set of elements of the vector of initial probabilities, denoted by $\mathbf{p}_x = \{p_x(1), p_x(2), \ldots, p_x(v)\}$, which are related to the probabilities $p(l)$ by

$$p_x(l) = p(l) \exp(x\delta_{l,1}) \tag{19}$$

The partition function $Z_n(x)$ for this chain is defined as

$$Z_n(x) = \sum_{l(1)} \cdots \sum_{l(n)} P_x\{E_{\{k=t-1\}} = q^{[l(t-1)]}\} \prod_{k=1}^{n-1} P_x\{E_{k+1} = q^{[l(k+1)]} | E_k = q^{[l(k)]}\} \tag{20}$$

This partition function is equal in matrix formulation to

$$Z_n(x) = \omega \mathbf{P}_x^{n-t+1} \mathbf{P}_x \tag{21}$$

In Eq. (21) ω is a unit row vector with v components and $\mathbf{P}_x$ is a $v \times v$ matrix with elements given by Eq. (14). This partition function can be expanded as

$$Z_n(x) = \sum_{i=1}^{v} \lambda_i^{n-t+1}(\mathbf{s}_i \cdot \mathbf{p}_x)(\mathbf{1} \cdot \mathbf{r}_i) \tag{22}$$

which replaces Eq. (16). For $n = t$, Eq. (22) expresses the exact partition function for a non-self-intersecting chain with $n = t$ links.

In the above example of a square lattice ($t = v + 1 = 4$), the normalized components of the vector p_x are

$$\mathbf{p}_x = \left(\frac{7}{9} + \frac{2}{9}x\right)^{-1} \left(\frac{2}{9}x, \frac{4}{9}, \frac{1}{3}\right)$$

For sufficiently large values of $n - t$, Eq. (22) can be approximated by Eq. (23)

$$Z_n(x) \approx \lambda_1^{n-t+1}(\mathbf{1} \cdot \mathbf{r}_1)(\mathbf{s}_1 \cdot \mathbf{p}_x) \tag{23}$$

λ_1 is the largest eigenvalue of the transition matrix $\mathbf{P}_x$, and $\mathbf{r}_1$ and $\mathbf{s}_1$ are the corresponding right and left eigenvectors.

The partition function, given by Eqs. (15–17) for chains with no chain-end effects, and by Eqs. (20–23) for chains with end effects, is restricted to the chain models in which only the lowest-order polygons are excluded. We can extend the derivation of these partition functions to a more general case, in which we eliminate all polygons of sizes t or less and restrict nearest-neighbor interactions to contacts which are separated by $t - 1$ and fewer chain elements.

We number the sizes of the excluded polygons, in increasing order, by $t_1 < t_2 < \cdots < t_s$. The number of excluded polygons of different sizes is s, which is also designated as the dimension of the Markov chain.[11] Thus, $t_s = t$. Let the smallest number of random steps needed to form a polygon of size t_1 be v_1, that to form polygon of size t_2 be v_2, etc. We can, as before, describe the chain as a sequence of consecutive events, $E_1, \ldots, E_n$. Each of the events results in a configuration with no more than $t-1$ chain elements, and which is denoted by $q(l_1, \ldots, l_s)$. l_1 is a parameter that can have one of the possible values $1, \ldots, v_1$, l_2 is a parameter that can have one of the possible values $1, \ldots, v_2$, etc. For example, in a square lattice in which all squares and hexagons are excluded, $s = 2$, $v_1 = 3$ and $v_2 = 4$, since in forming a square the first step is arbitrary while in forming a hexagon the first two steps are arbitrary. The event $E_k = q^{(l_1 = 1, \, l_2 = 2)}$ describes a configuration of five steps which requires one step to form a square and two steps to form a hexagon.

In order to formulate the matrix of transition probabilities, we will have to consider all possible combinations of l_1, l_2, etc. What complicates the problem of arranging these combinations is the fact that, on one hand, certain combinations of the indices $l_1, \ldots, l_s$ cannot occur, while on the other hand, more than one distinct outcome of the event E_k can result for a given set of values of the indices $l_1, \ldots, l_s$. This latter fact is the consequence of the general nonuniqueness of the eliminated polygons. For example, for a cubic lattice with $s = 2$, the combination $l_1 = 1$ and $l_2 = 4$ does not exist, while 3 distinct events with $l_1 = 2$ and $l_2 = 1$ and 2 distinct events $l_1 = 2$ and $l_2 = 2$ are possible.

We will not go into detail of the derivation of the chain partition function for the general case of $s > 1$. We will only state, that, in order to formulate the matrix of transition probabilities, the various permissible combinations of the indices $l_1, \ldots, l_s$ with $l_1 = 1, \ldots, v_1; \ldots; l_l = l_1, \ldots, v_s$ have to be arranged in an array l. If the number of the elements in the array l is L, the matrix $\mathbf{P}_x$ of the transition probabilities is of the order L. The number of elements, L, increases very rapidly with increasing s, as the following example will show: Consider the walk on a square lattice. We found that $L = v = 3$ for $s = 1$, $L = 11$ for $s = 2$ and $L = 48$ for $s = 3$. The corresponding values of t are 4, 6, and 8, respectively.

In the presence of nearest-neighbor interactions, the $p_x(l, m)$ elements of the matrix $\mathbf{P}_x$ are related to the $p(l, m)$ elements of the matrix $\mathbf{P}$ by

$$p_x(l, m) = p(l, m) \exp(xh_l)$$

$$h_l = \sum_{r=1}^{s} \delta_{l_r, 1} \tag{24}$$

Thus, h_l is the total number of indices l_r having the value of one, in the array l. The maximum value of h is either s or $q - 2$, depending on whether s is smaller, or greater than $q - 2$. (The restriction $h \leq q - 2$ is imposed by the impossibility of the chain to trap itself.)

Expanding the partition function in terms of the eigenvalues and eigenvectors of the transition matrix $\mathbf{P}_x$, we obtain

$$Z_n(x) = \sum_{i=1}^{L} \lambda_i^n(\mathbf{s}_i \cdot \mathbf{1})(\mathbf{1} \cdot \mathbf{r}_i) \tag{25}$$

or, if the chain-end effects are considered,

$$Z_n(x) = \sum_{i=1}^{L} \lambda_i^{n-t+1}(\mathbf{s}_i \cdot \mathbf{p}_x)(\mathbf{1} \cdot \mathbf{r}_i) \tag{26}$$

$\mathbf{p}_x$ is a column vector with L components. Each component of this vector represents the initial probability of one of L possible outcomes of the events $E_{\{k+t-1\}}$. In other words, each of the initial events describes one of the L possible distinct chain configurations with $t - 1$ chain elements, with t being the size of the largest excluded polygon.

In a more realistic chain model, no restrictions would be imposed on the size of the largest disallowed polygon. Therefore, $t = n$, the total number of chain elements, and the chain is no longer Markovian. For an infinitely long chain, the matrix of transition probabilities is of an infinite order. We submit that the order of the transition matrix is approximately given by the total number of possible configurations, which can be approximated by μ^n. The reason is that, at sufficiently large n, the total number of possible configurations represents a much lower bound on the order of the matrix than does the bound based on all possible combinations of the indices each of which represents the number of steps needed to form a polygon of a given size and which can be shown to be of the order of magnitude of $[n/2]!$[4] We can thus make a reasonable assumption, that the order of the transition matrix is given approximately by the total number of chains of n steps and, therefore, the order increases exponentially with increasing n.

IV. SOME PRELIMINARY RESULTS

We submitted before that if the Monte Carlo computations point to the possibility of configurational transition in the chain, the largest eigenvalue of the partition function for the infinitely long chain might become degenerate at some particular value of $x = x^*$. Some evidence supporting this possibility is presented in Figure 6. We notice from Figure 6 that, as

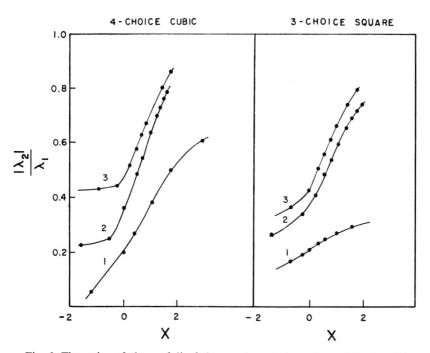

Fig. 6. The ratios of the moduli of the two largest eigenvalues of the transition matrix, $|\lambda_2|/\lambda_1$, versus x, for chains on four-choice cubic lattice and three-choice square lattice. Curves 1, 2, and 3 represent chains with increasing sizes of the largest excluded polygons.

the range of interactions (measured by the value of t) increases, the ratio of the modulus of the second largest eigenvalue, $|\lambda_2|$, to the largest eigenvalue, λ_1, at a given value of x rapidly increases for $x < 1$. While $|\lambda_2|/\lambda_1$ increases rather gradually with increasing x in the case of a chain with the excluded first-order overlaps (curves 1 in Fig. 6) this increase is much more abrupt when higher order overlaps are also excluded (curves 2 and 3 in Fig. 6). However, computations with still higher-order eliminated overlaps are required before the extrapolation to an infinitely large range of interaction can be made, and a value of x^* can be determined. In any case, the ratio of $|\lambda_2|/\lambda_1$ can provide a rough estimate of the range to which the local order associated with excluded volume and nearest-neighbor interactions extends in the chain.[12]

Our numerical studies on the distribution of the eigenvalues of transition matrix reveal that for low values of x there appears to develop a set of k eigenvalues, which have practically identical moduli, equal to $|\lambda_2|$, but with widely different arguments.[13] For $x < 0$, the modulus of this set of eigenvalues is considerably smaller than λ_1. This set of k eigenvalues increases rapidly with increasing t. As x increases, the moduli in this set of eigenvalues become more spread out, and the eigenvalues tend to be more uniformly distributed inside the circle of the radius equal to the largest eigenvalue. At the same time, there emerges a single real eigenvalue λ_2, which approaches λ_1 rapidly.[13] Some of the numerical studies on the distribution of eigenvalues are shown in Figure 7. In this figure, the distribution of several consecutive eigenvalues of the transition matrix in a complex plane, starting with the largest one, is shown. The lattice model employed is the four-choice cubic, with $t = 8$. In Figure 7, the individual chains are represented as stochastic processes, hence λ_1 is invariably equal

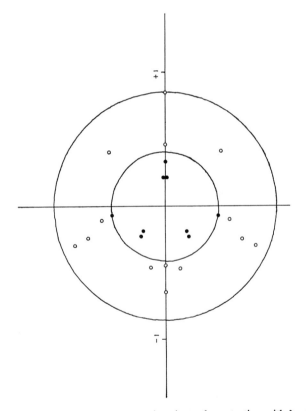

Fig. 7. Distribution of several consecutive eigenvalues starting with λ_1, in complex plane for chains on four-choice cubic lattice. Outer circle ($\circ$): $x = \log 6$. Inner circle ($\bullet$): $x = \log 0.4$. Radii of the circles $= |\lambda_2|$.

to 1. In Figure 7, two different values of x are used: $x = \log 0.4$ (nearest-neighbor forces of repulsion) and $x = \log 6.0$ (nearest-neighbor forces of attraction). The circles drawn in Figure 7, have their radii equal to $|\lambda_2|$.

We also calculated the partition function, based on Eq. (26), with $n = t$.[13] In this case, Eq. (28) expresses an exact partition function for a short chain with no restrictions being imposed on the maximal range of interactions between chain elements. Our calculations showed that, for low values of x and t, the partition function is given almost exactly by the term which is proportional to the largest eigenvalue. It is found that $1 - Z_n(x)/Z_n^{(0)}(x)$, with $Z_n^{(0)}(x) = \lambda_1 \cdot (\mathbf{s}_1 \cdot \mathbf{p}_x)(\mathbf{1} \cdot \mathbf{r}_1)$, is a very small number, never exceeding 10^{-2}, whenever $x < 0.5$. This small value for the deviation of $Z_n(x)$ from its approximation by $Z_n^{(0)}(x)$ is explained by the mutual cancellation of the contributions of all eigenvalues except λ_1 to the exact partition function $Z_n(x)$. For this reason, for the cases with low x, $Z_n(x) - Z_n^{(0)}(x)$ cannot be approximated by $\lambda_2^{n-1+t} (\mathbf{s}_2 \cdot \mathbf{p}_x)(\mathbf{1} \cdot \mathbf{r}_2)$, but the entire partition function has to be calculated. However, as x increases $|Z_n(x) - Z_n^{(0)}(x)|$ rapidly increases. As an example, we plotted in Figure 8 $(Z_n(x) - Z_n^{(0)}(x))/Z_n(x)$ versus x for chains with $t = 6$ (open circles) and

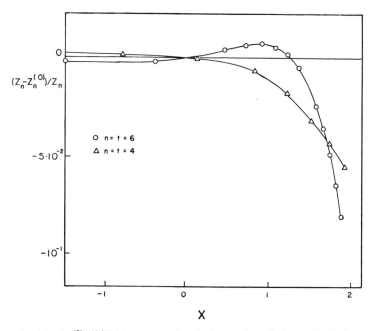

Fig. 8. $(Z_n(x) - Z_n^{(0)}(x))/Z_n(x)$ versus x for chains on four-choice cubic lattice. Open triangles: $t = 4$. Open circles: $t = 6$.

with $t = 4$ (open triangles), both on a four-choice cubic lattice. We notice from Figure 8 that, for the case of $t = 6$, $Z_n(x) - Z_n^{(0)}(x)$ changes its sign at a certain value of x, in the domain of positive x. Thus, in general, there might exist a certain value of x for which $Z_n(x) = Z_n^{(0)}(x)$ exactly. Figure 8 also demonstrates the rapid increase in the deviation of the partition function from its approximation by $Z_n^{(0)}(x)$ as t increases from 4 to 6, for $x > 1.5$.

We conclude, that the computations of the approximate partition function for long chains with finite range of interactions and of the exact partition function for short chains with no restriction imposed on the range of interaction, could lead to the explanation of the results obtained from the Monte Carlo calculations. Particularly, the observed change of the sign of the long-range interaction parameter α at $x = x_c$, and the configurational transition in the infinitely long chain might be investigated by the stochastic matrix method.

Acknowledgment

The author wishes to thank Dr. C. Guttman of the National Bureau of Standards for his helpful suggestions and critical review of the manuscript.

References

1. C. Domb, this volume.
2. J. Mazur and F. McCrackin, *J. Chem. Phys.*, **49**, 648 (1968).
3. M. E. Fisher and B. J. Hiley, *J. Chem. Phys.*, **34**, 1251 (1961).
4. M. E. Fisher and M. F. Sykes, *Phys. Rev.*, **114**, 45 (1959).
5. B. J. Hiley and M. E. Fisher, *J. Chem. Phys.*, **34**, 1253 (1961); M. F. Sykes, *J. Chem. Phys.*, **39**, 410 (1963).
6. C. Domb, *J. Roy. Stat. Soc.*, **B25**, 367 (1964).
7. J. Ashkin and W. B. Lamb, *Phys. Rev.*, **64**, 159 (1943).
8. See L. Takacs, *Stochastic Processes*, Methuen, London, 1966, for the definitions of the symbols and of the nomenclature employed in this work.
9. J. G. Kemeny and J. L. Snell, *Finite Markov Chains*, Van Nostrand, Princeton, N.J., 1960, Chap. III.
10. E. Montroll, *Ann. Math. Stat.*, **18**, 18 (1947).
11. For a general definition of multidimensional Markov chains see, for example, N. Bailey, *Elements of Stochastic Processes*, Wiley, New York, 1964, Chap. 10.
12. C. Domb, *Advan. Phys.*, **9**, 150 (1960).
13. J. Mazur, unpublished results.

REVERSIBLE KINETICS ON LINEAR LATTICES WITH NEIGHBOR EFFECTS

P. RABINOWITZ and A. SILBERBERG

The Weizmann Institute of Science, Rehovoth, Israel

ROBERT SIMHA and ELIZABETH LOFTUS

Case Western Reserve University, Cleveland, Ohio

CONTENTS

I. GENERAL CONSIDERATIONS

Reactions on a lattice are distinguished by the propagation of near-neighbor effects in time. While in two- or three-dimensional lattices this is an extremely difficult problem, in one dimension the problem can be treated exactly.[1]

The reaction scheme investigated may be expressed as follows:

$$
\begin{array}{ccc}
-0-0-0- & -0-0-1- & -1-0-1- \\
k_1 \Big\downarrow\Big\uparrow k_3{}' & k_2 \Big\downarrow\Big\uparrow k_2{}' & k_3 \Big\downarrow\Big\uparrow k_1{}' \\
-0-1-0- & -0-1-1- & -1-1-1-
\end{array}
\qquad (I)
$$

where "0" and "1" stand for the site in the two states considered. The k's are rate constants for the transition $0 \rightleftarrows 1$ and their magnitudes depend on the state of reaction of the two neighboring sites, as indicated in (I). The lattice is essentially infinite and end-effects can be neglected. It is assumed, moreover, that the intrinsic reactivity does not vary in space or time.

Under these circumstances the two following properties will hold at any time:

$$N\{X_j\} = N\{X_j^{-1}\} \tag{1}$$

$$N\{X_j; 0\} + N\{X_j; 1\} = N\{1; X_j\} + N\{0; X_j\} = N\{X_j\} \tag{2}$$

where X_j is a consecutive group of j sites in a particular sequence of 0's and 1's, X_j^{-1} is the inverse sequence which results when the order in X_j is reversed and $N\{X_j\}$ is the number of times the sequence X_j occurs in the chain. Property (1) is a consequence of the homogeneity of the reaction environment along the chain and property (2) expresses the fact that any sequence X_j can be preceded or followed only by a 0 or 1.

On the basis of (1) and (2) not all sequences of length j can vary independently in number, and it becomes possible to define an irreducible set of sequences which cannot be interconverted by operations (1) and (2) but by means of which all sequences not members of the set can be expressed. A number of such schemes can be evolved and it is necessary to introduce a convention in order to make the scheme unique. The selection

TABLE I

Sequence Hierarchy

Length of sequence	Structure of retained sequence	Number of retained sequences
1	$\{0\}$	1
$2(j+1)$	$\{0; Z_j; Z_j^{-1}; 1\}$	2^j
$j = 0, 1, \ldots$	$\{0; Y_i; 0; U_{j-i-1}; T_{j-i-1}; 1; Y_i^{-1}; 1\}$	$2^j(2^{j-1} - \tfrac{1}{2})$
$i = 0, \ldots, (j-1)$		$2^j(2^{j-1} + \tfrac{1}{2})$
$2j + 3$	$\{0; Z_j; 0/1; Z_j^{-1}; 1\}$	2^{j+1}
$j = 0, 1, \ldots$	$\{0, Y_i; 0; U_{j-i-1}; 0/1; T_{j-i-1}; 1; Y_i^{-1}; 1\}$	$2^j(2^j - 1)$
$i = 0, \ldots, (j-1)$		$2^j(2^j + 1)$

rules followed by us are outlined in Table I so that the first seven sequences of the scheme, of length 1–4 are given below:

$$\{0\}; \{01\}; \{001\}; \{011\}; \{0001\}; \{0011\}; \{0111\} \tag{3}$$

Use of this hierarchy reduces the number of variables which have to be considered to about 1/8 the total number possible. The main advantage of the scheme, however, is the independence of the variables so produced. The number of rate equations which have to be derived is clearly specified at each level by Table I.

II. DERIVATION OF KINETICS

The rate equations may be established by considering all distinguishable ways by which a given sequence can react or be formed by reaction at a site. There are two types of sites in the sequence, namely, terminal ones and sites which are at least one place removed from each end. For the latter, the near-neighbor reaction environment is completely specified by the sequence itself. For a terminal site, however, we must additionally specify the occupation of the site neighboring the sequence at the end considered. This can be either a 0 or a 1. It is thus clear that the rate equation of a sequence of length j will depend on the numbers of hierarchic sequences of length $j + 1$, j, and less. The infinite set of rate equations is thus required for a complete solution.

The method of deriving the coefficients of the rate equations in a particular case is shown in Table II, where the sequences appearing in the rate

TABLE II

Creation and Disappearance of Sequences
{0001}

Reaction on left terminal site* (two cases)		Reaction on interior sites*		Reaction on right terminal site* (two cases)	
*	*	*	*	*	*
1 | 0001	0 | 0001	0001	0001	0001 | 1	0001 | 0
$k_2\!\downarrow\!\uparrow k_2'$	$k_1\!\downarrow\!\uparrow k_3'$	$k_1\!\downarrow\!\uparrow k_3'$	$k_2\!\downarrow\!\uparrow k_2'$	$k_2'\!\downarrow\!\uparrow k_2$	$k_3'\!\downarrow\!\uparrow k_1$
1 | 1001	0 | 1001	0101	0011	0000 | 1	0000 | 0
*	*	*	*	*	*

$$\dot{N}\{0001\} = -[k_2 N\{10001\} + k_1 N\{00001\} + k_1 N\{0001\}$$
$$+ k_2 N\{0001\} + k_2' N\{00011\} + k_3' N\{00010\}]$$
$$+ [k_2' N\{11001\} + k_3' N\{01001\} + k_3' N\{0101\}$$
$$+ k_2' N\{0011\} + k_2 N\{00001\} + k_1 N\{00000\}]$$

equation must, however, still be expressed in terms of the hierarchic sequences. This can always be done by means of the scheme outlined in Table III. In this way the coefficient matrix for the first seven members of the hierarchy of sequences given in (3) has been previously derived.[1] This matrix has now been extended to include the rate equations for the next

TABLE III

Reduction of a Given Sequence $\{Z_{j+2}\}$ into a Hierarchic
Sequence of Length $j + 2$.

		Retained $\{Z_{j+2}\}$		Overflow $\{Z_{j+1}\}$			
		$\{0X_j1\}$	$\{0X_j{}^{-1}1\}$	$\{0X_j\}$	$\{X_j0\}$	$\{1X_j\}$	$\{X_j1\}$
	$\{0X_j0\}$ $-[B]\to\{$	-1 ...	... -1	$+1$ ...	... $+1$	... ...	... ...
$\{Z_{j+2}\}$ $[A]$	$\{0X_j1\}$ $-[B]\to\{$	$+1$ ...	... $+1$	... $+1$	... -1	... ...	... ...
	$\{1X_j0\}$ $-[B]\to\{$	$+1$ ...	... $+1$	-1 ...	$+1$ ...	... ...	... ...
	$\{1X_j1\}$ $-[B]\to\{$	-1 ...	... -1	... ...	... ...	... $+1$	$+1$ ...

$[A]$: Sorting Z_{j+1} into one of 4 categories.
$[B]$: Use of equations (1) and (2) and the convention Table I.

sixteen sequences up to length six involving runs of seven. The whole set derived so far is exhibited in Table IV.

III. EQUILIBRIUM RELATIONS

The equilibrium resulting from this reaction is characterized by setting all rates $\dot{N}\{X_j\}$ equal to zero. This set, too, is infinite but it can be shown that exact closure of the scheme is possible provided[1]

$$(k_1/k_3{}')(k_3/k_1{}') = (k_2/k_2{}')^2 \tag{4}$$

Our kinetic model in this case corresponds to the Ising model with symmetrical nearest-neighbor interactions*. Equation (4) is consistent with the result of detailed balancing when applied to each pair of elementary steps in scheme I. The solution for the experimentally most important quantities can be expressed as follows (see Eqs. (9)–(11a) in Ref. 1):

$$n\{1\} = N\{1\}/N_T = 1/(1 + S^2) \tag{5}$$

$$\langle 0\rangle_n = 1 + K_0S \qquad \langle 1\rangle_n = 1 + K_1/S \tag{6}$$

$$\langle 0\rangle_w = 1 + 2K_0S \qquad \langle 1\rangle_w = 1 + 2K_1/S \tag{7}$$

$$\rho_{01} = (1 + S^2)/(1 + K_0S) \tag{8}$$

*A relation between the free energy levels of the three pairs 00,01,11, given earlier,[1] does not represent the most general case under which the model, Eq. (I), is valid.

where $n\{1\}$ is the degree of conversion of the chain from 0 to 1 and N_T the total number of sites. The subscripts n and w indicate the number and weight average lengths of runs and ρ_{01} is the correlation coefficient. S is an intermediate parameter defined by

$$S = \tfrac{1}{2}(K_0 - K_1) + [\tfrac{1}{4}(K_0 - K_1)^2 + 1]^{1/2} \tag{9}$$

with

$$K_0 = (k_3'/k_1)^{1/2}; \qquad K_1 = (k_3/k_1')^{1/2}$$

The quantities K_0 and K_1 thus define the solution. As indicated in Appendix A, the result, Eqs. (5)–(9), is identical with the familiar statistical mechanical solution for the case of nearest-neighbor interactions, summarized for example, by Schwarz.[2] We note the ease with which the results have been obtained here. The procedure could be extended to other cases, for example, a copolymer (i.e., a linear lattice with two types of sites) distributed in a prescribed manner and undergoing a transition to two other types of sites. For the finite chain, however, the use of nearest-neighbor conditional probabilities and detailed balancing will not yield the complete solution.[3]

Representative examples are shown in Figure 1, where $n\{1\}$ is plotted as a function of K_0 with K_1 as a variable parameter. When K_0, $K_1 \ll 1$, S tends

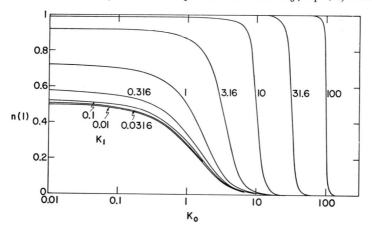

Fig. 1. Degree of conversion $n\{1\}$ at equilibrium for the nearest-neighbor case $(k_1 k_3/k_1' k_3') = (k_2/k_2')^2$ as a function of the parameters $K_0 = (k_3'/k_1)^{1/2}$, $K_1 = (k_3/k_1')^{1/2}$. Note that the cooperative transition region corresponds to K_0 and K_1 being very large and about equal. For very small values of K_0 and K_1 the conversion is about 1/2 and the strictly alternating polymer ... 01010 ... is preferred. K_0 and K_1 completely determine the equilibrium distribution.

TABLE IV. Coefficient

	N_T	$N\{0\}$	$N\{01\}$	$N\{001\}$	$N\{011\}$	$N\{0_3;1\}$	$N\{0011\}$
$\dot{N}\{0\}$	k_1'	$-k_1-k_1'$ $-k_3+k_3'$	k_1-k_1' $+k_3$	k_1-2k_2	$-k_1'+2k_2'$ $-k_3'$	—	—
$\dot{N}\{01\}$	k_1'	k_1-k_1'	$-k_1-k_1'$ $-k_3-k_3'$	k_3-k_1	$k_3'-k_1'$	—	—
$\dot{N}\{001\}$	—	k_1	$k_3'-k_1$	$-k_1-2k_2$ $-2k_3'$	$2k_2'-k_3'$	$2k_2-2k_1$	$2k_3'-2k_2'$
$\dot{N}\{011\}$	k_1'	$-k_1'$	k_3-k_1'	$2k_2-k_3$	$-k_1'-2k_2'$ $-2k_3$	—	$2k_3-2k_2$
$\dot{N}\{0_3;1\}$	—	k_1	$k_3'-k_1$	$-k_1$	$-k_3'$	$-2k_1-2k_2$ $-2k_3'$	$2k_2'$
$\dot{N}\{0011\}$	—	—	—	k_2	k_2'	k_2	$-3k_2-3k_2'$
$\dot{N}\{0;1_3\}$	k_1'	$-k_1'$	k_3-k_1'	$-k_3$	$-k_1'$	—	$2k_2$
$\dot{N}\{0_4;1\}$	—	k_1	$-k_1$	$-k_1+k_3'$	—	$-k_1$	$-k_3'$
$\dot{N}\{0_3;11\}$	—	—	—	—	—	k_2	k_2'
$\dot{N}\{00;1_3\}$	—	—	—	—	—	—	k_2
$\dot{N}\{0;1_4\}$	k_1'	$-k_1'$	$-k_1'$	—	k_3-k_1'	—	$-k_3$
$\dot{N}\{00101\}$	—	—	k_3'	k_2-k_3'	$k_2'-k_3'$	k_1-k_2	$-k_2-k_2'$ $+k_3'$
$\dot{N}\{01011\}$	—	—	k_3	k_2-k_3	$-k_3+k_2'$	$-k_2$	$-k_2+k_3$ $-k_2'$
$\dot{N}\{0_5;1\}$	—	k_1	$-k_1$	$-k_1+k_3'$	—	$-k_1$	$-k_3'$
$\dot{N}\{0_4;11\}$	—	—	—	—	—	—	—
$\dot{N}\{0_3;1_3\}$	—	—	—	—	—	—	—
$\dot{N}\{00;1_4\}$	—	—	—	—	—	—	—
$\dot{N}\{0;1_5\}$	k_1'	$-k_1'$	$-k_1'$	—	k_3-k_1'	—	$-k_3$
$\dot{N}\{0_3;101\}$	—	—	k_3'	$-k_3'$	$-k_3'$	k_1	k_3'
$\dot{N}\{001011\}$	—	—	—	k_2	k_2'	$-k_2$	$-k_2-k_2'$
$\dot{N}\{010011\}$	—	—	—	k_2	k_2'	—	$-k_2$
$\dot{N}\{010;1_3\}$	—	—	k_3	$-k_3$	$-k_3$	—	k_3
$\dot{N}\{001101\}$	—	—	—	k_2	k_2'	$-k_2$	$-k_2'$

atrix for the Rate Equations

{0; 1₃}	$N\{0_4; 1\}$	$N\{0_3; 11\}$	$N\{00; 1_3\}$	$N\{0; 1_4\}$	$N\{00101\}$	$N\{01011\}$
—	—	—	—	—	—	—
—	—	—	—	—	—	—
—	—	—	—	—	—	—
$2k_2' - 2k_1'$	—	—	—	—	—	—
—	$2k_2 - 2k_1$	$2k_3' - 2k_2'$	—	—	—	—
k_2'	—	$k_2 - k_1$	$k_2' - k_1'$	—	$k_3 - k_2$	$k_3' - k_2'$
$2k_3 - 2k_1'$ $2k_2'$	—	—	$2k_3 - 2k_2$	$2k_2' - 2k_1'$	—	—
—	$-3k_1 - 2k_2$ $-2k_3'$	$2k_2'$	—	—	k_3'	—
—	k_2	$-k_1 - 3k_2$ $-3k_2'$	k_2'	—	—	k_3'
k_2'	—	k_2	$-3k_2 - k_1'$ $-3k_2'$	k_2'	k_3	—
k_1'	—	—	$2k_2$	$-2k_3 - 3k_1'$ $-2k_2'$	—	k_3
k_2'	k_1	$-k_1 + k_2$	$k_1' + k_2'$	—	$-3k_2 - k_3$ $-3k_3'$	$k_2' - k_3'$
$k_1' - k_2'$	—	$k_1 + k_2$	$-k_1' + k_2'$	k_1'	$k_2 - k_3$	$-3k_3 - 3k_2'$ $-k_3'$
—	$-k_1$	—	—	—	$-k_3'$	—
—	k_2	k_2'	—	—	—	—
—	—	k_2	k_2'	—	—	—
—	—	—	k_2	k_2'	—	—
k_1'	—	—	—	$-k_1'$	—	$-k_3$
—	—	$-k_1$	—	—	—	$-k_3'$
k_2'	—	k_2	k_2'	—	—	—
k_2'	$-k_2$	$-k_2'$	k_1'	—	$-k_2 + k_3$	$-k_2'$
k_1'	—	—	$-k_1'$	—	$-k_3$	—
—	—	k_1	$-k_2$	$-k_2'$	$-k_2$	$-k_2' + k_3'$

(continued)

D.70 Shuler tablex for page 19—g.110

TABLE IV (*continued*)

	$N\{0_6; 1\}$	$N\{0_5; 11\}$	$N\{0_4; 1_3\}$	$N\{0_3; 1_4\}$	$N\{00; 1_5\}$	$N\{0; 1_6\}$	$N\{0_4; 101\}$	$N\{0_3; 1001\}$	$N\{0010011\}$	$N\{0_3; 1011\}$	$N\{0010101\}$
$\tilde{N}\{0_4; 1\}$	—	—	—	—	—	—	—	—	—	—	—
$\tilde{N}\{0_3; 11\}$	—	—	—	—	—	—	—	—	—	—	—
$\tilde{N}\{00; 1_3\}$	—	—	—	—	—	—	—	—	—	—	—
$\tilde{N}\{0; 1_4\}$	—	—	—	—	—	—	—	—	—	—	—
$\tilde{N}\{00101\}$	—	—	—	—	—	—	—	—	—	—	—
$\tilde{N}\{01011\}$	—	—	—	—	—	—	—	—	—	—	—
$\tilde{N}\{0_5; 1\}$	$-2k_1+2k_2$	$-2k_2'+2k_3'$	—	—	—	—	—	—	—	—	—
$\tilde{N}\{0_4; 11\}$	—	$-k_1+k_2$	$-k_1'+k_2'$	—	—	—	$-k_2+k_3$	—	—	—	—
$\tilde{N}\{0_3; 1_3\}$	—	—	$-k_1+k_2$	$-k_1'+k_2'$	—	—	—	—	—	—	—
$\tilde{N}\{00; 1_4\}$	—	—	—	$-k_1+k_2$	$-k_1'+k_2'$	—	—	—	—	—	—
$\tilde{N}\{0; 1_5\}$	—	—	—	—	$-2k_2+2k_3$	$-2k_1'+2k_2'$	—	—	—	—	—
$\tilde{N}\{0_3; 101\}$	—	—	—	—	—	—	$-k_1+k_2$	$-k_1+k_2$	$-k_2'+k_3'$	$-k_2'+k_3'$	—
$\tilde{N}\{001011\}$	—	—	—	—	—	—	—	—	—	$-k_1+k_2$	k_3-k_2
$\tilde{N}\{010011\}$	—	—	—	—	—	—	—	—	$-2k_2+2k_3$	—	—
$\tilde{N}\{010; 1_3\}$	—	—	—	—	—	—	—	—	—	—	—
$\tilde{N}\{001101\}$	—	—	—	—	—	—	—	—	—	—	—

	$N\{0_5; 1\}$	$N\{0_4; 11\}$	$N\{0_3; 1_3\}$	$N\{00; 1_4\}$	$N\{0; 1_5\}$	$N\{0_3; 101\}$	$N\{001011\}$	$N\{010011\}$	$N\{010; 1_3\}$	$N\{001101\}$
$\bar N\{0_4; 1\}$	$-2k_1+2k_2$	$-2k_2'+2k_3'$	—	—	—	—	—	—	—	—
$\bar N\{0_3; 11\}$	—	$-k_1+k_2$	$-k_1'+k_2'$	—	—	$-k_2+k_3$	—	$-k_2'+k_3'$	$-k_2'+k_3'$	$-k_2+k_3$
$\bar N\{00; 1_3\}$	—	—	$-k_1+k_2$	$-k_1'+k_2'$	—	—	—	—	—	—
$\bar N\{0; 1_4\}$	—	—	—	$-2k_2+2k_3$	$-2k_1'+2k_2'$	—	—	—	—	—
$\bar N\{00101\}$	—	—	—	—	—	$-2k_1+2k_2$	$-2k_2'+2k_3'$	—	$-2k_1'+2k_2'$	—
$\bar N\{01011\}$	—	—	—	—	—	—	$-2k_2+2k_3$	—	$-2k_1'+2k_2'$	—
$\bar N\{0_5; 1\}$	$-4k_1-2k_2-2k_3'$	$2k_2'$	k_2'	—	—	$2k_3'$	—	—	—	—
$\bar N\{0_4; 11\}$	k_2	$-2k_1-3k_2-3k_2'$	k_2	k_2'	—	—	—	—	—	—
$\bar N\{0_3; 1_3\}$	—	k_2	$-k_1-3k_2-k_1'-3k_2'$	—	—	k_3	k_3'	k_3'	—	k_3
$\bar N\{00; 1_4\}$	—	—	—	$-3k_2-2k_1'-3k_2'$	k_2'	—	—	—	k_3'	—
$\bar N\{0; 1_5\}$	—	—	—	$2k_2$	$-2k_3-4k_1'-2k_2'$	—	—	—	$2k_3$	—
$\bar N\{0_3; 101\}$	k_1	—	k_1'	k_1'	—	$-2k_1-2k_2-k_3-3k_3'$	k_3	$k_2'-k_3'$	k_2'	k_2'
$\bar N\{001011\}$	—	k_1	$k_2'-k_1$	—	k_1'	k_2	$-3k_2-k_3-3k_2'-k_3'$	—	—	k_2'
$\bar N\{010011\}$	—	k_1+k_2	k_1	—	—	—	—	$-2k_2-2k_3-3k_2'-k_3'$	k_2'	k_2-k_3
$\bar N\{010; 1_3\}$	—	—	—	—	—	k_2-k_3	—	k_2	$-3k_3-2k_1'-2k_2'-k_3'$	—
$\bar N\{001101\}$	—	—	$-k_1+k_2$	$k_1'+k_2'$	—	$2k_2$	k_3	—	$k_2'-k_3$	$-3k_2-k_3-2k_2'-2k_3'$

(continued)

TABLE IV (*continued*)

	$N\{0101011\}$	$N\{0011011\}$	$N\{0010; 1_3\}$	$N\{01; 0_3; 11\}$	$N\{0_3; 1101\}$	$N\{00; 1_3; 01\}$	$N\{010; 1_4\}$	$N\{0110; 1_3\}$	$N\{0100; 1_3\}$
$\dot{N}\{0_4; 1\}$	—	—	—	—	—	—	—	—	—
$\dot{N}\{0_3; 11\}$	—	—	—	—	—	—	—	—	—
$\dot{N}\{00; 1_3\}$	—	—	—	—	—	—	—	—	—
$\dot{N}\{0; 1_4\}$	—	—	—	—	—	—	—	—	—
$\dot{N}\{001101\}$	—	—	—	—	—	—	—	—	—
$\dot{N}\{01011\}$	—	—	—	—	—	—	—	—	—
$\dot{N}\{0_5; 11\}$	—	—	—	—	—	—	—	—	—
$\dot{N}\{0_4; 11\}$	—	—	—	$-k_2' + k_3'$	—	—	—	—	—
$\dot{N}\{0_3; 1_3\}$	—	—	—	—	$-k_2 + k_3$	—	—	—	$-k_2' + k_3'$
$\dot{N}\{00; 1_4\}$	—	—	—	—	—	$-k_2 + k_3$	$-k_2' + k_3'$	—	—
$\dot{N}\{0; 1_5\}$	—	—	—	—	—	—	—	—	—
$\dot{N}\{0_3; 101\}$	—	—	—	—	—	—	—	—	—
$\dot{N}\{001011\}$	$-k_2 + k_3'$	—	$-k_1' + k_2'$	—	—	—	—	—	—
$\dot{N}\{010011\}$	—	—	—	—	—	—	—	—	—
$\dot{N}\{010; 1_3\}$	—	$-k_2 + k_3$	$-k_2 + k_3$	—	—	—	$-k_1' + k_2'$	$-k_1' + k_2'$	—
$\dot{N}\{001101\}$	—	$-2k_2' + 2k_3'$	—	—	$-2k_1 + 2k_2$	—	—	—	$-2k_1' + 2k_2'$

to unity and n_1 to $\frac{1}{2}$ according to Eq. (5) and Figure 1. The definitions (9) and the reaction scheme I or Eqs. (6) and (7) indicate under these conditions strict alternation 0101. ... When, on the other hand, K_0 and K_1 are equal and very large, $S = 1$ and the ratio of weight to number average for either 0's or 1's tends to 2. When K_0 and K_1 are large, the right-hand side of Figure 1 displays the well-known cooperative effect.

IV. NUMERICAL APPROXIMATIONS

A sudden change in the rate constants (consistent with Eq. (4)) causes a system in equilibrium at one pair of values (K_0, K_1) to move to the state characterized by the new pair. The rate of this transition is determined by the infinite set of equations, a subset of which is given in Table IV. This extends our earlier results[1] to include rate equations for sextuplets.

In order to compute these time dependent changes, an approximate method must be found to break off the infinite set at some level j. The rule we used may be expressed for a sequence terminated by a 1 as

$$N\{Y_i; Z_{j-1}; 1\} = N\{Y_i; Z_{j-1}\}[N\{Z_{j-1}; 1\}/N\{Z_{j-1}\}]; \qquad i \geq 1 \quad (10)$$

and it is clear that by this closure approximation all sequences of length $j + 1$ become functions of sequences of length j and shorter. The rate equations were then solved numerically on the GOLEM computer of the Weizmann Institute by the Runge-Kutta method. Referring to Table IV, we have so far broken off either at level 3 (4 equations) or at level 4 (7 equations). Defining the ratios

$$x = k_2/k_1; \qquad y = k_3/k_2; \qquad x' = k_2'/k_1'; \qquad y' = k_3'/k_2';$$
$$u = k_1'/k_1 \quad (11)$$

we have computed the variation in time of the conversion $n\{1\}$ and the averages $\langle 0 \rangle_n = n\{0\}/n\{01\}$, and $\langle 0 \rangle_w$ (see Appendix B) of runs of 0's using values of x, y, x', y' and u ranging from 10^{-3} to 10^3 and treating a number of initial conditions. For most of the above range no significant difference in the values computed on the basis of 4 and 7 equations, respectively, could be detected over the entire time scale as is demonstrated by some representative results exhibited in Table V. This may be indicative of a very good approximation or alternatively, of a nearly constant error at the closure levels explored so far. At equilibrium, Eq. (10) is rigorous, with a value of j determined by the range of the neighbor interaction.

Figures 2–5 show typical rate curves computed by means of the closure assumption. Here $n\{1\}$ is plotted as a function of reduced time $k_1 t$, assuming throughout values of the rate constants consistent with the

TABLE V

Effect of Closure at Level 3 Compared with Closure at Level 4[a]

Case	k_1/k_1	k_2/k_1	k_3/k_1	k_1'/k_1	k_2'/k_1	k_3'/k_1	k_1t	$\langle 0 \rangle_n$	$\langle 0 \rangle_w$	$n\{0\}$	$n\{01\}$	$n\{001\}$	$n\{011\}$
1	1	20	40	0.1	0.01	0.02	0	∞	∞	1.00000	0.00000	0.00000	0.00000
							10^{-3}	4862.63	9724.25	0.99979	0.00021	0.00021	0.00000
								—	—	—	—	—	—
							10^{-2}	109.141	217.277	0.98925	0.00906	0.00898	0.00149
								—	—	—	—	—	—
							10^{-1}	10.5845	20.1832	0.75583	0.07141	0.06462	0.05503
								—	—	—	—	—	—
							1	1.00052	1.00105	0.00248	0.00248	0.00000	0.00248
								—	—	—	—	—	—
							Equil.	1.00050	1.00101	0.00248	0.00248	0.00000	0.00248
2	1	100	10000	0.1	10	1000	0	∞	∞	1.00000	0.00000	0.00000	0.00000
							10^{-6}	4,862620	9,725230	1.00000	0.00000	0.00000	0.00000
								—	—	—	—	—	—
							10^{-5}	109130	218258	0.99999	0.00001	0.00001	0.00000
								—	—	—	—	—	—
							10^{-4}	10585.7	21169.9	0.99990	0.00009	0.00009	0.00000
								—	—	—	—	—	—
							10^{-3}	1536.46 (1536.45)	3070.43 (3070.42)	0.99927	0.00065	0.00065	0.00007
								—	—	—	—	—	—
							10^{-2}	436.734 (435.012)	870.675 (867.204)	0.99491 (0.99499)	0.00228 (0.00229)	0.00228 (0.00229)	0.00144 (0.00145)

3	1	1000	0.1	100	100	0	∞	∞	1.00000	0.00000	0.00000	0.00000

Section	Params						Col 1	Col 2	Col 3	Col 4	Col 5	Col 6
3	1	1000	0.1	100	100	0	∞	∞	1.00000	0.00000	0.00000	0.00000
						10^{-3}	4906.53	9812.18	0.99975	0.00020	0.00020	0.00004
							—	—	—	—	—	—
						10^{-2}	114.048	228.332	0.92131	0.00808	0.00796	0.00757
							(114.009)	(228.508)	(0.92129)	—	—	(0.00760)
						0.05012	18.4469	37.4416	0.11184	0.00606	0.00549	0.00601
							(20.4969)	(42.0829)	(0.12314)	(0.00610)	(0.00545)	(0.00595)
4	1	10	100	0.1	10	0	2.00000	3.00000	0.50000	0.25000	0.12500	0.01250
						10^{-3}	2.01118	3.01482	0.49722	0.24723	0.12477	0.12521
							—	—	—	—	—	—
						10^{-2}	2.44845	3.51521	0.41004	0.16747	0.11410	0.11753
							(2.44857)	(3.52387)	(0.41003)	(0.16746)	(0.11407)	(0.11744)
						10^{-1}	3.12456	4.22191	0.17611	0.05636	0.05054	0.05382
							(3.13144)	(4.21048)	(0.17646)	(0.05635)	(0.05061)	(0.05423)
						1	1.12731	1.26044	0.00127	0.00112	0.00012	0.00112
							(1.12382)	(1.25559)	(0.00126)			
5	1	0.1	0.01	0.1	1	0	2.00000	3.00000	0.50000	0.25000	0.12500	0.12500
						10^{-3}	2.00295	3.00665	0.50028	0.24977	0.12502	0.12498
							—	—	—	—	—	—
						10^{-2}	2.13114	3.29330	0.51201	0.24025	0.12579	0.12397
							—	(3.29215)	—	—	—	—
						10^{-1}	3.23952	5.59007	0.59098	0.18243	0.12307	0.11415
							(3.23933)	(5.57665)	—	(0.18244)	(0.12279)	—
		10				1	7.07726	13.0894	0.79382	0.11216	0.09684	0.05027
							(7.06811)	(13.0322)	(0.79388)	(0.11232)	(0.09725)	(0.05047)
						10	10.9999	20.9999	0.90909	0.08265	0.07513	0.00751
							—	(20.9997)	—	—	—	—
						Equil.	11.0000	21.0000	0.90909	0.08264	0.07513	0.00751

[a] Results given refer to closure at level 3. Where closure at level 4 gives the identical result a line is drawn under the number. When the result differs it is given in parentheses. The weight average $\langle 0 \rangle_w$ is the most sensitive indicator.

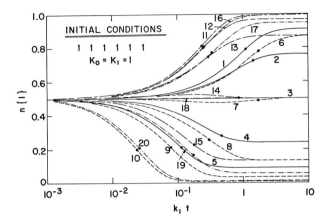

Fig. 2. Degree of conversion $n\{1\}$ as a function of reduced time $k_1 t$. Initial equilibrium correspond to $K_0 = K_1 = 1$, for example, to $k_1 = k_2 = k_3 = k_1' = k_2' = k_3'$. Stepwise transition to

Case:	k^1/k^1	k_2/k_1	k_3/k_1	k_1'/k_1	k_2'/k_1	k_3'/k_1	$x=y$	$x'=y'$	u	K_0	K_1
1	1	1	1	10^{-1}	10^{-1}	10^{-1}	1	1	10^{-1}	$10^{-1/2}$	$10^{1/2}$
2				$10^{-1/2}$	$10^{-1/2}$	$10^{-1/2}$			$10^{-1/2}$	$10^{-1/4}$	$10^{1/4}$
3				1	1	1			1	1	1
4				$10^{1/2}$	$10^{1/2}$	$10^{1/2}$			$10^{1/2}$	$10^{1/4}$	$10^{-1/}$
5				10	10	10			10	$10^{1/2}$	$10^{-1/}$
6				10^{-1}	$10^{-1/2}$	1	1	$10^{1/2}$	10^{-1}	1	$10^{1/2}$
7				$10^{-1/2}$	1	$10^{1/2}$			$10^{-1/2}$	$10^{1/4}$	$10^{1/4}$
8				1	$10^{1/2}$	10			1	$10^{1/2}$	1
9				$10^{1/2}$	10	$10^{3/2}$			$10^{1/2}$	$10^{3/4}$	$10^{-1/}$
10				10	$10^{3/2}$	10^2			10	10	$10^{-1/}$
11	1	$10^{1/2}$	10	10^{-1}	10^{-1}	10^{-1}	$10^{1/2}$	1	10^{-1}	$10^{-1/2}$	10
12				$10^{-1/2}$	$10^{-1/2}$	$10^{-1/2}$			$10^{-1/2}$	$10^{-1/4}$	$10^{3/4}$
13				1	1	1			1	1	$10^{1/2}$
14				$10^{1/2}$	$10^{1/2}$	$10^{1/2}$			$10^{1/2}$	$10^{1/4}$	$10^{1/4}$
15				10	10	10			10	$10^{1/2}$	1
16				10^{-1}	$10^{-1/2}$	1	$10^{1/2}$	$10^{1/2}$	10^{-1}	1	10
17				$10^{-1/2}$	1	$10^{1/2}$			$10^{-1/2}$	$10^{1/4}$	$10^{3/4}$
18				1	$10^{1/2}$	10			1	$10^{1/2}$	$10^{1/2}$
19				$10^{1/2}$	10	$10^{3/2}$			$10^{1/2}$	$10^{3/4}$	$10^{1/4}$
20				10	$10^{3/2}$	10^2			10	10	1

Notes:

(1) Cases with the same K_0, K_1 combination tend to the same equilibrium state.

(2) Points "•" mark the relaxation time calculated from Eq. (13).

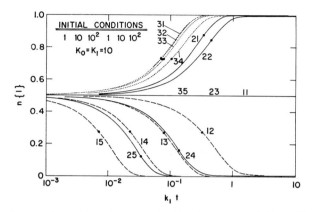

Fig. 3. Degree of conversion $n\{1\}$ as a function of reduced time k_1t. Initial equilibrium corresponds $K_0 = K_1 = 10$, for example, to $k_1/k_1 = k_1'/k_1 = 1$, $k_2/k_1 = k_2'/k_1 = 10$, $k_3/k_1 = k_3'/k_1 = 10^2$ epwise transition to

se:	k_1/k_1	k_2/k_1	k_3/k_1	k_1'/k_1	k_2'/k_1	k_3'/k_1	$x=y$	$x'=y'$	u	K_0	K_1
1	1	$10^{1/2}$	10	10^{-1}	$10^{1/2}$	10^2	$10^{1/2}$	$10^{3/2}$	10^{-1}	10	10
2				$10^{-1/2}$	10	$10^{5/2}$			$10^{-1/2}$	$10^{5/4}$	$10^{3/4}$
3				1	$10^{3/2}$	10^3			1	$10^{3/2}$	$10^{1/2}$
4				$10^{1/2}$	10^2	$10^{7/2}$			$10^{1/2}$	$10^{7/4}$	$10^{1/4}$
5				10	$10^{5/2}$	10^4			10	10^2	1
1	1	10	10^2	10^{-1}	1	10	10	10	10^{-1}	$10^{1/2}$	$10^{3/2}$
2				$10^{-1/2}$	$10^{1/2}$	$10^{3/2}$			$10^{-1/2}$	$10^{3/4}$	$10^{5/4}$
3				1	10	10^2			1	10	10
4				$10^{1/2}$	$10^{3/2}$	$10^{5/2}$			$10^{1/2}$	$10^{5/4}$	$10^{3/4}$
5				10	10^2	10^3			10	$10^{3/2}$	$10^{1/2}$
1	1	$10^{3/2}$	10^3	10^{-1}	$10^{-1/2}$	1	$10^{3/2}$	$10^{1/2}$	10^{-1}	1	10^2
2				$10^{-1/2}$	1	$10^{1/2}$			$10^{-1/2}$	$10^{1/4}$	$10^{7/4}$
3				1	$10^{1/2}$	10			1	$10^{1/2}$	$10^{3/2}$
4				$10^{1/2}$	10	$10^{3/2}$			$10^{1/2}$	$10^{3/4}$	$10^{5/4}$
5				10	$10^{3/2}$	10^2			10	10	10

te: Points "•" mark the relaxation time calculated according to Eq. (13).

nearest-neighbor equilibrium model, Eq. (4). We start in Figure 2 from an equilibrium distribution corresponding to the choice $k_i = k_i' = k$, $K_0 = K_1 = 1$ which has been perturbed at $t = 0$ to a new set of rate constants, as specified in the graphs. In general, a monotonic sigmoid approach to the new equilibrium value occurs. However, when the initial and final equilibrium value of $n\{1\}$ are identical, corresponding to different values of K_0, K_1, but with $K_0 = K_1$, an extremum can result, as is seen in Figure 2. Figure 3 shows the perturbation of $n\{1\}$ from an initial equilibrium state in the highly cooperative region of Figure 1. For relative perturbations of the initial states similar to those in Figure 2 conversion to practically all 0's or 1's results in this case, unless the equilibrium remains at the $\frac{1}{2}$ level.

It is appropriate at this point to consider briefly the formalism of relaxation times for this model. The rigorous solution of the set, Table IV, will

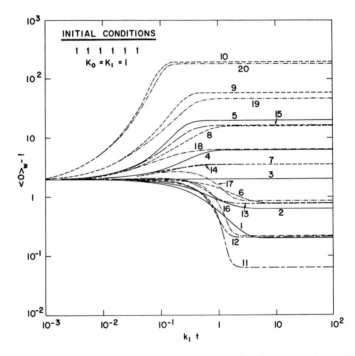

Fig. 4. Weight average length of runs of 0's, $\langle 0 \rangle_w$. Plot of ($\langle 0 \rangle_w - 1$) as a function of reduced time, $k_1 t$. Conditions and numbering as in Fig. 2.

consist of a sum of weighted exponentials describing the transition from the initial to the final state. Thus

$$n\{X_j\} = \sum_i A_i(X_j)\exp[-t/\tau_i]$$

and   (12)

$$\lim_{t \to 0} \dot{n}\{X_j\}/n\{X_j\} = -\sum_i [A_i(X_j)/\tau_i]/\sum_i A_i(X_j) = -\langle 1/\tau \rangle_{X_j}$$

which defines a series of mean reciprocal relaxation times[2] based on the initial rates. These will be derived from Table IV by expressing the right hand sides in terms of the initial conditions and dividing by the appropriate

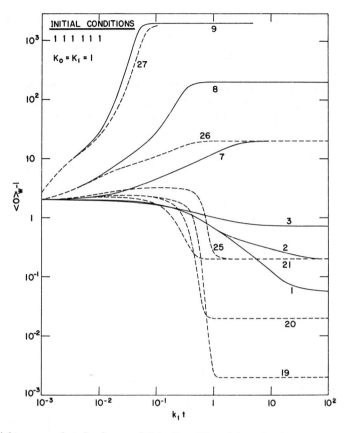

Fig. 5. Weight average length of runs of 0's, $\langle 0 \rangle_w$. Plot of $(\langle 0 \rangle_w - 1)$ as a function of reduced e, $k_1 t$. Initial equilibrium corresponds to $K_0 = K_1 = 1$, for example, to $k_1 = k_2 = k_3 = k_1' = = k_3'$. Stepwise transition to

e:	k_1/k_1	k_2/k_1	k_3/k_1	k_1'/k_1	k_2'/k_1	k_3'/k_1	$x=y$	$x'=y'$	u	K_0	K_1
	1	10^{-1}	10^{-2}	10^{-1}	10^{-2}	10^{-3}	10^{-1}	10^{-1}	10^{-1}	$10^{-3/2}$	$10^{-1/2}$
				1	10^{-1}	10^{-2}			1	10^{-1}	10^{-1}
				10	1	10^{-1}			10	$10^{-1/2}$	$10^{-3/2}$
				10^{-1}	1	10		10	10^{-1}	$10^{1/2}$	$10^{-1/2}$
				1	10	10^{2}			1	10	10^{-1}
				10	10^{2}	10^{3}			10	$10^{3/2}$	$10^{-3/2}$
	1	10	10^{2}	10^{-1}	10^{-2}	10^{-3}	10	10^{-1}	10^{-1}	$10^{-3/2}$	$10^{3/2}$
				1	10^{-1}	10^{-2}			1	10^{-1}	10
				10	1	10^{-1}			10	$10^{-1/2}$	$10^{1/2}$
				10^{-1}	1	10		10	10^{-1}	$10^{1/2}$	$10^{3/2}$
				1	10	10^{2}			1	10	10
				10	10^{2}	10^{3}			10	$10^{3/2}$	$10^{1/2}$

initial concentration. The quantities are obtained from the equilibrium relations (5)–(9) where applicable. The equation for $\dot{n}\{0\}$,[1] Table IV, has previously been given by Schwarz.[2] There appears also an expression for $\dot{n}\{0_3\}$, see Appendix C.

If the initial state corresponds to the Ising model with nearest-neighbor interactions, Eqs. (4)–(9), we obtain the following expressions for the average reciprocal relaxation times of $n\{1\}$, $n\{0\}$, and $n\{01\}$:

$$\langle 1/\tau \rangle_1 (1 + K_0 S)^2 = -S^2[(K_0 S)^2 k_1 + 2(K_0 S)k_2 + k_3]$$
$$+ [(1 - S^2) + (K_0 S)]^2 k_1' + 2S^2[(1 - S^2) + (K_0 S)]$$
$$\times k_2' + S^4 k_3' \tag{13}$$
$$\langle 1/\tau \rangle_0 = -(1/S^2)\langle 1/\tau \rangle_1$$
$$\langle 1/\tau \rangle_{01}(1 + K_0 S) = -(K_0 S)^2 k_1 + k_3 - [(1 - S^2) + (K_0 S)]^2 S^{-2} k_1'$$
$$+ S^2 k_3'$$

Note that K_0 and S characterize the initial and the k_i and k_i' the new state of the system. From Eq. (13) we obtain at once the average relaxation time of the number average $\langle 0 \rangle_n$, since

$$\langle 1/\tau \rangle_{\langle 0 \rangle} = \langle 1/\tau \rangle_0 - \langle 1/\tau \rangle_{01}$$

The values for the reduced reciprocal of $\langle 1/\tau \rangle_1$ have been indicated by filled circles on the rate curves in Figures 2 and 3. As can be seen, reasonable estimates of the length of the reaction period are obtained in this manner, even though many details are, of course, lost. Finally, the sign of the average relaxation time may be positive or negative, depending upon whether $n\{X_j\}$ decreases or increases with time.

Figures 4 and 5 show the weight average length of zero runs as a function of time. In the former the numerical values of the rate constants are identical with those in Figure 2. Combination of Figure 2 and Figure 4 will yield the weight average as a function of the conversion. Similarities in the $n\{1\} - t$ curves are not necessarily accompanied by corresponding similarities in $\langle 0 \rangle_w$. For example, the maximum in Figure 2 (curve 14) does not result in an extremum in Figure 4. In turn the maximum in the latter figure (curve 17) is not reproduced in Figure 2.

Equation (13) contains the first two in the hierarchy of mean relaxation frequencies $\langle 1/\tau \rangle_{X_j}$. The matrix, Table IV permits the evaluation of further such quantities and thus of the set k_i, k_i' of rate constants from relaxation data. Equation (13) and its continuation is entirely general for the nearest-neighbor model under consideration and describes the *initial* kinetic stages of the transition from an arbitrary starting equilibrium to a second equilibrium, *arbitrarily* distant from the first. An extended Eq. (13) may be derived from Table IV and used to determine all six rate constants, provided the experimental relaxation spectrometry is capable of tracing a sufficient number of species X_j. There are five independent rate constants, see Eq. (4). If the parameters K_0 and K_1 characteristic for the second equilibrium are already known, three such species X_j have to be investigated by means of relaxation spectrometry. For a theoretical analysis one is not restricted, of course, to the mean relaxation frequencies, Eq. (12), since the rate equations are linear, except for the closure approximation introduced. Figures 2 and 3 are examples of complete solutions and thus complete kinetic descriptions, valid at all times.

In recent years Schwarz[2] has discussed a kinetics of the helix-coil transition corresponding to the same model and derived expressions for a single quantity, namely $\langle 1/\tau \rangle_1$. He treats the special case, where the two equilibrium states are very close and differ only in respect to the growth parameter $s = k_2/k_2'$ (see Appendix A). Details are discussed in Appendix D, but the limitations inherent in a treatment not based on at least a sufficiently large subset of rate equations, or the complete set for short chains,[3] are obvious.

V. SOME APPLICATIONS

An example of considerable interest is the helix-coil transition in polypeptides. This will fall into the pattern of the present model provided we treat groups of four amino acids as one unit. If the bonds linking the α-carbon atom to the planar peptide bond are free to rotate we assign the symbol "0." If they are twisted to give a helical configuration we write " 1 " and assign the configurational activation factor b; if four amino acids have come around the helix and the first interacts with the last in helical configuration on the one side we write " 2 " and assign a factor h; if a second helical turn has been completed (8 residues in helical conformation), segments 4 and 5 interact on both sides, we write " 3 " and put in another factor h. Table VI illustrates some of the situations which arise and the way the rate constants are related. It will be clear that while b and h characterize the passage from random coil to helix, b' and h' are the corresponding factors in the reverse direction.

Steps intermediate to those shown in Table VI are not considered explicitly. It then follows that the reaction scheme is in accordance with I and with Eq. (4) in particular. Moreover

$$x = y; \qquad x' = y'$$

in Eqs. (11). Hence the equilibrium states are characterized by K_0 and K_1 and Figures 1–5 are representative.

This model differs from Schwarz's[2] who uses the single residue as kinetic unit in analogy to the Zimm-Bragg equilibrium model. His rate parameters satisfy, of course, Eq. (4), but in his case $x \neq y$, $x' \neq y'$. The

TABLE VI

Reaction Scheme for Helix–Coil Transition

$$
\begin{array}{ll}
0000 \mid 0000 \mid 0000 & \\
\quad\quad \updownarrow & k_1 = b^3 h \Big\downarrow\Big\uparrow k_3' = (b')^3 h' \\
0000 \mid 2112 \mid 0000 &
\end{array}
$$

$$
\left.\begin{array}{l}
2112 \mid 0000 \mid 0000 \\
\quad\quad \updownarrow \\
2223 \mid 3222 \mid 0000 \\
3222 \mid 0000 \mid 0000 \\
\quad\quad \updownarrow \\
3333 \mid 3222 \mid 0000
\end{array}\right\} \quad k_2 = b^4 h^4 \Big\downarrow\Big\uparrow k_2' = (b')^4 (h')^4
$$

$$
\left.\begin{array}{l}
2112 \mid 0000 \mid 2112 \\
\quad\quad \updownarrow \\
2223 \mid 3333 \mid 3222 \\
3222 \mid 0000 \mid 2223 \\
\quad\quad \updownarrow \\
3333 \mid 3333 \mid 3333
\end{array}\right\} \quad k_3 = b^5 h^7 \Big\downarrow\Big\uparrow k_1' = (b')^5 (h')^7
$$

$$
\begin{aligned}
k_1'/k_1 &= (b')^5 (h')^7 / [(b)^3 h] \\
k_3/k_2 &= k_2/k_1 = bh^3 \\
k_3'/k_2' &= k_2'/k_1' = (b')^{-1} (h')^{-3}
\end{aligned}
$$

specification of four residues as the kinetic unit may be an overschematization. On the other hand, Engel[4] observes a significant molecular weight dependence of $\langle 1/\tau \rangle_0$ between 3300 and 21,000 in poly-L-proline. This may be more readily understood on the basis of a large effective unit.

The applicability of the model to binding, e.g., of protons (potentiometric titrations), is obvious. As a further illustration, let us consider the special case where the particle being bound occupies two neighboring sites at once and each site can be occupied only once. Examples of situations which can arise are the following:

$$\times(\times\ \times)\times \qquad \times(\times\ \times)(\times\ \times)\times \qquad \times(\times\ \times)\times(\times\ \times)\times$$

Both the unit process and the situations created are seemingly different.

Let us, however, consider what happens to the space between sites, and indicate the presence or absence of a bridging particle by 1 or 0, respectively.

$$\times \;(\times \;\;\times) \;\times \qquad\qquad \times \;(\times \;\;\times) \;(\times \;\;\times) \;\times$$
$$0 \quad 1 \quad\; 0 \qquad\qquad\quad 0 \quad 1 \quad 0 \quad 1 \quad\; 0$$

$$\times \;(\times \;\;\times) \;\times \;(\times \;\;\times) \;\times$$
$$0 \quad 1 \quad 0 \quad 0 \quad 1 \quad\; 0$$

A particular case of the general system results. That is, two 1's cannot be neighboring, and such sequences do not occur. Consequently $k_2 = k_3 = k_1' = k_2' = 0$ and only the first of the reactions in scheme (I) is operative.

There is no fundamental problem about extending Table IV. Also, certain special cases, where some of the rate constants are zero or equal and which have been treated previously, follow from this scheme.

The solution found when the rate equations are put equal to zero corresponds to equilibrium in the case of a uniform reaction environment, but also characterizes the steady state if it is assumed that the linear lattice separates two two-dimensional spaces such that on the one side the reaction is all $0 \to 1$ according to k_1, k_2, and k_3 and on the other all $1 \to 0$ according to k_1', k_2' and k_3'. As the k's can include functions of the environment within them such as the concentrations of a transported substance with which the lattice reacts, this model can be used to discuss transport through membranes with reactions governed by near neighbor effects. It will be clear that the reactivity of the linear lattice must be defined in an asymmetric fashion in order to obtain transport.

Appendix A

Identity of equilibrium solution derived from kinetics, Eqs. (5)–(9), and statistical mechanical result.

This is established by relating the usual nucleation and propagation parameters σ and s of the Zimm–Bragg theory[2] to the rate constants, Eq. (I), as follows:

$$s = K_1/K_0 = k_2/k_2'; \qquad \sigma s = K_0^{-2} = k_1/k_3'; \qquad s/\sigma = K_1^2 = k_3/k_1'$$

The parameters σ and σ' for nucleation of 0's (coil) and 1's (helix) are identical, with

$$\sigma = \sigma' = (k_1'/k_3)/(k_2'/k_2) = (k_1/k_3')/(k_2/k_2')$$

which displays clearly the meaning of the parameters in terms of our rate constants.

Appendix B

Derivation of weight average length $\langle 0 \rangle_w$; closure at level i.
We have by definition:

$$\langle 0 \rangle_w = \sum_{j=1}^{\infty} j^2 n\{10_j 1\} / \sum_{j=1}^{\infty} jn\{10_j 1\}$$

$$= S/n\{0\}$$

The sum S may be transformed in terms of our retained sequences $0_j 1$ as follows:

$$S = \sum_{j=1}^{\infty} j^2 [n\{0_j 1\} - n\{0_{j+1} 1\}] = \sum_{j=1}^{\infty} [j^2 - (j-1)^2] n\{0_j 1\}$$

$$= \sum_{j=1}^{\infty} (2j - 1)n\{0_j 1\}$$

Assuming now closure at level i, we have for $k \geq 1$ from Eq. (10)

$$n\{0_k 0_{i-1} X\} = n\{0_k 0_{i-1}\} n\{0_{i-1} X\}/n\{0_{i-1}\}$$

Repeated application of this relation to $n\{0_j 1\}$ and $n\{0_j\}$ for $j \geq i$ yields

$$n\{0_j 1\} = n\{0_{i-1} 1\} v_i^{j-i+1}; \qquad v_i = n\{0_i\}/n\{0_{i-1}\}$$

and

$$\sum_{j=i}^{\infty} n\{0_j 1\} = n\{0_i\};$$

$$\sum_{j=i}^{\infty} jn\{0_j 1\} = n\{0_i\}[in\{0_{i-1} 1\} + n\{0_i\}]/n\{0_{i-1} 1\}$$

Hence, we obtain $\langle 0 \rangle_w$ at closure level i in terms of runs of length i or less, viz:

$$\langle 0 \rangle_w \cdot n\{0\} = \sum_{j=1}^{i-1} (2j - 1)n\{0_j 1\} + (2i - 1)n\{0_i\} + 2[n\{0_i\}]^2/n\{0_{i-1} 1\}$$

Appendix C

Equation for $\dot{n}_3\{0_3\}$

From the first three equations of our set, Table IV, there follows, using transformations (1) and (2):

$$\dot{n}\{0_3\} = -k_1(n\{0_3\} + 2 n\{0_4\}) + k_3'(n\{010\}$$
$$+ 2n\{0010\}) - 2k_2 n\{0_3; 1\} + 2k_2' n\{0011\}$$

where each term is readily interpreted. Equations (30) and (31) in Ref. 2 are valid and become identical with the preceding result, provided $k_2 = k_3$ and $k_2' = k_3'$.

Appendix D

A special case of Eq. (13)

An equation for $\langle 1/\tau \rangle_1$ is implicit in Schwarz's[2] expression for $\dot{n}\{0\} = -\dot{n}\{1\}$, which is identical with ours, as noted before. However no doublet relaxation average is obtained. There is a difference in definition, as in Eq. (12) the quantity $\dot{n}\{X_j\}(t = 0)$ is replaced by $n\{X_j\}(t = 0) - n\{X_j\}(t = \infty)$. That is, the very largest relaxation time is omitted in the average, Eq. (12). In the actual computation the final equilibrium is assumed to be close to the initial one and only the growth parameter $s = k_2/k_2'$ is allowed to change, whereas $\sigma = \sigma'$ remains constant (see Appendix A). The final equilibrium and thus the ratios of rate constants in Eqs. (5)–(9) are therefore determined by the relations

$$k_1/k_3' = K_0^{-2} + (K_0 K_1)^{-1}\Delta s; \qquad k_3/k_1' = K_1^2 + (K_0 K_1)\Delta s;$$
$$k_2/k_2' = K_1/K_0 + \Delta s$$

where terms $0(\Delta s^2)$ are neglected and the final equilibrium relation is from Eqs. (5) and (9)

$$n\{1\} = 1/(1 + S^2) - 2S/(1 + S^2)^2(\partial S/\partial s)_\sigma \Delta s$$

with

$$(\partial S/\partial s)_\sigma = -(K_0^3\sigma/2)(dS/dK_0); \qquad K_1 = (K_0\sigma)^{-1}$$

References

1. A. Silberberg and R. Simha, *Biopolymers*, **6**, 479 (1968).
2. G. Schwarz, *J. Mol. Biol.*, **11**, 64 (1965).
3. R. Simha and E. Loftus, unpublished.
4. J. Engel, *Biopolymers*, **4**, 945 (1966).

STOCHASTIC MODELS
FOR CHAIN DYNAMICS*

R. A. ORWOLL and W. H. STOCKMAYER

*Department of Chemistry, Dartmouth College,
Hanover, New Hampshire*

CONTENTS

I. INTRODUCTION

During the past fifteen years a familiar bead-and-spring model often associated with the name of Rouse[1] has dominated discussions of the dynamic behavior of flexible long-chain molecules in solution or bulk. Independently developed in more or less equivalent degree by others,[2,3] the model has since been improved and embellished in several physically important respects, such as (*a*) the inclusion of hydrodynamic interactions between chain segments in either scalar[4] or tensor[5] approximation, (*b*) the inclusion of long-range "excluded volume" effects in some approximation[5-7] and, (*c*) the *ad hoc* introduction of an "internal viscosity."[8,9] The phenomenological success of the model, as applied to dynamic viscoelastic,[10,11,12] dielectric,[12,13,14] optical,[4,14,15] and nuclear magnetic relaxation[16] experiments, is noteworthy, except at high frequencies[17,18] or low temperatures, or under nonlinear (e.g., non-Newtonian viscoelastic) conditions. Further extensions[19] of the model may yet be offered.

The molecular basis of the Rouse model (and its more sophisticated relatives), however, has remained somewhat obscure. The more complete and realistic treatment of Kirkwood,[20] though itself rarely tractable save in a formal sense, could in principle offer a starting point for the derivation

* Supported by the National Science Foundation.

of the Rouse model, in rough analogy with the reduction of the Liouville equation to the Boltzmann equation in gas kinetic theory; but recorded attempts[21] along this line have not been wholly satisfactory. In particular, it is not clear whether a realistic molecular model would *demand* (as seems required by various experimental indications[17, 18, 22]) the introduction of some form of "internal viscosity" into the Rouse formalism, or whether and how the shape of the relaxation spectrum in the high-frequency region would deviate from the Rouse-Zimm[1, 4, 6] form.

As a contribution to the study of these problems, stochastic models are here developed for two cases: a freely-jointed chain in any number of dimensions, and a one-dimensional chain with nearest-neighbor correlations. Our work has been directly inspired by two different sources: the Monte Carlo studies by Verdier[23, 24] of the dynamics of chains confined to simple cubic lattices, and the analytical treatment by Glauber[25] of the dynamics of linear Ising models. No attempt is made in this work to introduce the effects of excluded volume or hydrodynamic interactions.

II. FREELY JOINTED CHAIN

Let a linear chain comprise $N + 1$ beads which are indexed serially along the chain from 0 to N. The centers of adjoining beads are separated by a constant bond distance b. The vector drawn from bead $i - 1$ to bead i is designated $b\boldsymbol{\sigma}_i$, where $\boldsymbol{\sigma}_i$ is a unit vector. Thus, the configuration of a chain is specified by the set of N vectors $\{\boldsymbol{\sigma}_1, \boldsymbol{\sigma}_2, \ldots, \boldsymbol{\sigma}_N\}$.

The chain configuration is made to vary in time by allowing the beads to move one at a time. When an interior bead i $(i = 1, 2, \ldots N - 1)$ moves (or "flips"), the vectors $\boldsymbol{\sigma}_i$ and $\boldsymbol{\sigma}_{i+1}$ before the flip are transformed to the vectors $\boldsymbol{\sigma}_i'$ and $\boldsymbol{\sigma}_{i+1}'$ after the flip according to the equations

$$\boldsymbol{\sigma}_i' = \boldsymbol{\sigma}_{i+1} \quad \text{and} \quad \boldsymbol{\sigma}_{i+1}' = \boldsymbol{\sigma}_i, \tag{1}$$

as illustrated in Figure 1. This process is essentially the same as that used by Verdier[24] for chains confined to a simple cubic lattice. For convenience, the terminal beads 0 and N are specified to move so that

$$\boldsymbol{\sigma}_1' = -\boldsymbol{\sigma}_1 \quad \text{and} \quad \boldsymbol{\sigma}_N' = -\boldsymbol{\sigma}_N \tag{2}$$

Let w_i denote the probability per unit time that the ith bead executes a flip. We consider a class of stochastic models for which this probability is given by

$$w_i = \alpha(1 - a\boldsymbol{\sigma}_i \cdot \boldsymbol{\sigma}_{i+1}) \tag{3}$$

with $|a| \leq 1$. By choice of a suitable value of a, the mobility of a bead can

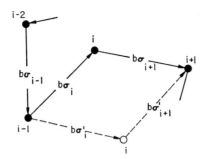

Fig. 1. The basic stochastic process. Position of bead i is indicated by a filled circle before it has flipped and an open circle after it has flipped. Solid lines represent the bond vectors $b\sigma_{i-1}$, $b\sigma_i$ and $b\sigma'_{i+1}$ before the ith bead flips; dashed lines indicate bond vectors $b\sigma_i'$ and $b\sigma_{i+1}'$ after the flip.

be weighted in favor of acute or obtuse bond angles as desired. The flip probability for an end bead is assigned the constant value

$$w_0 = w_N = \alpha\gamma \tag{4}$$

The probability that at time t the chain has the configuration $\{\sigma_1, \sigma_2, \ldots, \sigma_N\} \equiv \{\sigma^N\}$ is designated $p(\sigma_1, \sigma_2, \ldots, \sigma_N, t) \equiv p(\sigma^N, t)$. Let this probability be normalized, so that the ensemble average value of any chosen bond vector σ_i at time t is given by

$$\langle\sigma_i(t)\rangle = \int_{\text{all}\{\sigma^N\}} \cdots \int \sigma_i \, p(\sigma^N, t) \, d\{\sigma^N\} \equiv \mathbf{q}_i(t) \tag{5}$$

The time derivative of the probability function is expressed by the master equation[25]

$$dp(\sigma^N, t)/dt = -p(\sigma^N, t)\left[w_0 + \sum_{i=1}^{N-1} w_i(\sigma_i, \sigma_{i+1}) + w_N\right]$$

$$+ w_0\, p(-\sigma_1, \sigma_2, \ldots, \sigma_N, t)$$

$$+ \sum_{i=1}^{N-1} w_i(\sigma_{i+1}, \sigma_i) p(\sigma_1, \sigma_2, \ldots, \sigma_{i+1}, \sigma_i, \ldots, \sigma_N, t) \tag{6}$$

$$+ w_N\, p(\sigma_1, \sigma_2, \ldots, \sigma_{N-1}, -\sigma_N, t)$$

The first term on the right-hand side accounts for the destruction of the configuration $\{\sigma^N\}$ which results from the flipping of any one of the $N + 1$ beads; and the remaining terms describe the formation of $\{\sigma^N\}$ from other chain configurations.

The time derivative of $\mathbf{q}_i$ is obtained after both sides of Eq. (6) have been multiplied by $\boldsymbol{\sigma}_i$ and integrated over all possible configurations. For $2 \leq i \leq N - 1$,

$$d\mathbf{q}_i/dt = \int \cdots \int_{\text{all}\{\sigma^N\}} \{[-\boldsymbol{\sigma}_i w_{i-1}(\boldsymbol{\sigma}_{i-1}, \boldsymbol{\sigma}_i) - \boldsymbol{\sigma}_i w_i(\boldsymbol{\sigma}_i, \boldsymbol{\sigma}_{i+1})]p(\boldsymbol{\sigma}^N, t)$$

$$+ \boldsymbol{\sigma}_i w_{i-1}(\boldsymbol{\sigma}_i, \boldsymbol{\sigma}_{i-1})p(\boldsymbol{\sigma}_1, \boldsymbol{\sigma}_2, \ldots, \boldsymbol{\sigma}_i, \boldsymbol{\sigma}_{i-1}, \ldots, \boldsymbol{\sigma}_N, t) \qquad (7)$$

$$+ \boldsymbol{\sigma}_i w_i(\boldsymbol{\sigma}_{i+1}, \boldsymbol{\sigma}_i)p(\boldsymbol{\sigma}_1, \boldsymbol{\sigma}_2, \ldots, \boldsymbol{\sigma}_{i+1}, \boldsymbol{\sigma}_i, \ldots, \boldsymbol{\sigma}_N, t)\} \, d\{\boldsymbol{\sigma}^N\}$$

In writing Eq. (7), we have noted that the following integral vanishes when $j \neq i - 1, i$:

$$\int \cdots \int_{\text{all}\{\sigma^N\}} [-\boldsymbol{\sigma}_i w_j(\boldsymbol{\sigma}_j, \boldsymbol{\sigma}_{j+1})p(\boldsymbol{\sigma}^N, t)$$

$$+ \boldsymbol{\sigma}_i w_j(\boldsymbol{\sigma}_{j+1}, \boldsymbol{\sigma}_j)p(\boldsymbol{\sigma}_1, \boldsymbol{\sigma}_2, \ldots, \boldsymbol{\sigma}_{j+1}, \boldsymbol{\sigma}_j, \ldots, \boldsymbol{\sigma}_N, t)] \, d\{\boldsymbol{\sigma}^N\}$$

Substitution of w_j from Eq. (3) leads to

$$\alpha^{-1} \, d\mathbf{q}_i/dt = -2\mathbf{q}_i + \mathbf{q}_{i-1} + \mathbf{q}_{i+1} + a\langle(\boldsymbol{\sigma}_i - \boldsymbol{\sigma}_{i-1})(\boldsymbol{\sigma}_{i-1} \cdot \boldsymbol{\sigma}_i)\rangle$$

$$+ a\langle(\boldsymbol{\sigma}_i - \boldsymbol{\sigma}_{i+1})(\boldsymbol{\sigma}_i \cdot \boldsymbol{\sigma}_{i+1})\rangle; \qquad i = 2, \ldots, N - 1 \qquad (8)$$

Equations for the terminal bonds can be derived in a similar manner

$$\alpha^{-1} \, d\mathbf{q}_1/dt = -(1 + 2\gamma)\mathbf{q}_1 + \mathbf{q}_2 + a\langle(\boldsymbol{\sigma}_1 - \boldsymbol{\sigma}_2)(\boldsymbol{\sigma}_1 \cdot \boldsymbol{\sigma}_2)\rangle$$

$$\alpha^{-1} \, d\mathbf{q}_N/dt = -(1 + 2\gamma)\mathbf{q}_N + \mathbf{q}_{N-1} + a\langle(\boldsymbol{\sigma}_N - \boldsymbol{\sigma}_{N-1})(\boldsymbol{\sigma}_N \cdot \boldsymbol{\sigma}_{N-1})\rangle \qquad (9)$$

For $a \neq 0$, Eqs. (8) and (9) for the mean values $\mathbf{q}_i$ contain terms in higher-order correlations, a familiar and frequently frustrating type of event in statistical mechanics. However, as shown in the Appendix, when the system is not too far from equilibrium (i.e., small perturbations only) the terms $\langle\boldsymbol{\sigma}_i(\boldsymbol{\sigma}_i \cdot \boldsymbol{\sigma}_j)\rangle$ may be replaced by $\langle\boldsymbol{\sigma}_j\rangle d^{-1}$, when d is the dimensionality of the system.

Having made the above approximation we may rewrite Eqs. (8) and (9) in matrix form as

$$\alpha^{-1} \, d\mathbf{q}/dt = -(1 + ad^{-1})\mathbf{A}\mathbf{q} \qquad (10)$$

where $\mathbf{q}$ is a $N \times 1$ column matrix whose elements comprise the N vectors

$\mathbf{q}_i$. The elements of the $N \times N$ matrix $\mathbf{A}$ have the values

$$A_{11} = A_{NN} = 1 + 2\gamma(1 + ad^{-1})^{-1}$$

$$A_{ii} = 2; \qquad i \neq 1, N \qquad\qquad (11)$$

$$A_{ij} = -1; \qquad |i - j| = 1$$

$$= 0; \qquad |i - j| > 1$$

The matrix $\mathbf{A}$ is of course familiar in the model of Rouse or indeed in almost all studies of linear systems. (It has been suggested that the "A" stands for "Archimedes.") According to Rutherford,[26] eigenvalues of $\mathbf{A}$ for finite N can be simply expressed for the special cases $A_{11} = 1$ and $A_{11} = 2$. If λ_p represents the pth eigenvalue ($p = 1, 2, \ldots, N$) of $\mathbf{A}$, then

$$\lambda_p = 4 \sin^2 [(p - 1)\pi/2N] \qquad \text{for } A_{11} = 1; \qquad (12a)$$

or

$$\lambda_p = 4 \sin^2 [(p\pi/2(N + 1)] \qquad \text{for } A_{11} = 2 \qquad (12b)$$

For simplicity, we limit the remainder of this paper to the case $A_{11} = 2$. (Note that when $A_{11} = 1$, then $w_0 = w_N = 0$; i.e., the ends of the chain are stationary.) For long molecules, the end-effects become insignificant and the difference between the two sets of eigenvalues obviously becomes negligible.

There exists a symmetric $N \times N$ matrix $\mathbf{Q}$ such that

$$\mathbf{QA} = \mathbf{\Lambda Q}, \qquad\qquad (13)$$

with

$$\mathbf{Q}^{-1}\mathbf{Q} = \mathbf{QQ} = \mathbf{I} \qquad\qquad (14)$$

where $\mathbf{\Lambda}$ is a diagonal matrix whose i, i element is λ_i and where $\mathbf{I}$ is the $N \times N$ unit matrix. The i, j element of $\mathbf{Q}$, is[27]

$$Q_{ij} = \left(\frac{2}{N+1}\right)^{1/2} \sin \left[\frac{ij\pi}{(N+1)}\right] \qquad\qquad (15)$$

Premultiplication of Eq. (10) by $\mathbf{Q}$ and substitution of Eq. (13) gives

$$\alpha^{-1}d\xi/dt = -(1 + ad^{-1})\mathbf{\Lambda}\xi \qquad\qquad (16)$$

where

$$\xi = \mathbf{Qq} \qquad\qquad (17)$$

The elements of the column matrix ξ are the normal coordinates

$$\xi_p(t) = \sum_{j=1}^{N} Q_{pj}\mathbf{q}_j(t); \qquad p = 1, 2, \ldots, N \qquad (18)$$

The solutions of the differential equations represented by Eq. (16) are

$$\xi_p(t) = \xi_p(0) \exp\left(-t/\tau_p\right)$$

where

$$\tau_p^{-1} = \alpha(1 + ad^{-1})\lambda_p \tag{19}$$

Thus the relaxation spectrum resulting from the "average coordinates" equation[11] of our model has the same form as that of Rouse, of Kargin and Slonimiskii, or of Bueche. In order to relate the parameters of the model to those of the Rouse theory, the time scale factor α must somehow be connected to the frictional coefficient ζ for a single subchain of a Rouse molecule. To achieve this comparison, we may[23] study the translational diffusion coefficients as computed for the two models.

The translational diffusion coefficient D is $(2d)^{-1}$ times the mean square displacement per unit time of the center of mass of the molecule. When bead i flips from its position $\mathbf{R}_i$, as measured with respect to an arbitrary origin, to a new position $\mathbf{R}_i'$, the square of the resulting displacement of the center of mass of the chain is $(\mathbf{R}_i' - \mathbf{R}_i)^2/(N+1)^2$. Since bead i flips with a frequency w_i, we have

$$D = \frac{\sum_i \langle (\mathbf{R}_i' - \mathbf{R}_i)^2 w_i \rangle}{2(N+1)^2 d} \tag{20}$$

the average to be computed for an equilibrium ensemble. According to the rules governing the motions of the individual beads which were presented earlier (see Fig. 1),

$$\mathbf{R}_i' - \mathbf{R}_i = b(\boldsymbol{\sigma}_{i+1} - \boldsymbol{\sigma}_i) \tag{21}$$

Substitution in Eq. (20) from Eqs. (3) and (21) leads to

$$D = \alpha b^2(1 + ad^{-1})/(N+1)d \tag{22}$$

since $\langle \boldsymbol{\sigma}_i \cdot \boldsymbol{\sigma}_{i+1} \rangle_{eq} = 0$ and $\langle (\boldsymbol{\sigma}_i \cdot \boldsymbol{\sigma}_{i+1})^2 \rangle_{eq} = d^{-1}$. Then for long chains $(N+1 \simeq N)$ and for the slow modes of relaxation $(p \ll N; \lambda_p \simeq p^2\pi^2/N^2)$ our model leads to

$$\tau_p^{-1} = \lambda_p \, DN \, d/b^2 = p^2\pi^2 \, Dd/Nb^2 \tag{23}$$

Now in the Rouse model the diffusion constant is given by the Einstein relation

$$D = kT/n\zeta \tag{24}$$

for a chain made of n subchains, each with a friction constant ζ. It may be recalled that no unique choice of the size of the subchains is offered;

they must be long enough to be gaussian in respect to the statistics of their end-to-end displacements h but they must be short enough to justify somehow the concentration of all their dissipative effects into a single friction constant ζ. Then the long relaxation times of the model, with $\lambda_p' = 4 \sin^2(p\pi/2n)$, are given by[1]

$$\tau_p^{-1} = \lambda_p' kTd/\zeta\langle h^2\rangle = \lambda_p' Dnd/\langle h^2\rangle$$
$$= p^2\pi^2 Dd/n\langle h^2\rangle \qquad (p \ll n) \qquad (25)$$

A comparison of Eq. (25) with Eq. (23) shows that the two expressions for τ_p are identical, since $n\langle h^2\rangle = Nb^2$, the mean square end-to-end length of the entire chain. This is true for an arbitrary choice of the size of a Rouse subchain.

Furthermore, it may be seen that for *all* the normal modes of relaxation, including the most rapid, the freely jointed chain model and the Rouse model are identical if we set $n = N + 1$; that is, the relaxation time τ_p of the pth normal mode of a freely-jointed chain is the same as that of a Rouse marcromolecule composed of $N + 1$ subchains, each of mean square end-to-end length b^2. Moreover, for the special choice $a = 0$, Eq. (10) is true for arbitrarily large departures from equilibrium. We thus seem to have confirmed analytically the discovery of Verdier[24] that quite short chains executing a stochastic process described by Eqs. (1) and (3) on a simple cubic lattice display Rouse relaxation behavior. Of course, Verdier's Monte Carlo technique permits study of excluded volume effects, quite beyond the range of our present efforts.

However tempting it may be, further physical exploitation of the above results must be tempered by the realization that both the Rouse and the freely jointed chain models are in some sense artificial. We have nevertheless extended, somewhat beyond the ball-and-spring concept, the validity of the Rouse equations, and the prospect of developing the special case $a = 0$ for nonlinear phenomena is not without possible phenomenological interest.

III. ONE-DIMENSIONAL CHAIN WITH CORRELATIONS

We now undertake the formulation of a one-dimensional stochastic model describing a chain for which the directions of adjacent bonds are correlated. Since the chain is confined to one dimension, the bond vectors σ_i become scalars σ_i which can take on only values of ± 1 depending on whether bead i is to the right or left of bead $i - 1$. Therefore bead i can move only if bonds i and $i + 1$ point in opposite directions, i.e., $\sigma_i = -\sigma_{i+1}$. When bead i flips, the bond directions σ_i and σ_{i+1} change to $-\sigma_i$ and $-\sigma_{i+1}$, respectively. (We obviously can take no account of excluded volume.) We consider only very long chains and do not trouble to describe the motions of beads at or near the ends.

To develop a formulation of the flip rates, we consider the chain in dynamic equilibrium. If $p^{(2)}(\sigma_i, \sigma_{i+1})$ is the probability that the directions of bonds i and $i + 1$ are σ_i and σ_{i+1} and if $w_i(\sigma_i, \sigma_{i+1})$ is the probability per unit time that bead i flips, then at equilibrium the condition of microscopic reversibility requires

$$w_i(\sigma_i, \sigma_{i+1})p^{(2)}_{\text{eq}}(\sigma_i, \sigma_{i+1}) = w_i(-\sigma_i, -\sigma_{i+1})p^{(2)}_{\text{eq}}(-\sigma_i, -\sigma_{i+1}) \quad (26)$$

Correlations between adjacent bond vectors are introduced by assigning to the Hamiltonian H an energy E for each pair of consecutive bonds which point in opposite directions and an energy $-E$ for each pair of adjacent bonds which point in the same direction, i.e.,

$$H = -E \sum_{i=1}^{N-1} \sigma_i \sigma_{i+1} \quad (27)$$

Therefore at equilibrium

$$\frac{p^{(2)}_{\text{eq}}(\sigma_i, \sigma_{i+1})}{p^{(2)}_{\text{eq}}(-\sigma_i, -\sigma_{i+1})} = \frac{\exp\left[(\sigma_{i-1}\sigma_i + \sigma_{i+1}\sigma_{i+2})E/kT\right]}{\exp\left[-(\sigma_{i-1}\sigma_i + \sigma_{i+1}\sigma_{i+2})E/kT\right]} \quad (28)$$

It follows from Eqs. (26) and (28) that $w_i(\sigma_i, \sigma_{i+1})$ is proportional to $\exp[-(\sigma_{i-1}\sigma_i + \sigma_{i+1}\sigma_{i+2})E/kT]$. The transition probability is also again made proportional to $(1 - a\sigma_i\sigma_{i+1})$, where $|a| \leq 1$. Thus we take

$$w_i(\sigma_i, \sigma_{i+1}) = \alpha(1 - a\sigma_i\sigma_{i+1}) \exp\left[-(\sigma_{i-1}\sigma_i + \sigma_{i+1}\sigma_{i+2})E/kT\right] \quad (29)$$

The transition probability is a property independent of the restrictions of equilibrium, so that Eq. (29) is equally applicable to nonequilibrium situations.

Since even powers of any σ_i equal unity, series expansion of the exponential factors allows Eq. (29) to be rewritten as

$$w_i(\sigma_i, \sigma_{i+1}) = \alpha(1 - \beta^2)^{-1}(1 - a\sigma_i\sigma_{i+1})(1 - \beta\sigma_{i-1}\sigma_i)(1 - \beta\sigma_{i+1}\sigma_{i+2}) \quad (30)$$

where

$$\beta = \tanh(E/kT).$$

For this model the master equation corresponding to Eq. (6) for the multidimensional model discussed earlier is

$$\frac{dp(\sigma_1, \ldots, \sigma_N, t)}{dt} = -p(\sigma_1, \ldots, \sigma_N, t) \sum_{j=0}^{N} w_j(\sigma_j, \sigma_{j+1})$$

$$+ \sum_{j=0}^{N} w_j(\sigma_{j+1}, \sigma_j) p(\sigma_1, \ldots, \sigma_{j+1}, \sigma_j, \ldots, \sigma_N, t) \quad (31)$$

After multiplication by σ_i and summation over all 2^N possible configurations,

$$-[\alpha(1+a)]^{-1}(1-\beta^2)dq_i/dt = 2q_i - (1+\beta)(q_{i-1} + q_{i+1}) + \beta(q_{i-2} + q_{i+2})$$

$$- \beta\langle \sigma_{i-2}\sigma_{i-1}\sigma_i - 2\sigma_{i-1}\sigma_i\sigma_{i+1} + \sigma_i\sigma_{i+1}\sigma_{i+2} \rangle \quad (32)$$

$$+ \beta^2\langle \sigma_{i-2}\sigma_{i-1}\sigma_{i+1} - \sigma_{i-2}\sigma_i\sigma_{i+1} - \sigma_{i-1}\sigma_i\sigma_{i+2}$$

$$+ \sigma_{i-1}\sigma_{i+1}\sigma_{i+2} \rangle$$

where

$$q_i(t) \equiv \sum_{\text{all } \{\sigma^N\}} \sigma_i p(\sigma^N, t) \quad (33)$$

As with Eq. (8), the inclusion of triple-correlations in Eq. (32) makes them intractable unless some trick of linearization can be invoked. Fortunately, for small departures from equilibrium the triple-correlation terms can be evaluated from an equilibrium model in which each bond can have a slightly preferred orientation, i.e., $\langle \sigma_k \rangle_{\text{eq}} \neq 0$. For this model, which is treated in detail in the Appendix, we find

$$\langle \sigma_i\sigma_j\sigma_k \rangle = \beta^{k-j}q_i - \beta^{k-i}q_j + \beta^{j-i}q_k \quad (34)$$

where $i < j < k$, and then Eq. (32) reduces to

$$\alpha^{-1}dq_k/dt = -(1+a)(1-\beta)$$

$$\times [2(1+\beta+\beta^2)q_k - (1+\beta)^2(q_{k-1} + q_{k+1}) + \beta(q_{k-2} + q_{k+2})] \quad (35)$$

The N equations of which Eq. (35) is an example can be represented by the matrix equation

$$\alpha^{-1}d\mathbf{q}/dt = -(1+a)\mathbf{B}\mathbf{q} \quad (36)$$

where $\mathbf{q}$ is a column matrix whose ith element is q_i as defined by Eq. (33).

The elements of the $N \times N$ symmetric matrix $\mathbf{B}$ are given by

$$B_{ii} = 2(1 - \beta^3)$$
$$B_{ij} = -(1 - \beta)(1 + \beta)^2 ; \qquad |i - j| = 1$$
$$= +\beta(1 - \beta) \qquad ; \qquad |i - j| = 2 \qquad (37)$$
$$= 0 \qquad ; \qquad |i - j| > 2$$

Comparing $\mathbf{B}$ with the familiar Rouse $\mathbf{A}$ matrix of Eq. (11), we see that the bond correlations have produced second-neighbor effects in the chain dynamics.

The matrix product $\mathbf{Q} \cdot \mathbf{B} \cdot \mathbf{Q}$ is a diagonal matrix $\mathbf{M}$ whose p, p element is μ_p, and the matrix $\mathbf{Q}$ is the same as that described in Eqs. (14) and (15). According to Rutherford[28]

$$\mu_p = 4(1 - \beta)^3 \sin^2 u [1 + 4\beta(1 - \beta)^{-2} \sin^2 u]; \quad u \equiv p\pi/2(N + 1) \quad (38)$$

The column matrix ξ whose N elements are the normal coordinates $\xi_p(t)$, $(p = 1, 2, \ldots, N)$, is defined by an orthogonal transformation of the matrix $\mathbf{q}$

$$\xi = \mathbf{Q}\mathbf{q} \qquad (39)$$

From Eqs. (36) and (39) we have

$$\xi_p(t) = \xi_p(0) \exp(-t/\tau_p) \qquad (40)$$

where

$$\tau_p^{-1} = \alpha(1 + a)\mu_p \qquad (41)$$

As for the multidimensional freely jointed chain, it is possible to relate α to the parameters which describe a Rouse chain by evaluating the translational diffusion constant D for the center of mass. In the stochastic model, we determine the square of the displacement per unit time of a single bead averaged over an equilibrium ensemble. For bead j,

$$\langle (R_j' - R_j)^2 w_j \rangle_{eq} = \sum_{\{\sigma\}} w_j(\sigma_j, \sigma_{j+1})(R_j' - R_j)^2$$
$$\times p_{eq}^{(4)}(\sigma_{j-1}, \sigma_j, \sigma_{j+1}, \sigma_{j+2}) \qquad (42)$$
$$= 2\alpha b^2 (1 + a)(1 + \beta)(1 - \beta)^2$$

where $(R_j' - R_j)$ is the difference between the final and the initial positions of bead j. The reduced probability function $p_{eq}^{(4)}(\sigma_{j-1}, \sigma_j, \sigma_{j+1}, \sigma_{j+2})$ is determined from the Hamiltonian for the system [Eq. (27)];

$$p_{eq}^{(4)}(\sigma_{j-1}, \sigma_j, \sigma_{j+1}, \sigma_{j+2}) = (\tfrac{1}{2})[2 \cosh(E/kT)]^{-3}$$
$$\times \exp[(E/kT)(\sigma_{j-1}\sigma_j + \sigma_j\sigma_{j+1} + \sigma_{j+1}\sigma_{j+2})] \quad (43)$$

When bead j moves by an amount $(R_j' - R_j)$, the square of the displacement of the center of mass is $(R_j' - R_j)^2/(N + 1)^2$. The diffusion constant is then

$$D = \sum \langle (R_j' - R_j)^2 w_j \rangle_{eq}/2(N + 1)^2$$
$$= \alpha b^2(1 + a)(1 + \beta)(1 - \beta)^2/(N + 1). \qquad (44)$$

Entering Eq. (41) with Eq. (44) to eliminate $\alpha(1 + a)$ and taking $p \ll N$ in Eq. (38), we find for the slow relaxation processes

$$\tau_p^{-1} = p^2\pi^2 D/\langle r^2 \rangle \qquad (45)$$

where

$$\langle r^2 \rangle = Nb^2(1 + \beta)/(1 - \beta) \qquad (46)$$

From the Appendix, Eq. (68), we have

$$\langle \sigma_i \cdot \sigma_{i+1} \rangle_{eq} = \beta \qquad (47)$$

and hence, the quantity $\langle r^2 \rangle$ of Eq. (46) is just the equilibrium mean square end-to-end length of a chain of N links with nearest-neighbor correlations. Therefore Eq. (45) demonstrates that the present model also conforms to a Rouse chain, as far as the *slow* relaxations are concerned. For $\beta = 0$, the equations reduce in all ways to their counterparts in Section II for $d = 1$.

The longer relaxation times ($p \ll N$) when measured relative to τ_1 are independent of β; i.e., they are identical to the relaxation times in the Rouse model:

$$\tau_p = p^{-2}\tau_1; \qquad p \ll N \qquad (48)$$

For higher modes, the ratio τ_p/τ_1 becomes sensitive to the correlations. As β increases, τ_p/τ_1 decreases, as shown by Eq. (38). For illustration, this ratio is plotted semilogarithmically in Figure 2 as a function of p/N for a chain with 10^4 beads and for $\beta = 0, 0.2, 0.5$, and 0.9. It is seen that in this one-dimensional model the relaxation spectrum is broadened as the energetic preference for extended conformations ($\beta > 0$) is increased. In particular, the longest and shortest relaxation times are related by

$$N^2\tau_N/\tau_1 = N^2\mu_1/\mu_N = \pi^2(1 - \beta)^2/4(1 + \beta)^2 \qquad (49)$$

As recalled in the Appendix, the rate of tensile relaxation is principally controlled by the slowest modes, while that for dielectric relaxation is most commonly dominated by the fastest modes. Hence, Eq. (49) may not be without interest in certain physical applications.

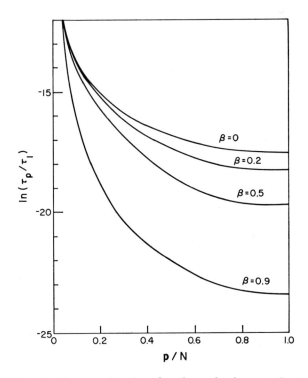

Fig. 2. Relaxation times as a function of mode number in a one-dimensional chain of 10,000 links, for different values of the bond correlation parameter β. Reduced relaxation time τ_p/τ_1 is plotted semilogarithmically against reduced mode number p/N.

The shear modulus $G(t)$ of a relaxing viscoleastic substance is a more sensitive probe of the overall distribution of relaxation times, as it does not depend so completely on either end of the relaxation spectrum. Although the present one-dimensional model cannot comprehend shear, it may be useful to study the analogous relaxation function. The relaxation function $H(\ln \tau)$, is defined[10] by

$$G(t) = \int_0^\infty H(\ln \tau) \exp\left(-t/\tau\right) d \ln \tau \qquad (50)$$

and for Rouse models is well approximated[29] by

$$H(\ln \tau) = -ckT \, dp/d \ln \tau \qquad (51)$$

where c is polymer concentration and p is treated as a continuous variable,

$1 \leqq p \leqq N$. For the present model, Eqs. (38), (41), and (51) for large N lead to

$$H(\ln \tau) = ckTN (\tan u)(1 + K \sin^2 u)/(1 + 2K \sin^2 u)\pi \qquad (52)$$

with

$$u = p\pi/2N$$
$$K = 4\beta(1 - \beta)^{-2}$$

In Figure 3, the slope $d \ln H/d \ln \tau$ as computed from Eq. (52) has been plotted as a function of $\ln (\tau/\tau_1)$ for several values of β, again for a chain of 10^4 bonds. It is seen that the effect of local equilibrium "stiffness" as measured by the value of β, tends to counteract the well-known effect of hydrodynamic interactions among chain elements. As is well known,[10] $d \ln H/d \ln \tau = -\frac{1}{2}$ for a free-draining (Rouse) chain in the long-time region, while a nondraining (Zimm) chain gives $d \ln H/d \ln \tau = -\frac{2}{3}$ in the same region. It is interesting that Frederick, Tschoegl, and Ferry[30]

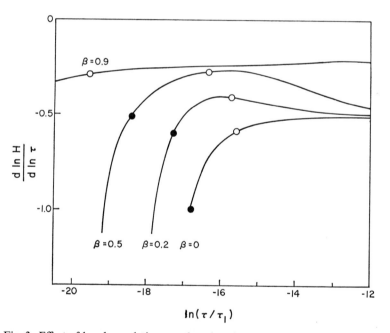

Fig. 3. Effect of bond correlations on the relaxation spectrum of a one-dimensional chain of 10,000 links. The slope $d \log H/d \log \tau$ of the relaxation function is plotted as a function of reduced relaxation time τ/τ_1. Open circles indicate points at which $p/N = 0.25$; filled circles, $p/N = 0.5$.

observed apparent deviations from Zimm theory in high-molecular weight dilute solutions of polystyrene, in a direction consistent with incomplete hydrodynamic shielding. Although the effect is considered[30] to be due principally to the difficulties of extrapolation to the region of nonoverlapping independent chains, it is conceivable that some real departures from the Zimm spectrum are involved, possibly along the lines suggested by the present one-dimensional model.

IV. DISCUSSION

Very recently Monnerie[31] has described Monte Carlo calculations for a quite realistic lattice model: nonintersecting chains confined to tetrahedral lattices performing local stochastic processes involving the simultaneous motion of three or four bonds. Without volume exclusion and with no correlations in the orientation probabilities of neighboring bonds, the model has also been treated analytically,[32] with application to the fluorescence depolarization experiment. It is easy to show that this model also leads to the long-time Rouse spectrum.

By now it may have dawned on the reader that the long-time Rouse spectrum (i.e., proportionality of τ_p to p^{-2}) is to be expected for any chain model in which the correlation lengths for both equilibrium conformations and frictional processes are small compared to the chain dimensions (and thus to the wavelength of the slow normal modes). A possible exception is that of the continuous wormlike chain of invariant contour length, which has been studied by Saito, Takahashi, and Yunoki.[33] In this latter case, the low-frequency spectrum makes τ_p proportional to p^{-4}, which resembles our special one-dimensional model in the limit $1 - \beta \ll 1$.

So far we have not been able to treat chains with bond correlations in more than one dimension. The introduction of more detailed or realistic models of local conformational processes, such as those of Reneker[34] or of Schatzki,[35] has, therefore, not been feasible. We may remark that the theory of dielectric relaxation by Work and Fujita,[36] which applies Glauber's methods[25] to *delayed* (dynamic) correlations between chain dipoles, is also in essence a one-dimensional affair.

It may be surprising that the effect of the nearest-neighbor bond correlations on the one-dimensional chain depends on the *sign* of β; i.e., that the spectrum broadens when extended conformations are favored and narrows when compact conformations are favored. No simple qualitative explanation of this result has occurred to us. The usual "internal viscosity" always produces a narrowing of the spectrum. This effect is easily introduced into a one-dimensional Rouse model; an internal viscous force is appended, proportional to the rate of extension of each subchain, and results[13] in the addition of a constant to each of the Rouse relaxation times. The treatment of internal viscosity in three dimensions is of course far more difficult, but present attempts[9,18] also appear to narrow the spectrum. It seems clear on physical grounds that in three dimensions chains for which local conformational processes (such as the bead "flips" of the present work) are strongly retarded can relax by rotational diffusion, as of a more or less rigid particle. Such a possibility is of course completely beyond the reach of any one-dimensional models; and it is also not encompassed by the Rouse-Zimm formalism. In the Rouse model, for example, there is only a single dissipative mechanism, as symbolized by the subchain frictional coefficient; furthermore, the Gaussian character of the subchains permits the separation of the unperturbed three-dimensional problem into three one-dimensional problems.

In view of the above considerations, it should be evident that our present results do not offer new formulas for practical application, but it is hoped that they will contribute to an understanding of chain dynamics.

Appendix

(a) In Section II, correlations $\langle \sigma_i(\sigma_i \cdot \sigma_j)\rangle$ were set equal to $d^{-1}\langle \sigma_j\rangle$ $= d^{-1}\mathbf{q}_j$ in d-dimensional space for freely jointed chains not too far from equilibrium. To demonstrate this equality, we take a three-dimensional example, with unit cartesian vectors $\mathbf{e}_x$, $\mathbf{e}_y$, and $\mathbf{e}_z$. Then

$$\langle \sigma_i(\sigma_i \cdot \sigma_j)\rangle = \langle x_i^2 x_j + x_i y_i y_j + x_i z_i z_j\rangle \mathbf{e}_x$$
$$+ \langle x_i y_i x_j + y_i^2 y_j + y_i z_i z_j\rangle \mathbf{e}_y + \langle x_i z_i x_j + y_i z_i y_j + z_i^2 z_j\rangle \mathbf{e}_z \qquad (53)$$

Because the bond directions are not correlated, we have $\langle x_i^2 x_j\rangle = \langle x_i^2\rangle$ $\times \langle x_j\rangle$, $\langle x_i y_i y_j\rangle = \langle x_i y_i\rangle\langle y_j\rangle$, etc.; and at zero-field equilibrium $\langle x_i^2\rangle = \frac{1}{3}$ while cross correlations like $\langle x_i y_i\rangle$ vanish. Hence, for small departures from equilibrium we get just

$$\langle \sigma_i(\sigma_i \cdot \sigma_j)\rangle = (\tfrac{1}{3})\langle \sigma_j\rangle \qquad (54)$$

which is easily generalized to other dimensionalities.

(b) Multiple-spin correlations are required for a one-dimensional, N-spin Ising chain at equilibrium in a small inhomogeneous field. An obvious generalization of the treatment of Marsh[37] gives the desired results. Let the spins have unit magnitude, and let the field at the locus of spin i be $h_i kT$. Then the Hamiltonian of the spin system is

$$H = -E \sum_i \sigma_i \sigma_{i+1} - kT \sum_i h_i \sigma_i \qquad (55)$$

and the partition function can be written as

$$Z = \text{tr}\left[V_1 \prod_{i=2}^{N}(UV_i)X\right] \tag{56}$$

where the matrices are defined as

$$V_i = \begin{bmatrix} \exp(h_i) & 0 \\ 0 & \exp(-h_i) \end{bmatrix} \tag{57}$$

$$U = \begin{bmatrix} \exp(E/kT) & \exp(-E/kT) \\ \exp(-E/kT) & \exp(E/kT) \end{bmatrix} \tag{58}$$

and

$$X = \begin{pmatrix} 1 & 1 \\ 1 & 1 \end{pmatrix} \tag{59}$$

Equilibrium averages for products of selected sets of spin variables $\sigma_j, \sigma_k, \ldots, \sigma_s$ are given by

$$\langle\sigma_j\sigma_k\cdots\sigma_s\rangle = Z^{-1}\,\text{tr}\left[V_1\left(\prod_{i=2}^{j}UV_i\right)F\left(\prod_{i=j+1}^{k}UV_i\right)F\cdots\right.$$
$$\left.\times\cdots\left(\prod_{i=s+1}^{N}UV_i\right)X\right] \tag{60}$$

where

$$F = \begin{pmatrix} 1 & 0 \\ 0 & -1 \end{pmatrix} \tag{61}$$

The matrix U is diagonalized under the transformation

$$S^{-1}US = L; \qquad S\,S^{-1} = I \tag{62}$$

where

$$S = S^{-1} = 2^{-1/2}\begin{pmatrix} 1 & 1 \\ 1 & -1 \end{pmatrix} \tag{63}$$

and

$$L = \begin{bmatrix} 2\cosh(E/kT) & 0 \\ 0 & 2\sinh(E/kT) \end{bmatrix} \tag{64}$$

If we take the field to be zero except at selected spins numbered $j, k, \ldots, r, s$, the matrix V_i reduces to the idemfactor I for all other spins, and the partition function collapses to

$$Z = \text{tr}\,[U^{j-1}V_j U^{k-j}V_k\cdots U^{s-r}V_s U^{N-s}X] \tag{65}$$

which after using Eq. (62) becomes

$$Z = \text{tr}\,[SL^{j-1}S^{-1}V_j SL^{k-j}S^{-1}V_k\cdots SL^{s-r}S^{-1}V_s SL^{N-s}S^{-1}X] \tag{66}$$

Similar operations are performed on Eq. (60). Then for small fields, $|h_i| \ll 1$, with $l \leq m \leq n \leq p$ the averages and correlations are found to be

$$\langle \sigma_l \rangle = \sum_{\alpha=j}^{s} \beta^{|l-\alpha|} h_\alpha \; ; \; \beta \equiv \tanh (E/kT) \tag{67}$$

$$\langle \sigma_l \sigma_m \rangle = \beta^{m-l} \tag{68}$$

$$\langle \sigma_l \sigma_m \sigma_n \rangle = \sum_{\alpha=j}^{m-1} \beta^{n-m+|l-\alpha|} h_\alpha + \sum_{\alpha=m}^{s} \beta^{m-l+|n-\alpha|} h_\alpha \tag{69}$$

$$\langle \sigma_l \sigma_m \sigma_n \sigma_p \rangle = \beta^{m-l+p-n}, \text{ etc.} \tag{70}$$

with neglect of terms of $O(h_i^2)$. Using Eq. (67) in Eq. (69), the triple correlations can be expressed as

$$\langle \sigma_l \sigma_m \sigma_n \rangle = \beta^{n-m} \langle \sigma_l \rangle - \beta^{n-l} \langle \sigma_m \rangle + \beta^{m-l} \langle \sigma_n \rangle \tag{71}$$

Since a small arbitrary inhomogeneous field must affect the correlations like small fluctuations from zero-field equilibrium, we may use Eq. (71) in Section III to linearize Eq. (32).

(c) Tensile relaxation is easily calculated for the one-dimensional model of Section III. The average value of the distance separating the two ends of the chain, $\langle L(t) \rangle$, is the sum of the average values of the N-bond vectors.

$$\langle L(t) \rangle = b \sum_{i=1}^{N} q_i(t) \tag{72}$$

Since

$$q = Q\xi$$

therefore

$$\langle L(t) \rangle = \left(\frac{2}{N+1} \right)^{1/2} b \sum_{i=1}^{N} \sum_{p=1}^{N} \sin \left(\frac{ip\pi}{N+1} \right) \xi_p(0) \exp (-t/\tau_p) \tag{73}$$

Summing[38] over i, we find

$$\langle L(t) \rangle = \left(\frac{2}{N+1} \right)^{1/2} b \sum_{(p \text{ odd})}^{N} \cot \left[\frac{p\pi}{2(N+1)} \right] \xi_p(0) \exp (-t/\tau_p) \tag{74}$$

where the remaining summation is over only odd values of the index p. If, at $t=0$, the mean value of the end-to-end distance is

$$\langle L(0) \rangle = b \sum_i q_i(0) = Nbq(0) \tag{75}$$

then

$$\xi_p(0) = \left(\frac{2}{N+1}\right)^{1/2} \frac{\langle L(0)\rangle}{Nb} \sum_{i=1}^{N} \sin\left(\frac{ip\pi}{N+1}\right) \tag{76}$$

$$\langle L(t)\rangle = \langle L(0)\rangle \frac{2}{N(N+1)} \sum_{(p\,\text{odd})}^{N} \cot^2\left[\frac{p\pi}{2(N+1)}\right] \exp\left(-t/\tau_p\right) \tag{77}$$

For large N, the well-known[4] result is

$$\langle L(t)\rangle/\langle L(0)\rangle = 8\pi^{-2} \sum_{(p\,\text{odd})} p^{-2} \exp\left(-t/\tau_p\right) \tag{78}$$

The series converges rapidly, with the first mode making the major contribution to $\langle L(t)\rangle$. Tensile relaxation is active in only the odd modes since the motion of only these modes affects the distance between the two ends.

(d) Another interesting example is the dielectric relaxation of a chain on which adjacent bonds carry dipoles of magnitude m_0 and of alternating sign. The ensemble-average dipole moment in the absence of an electrical field is

$$\langle M(t)\rangle = m_0 \sum_{i=1}^{N} (-1)^i q_i(t) \tag{79}$$

Replacing $q_i(t)$ by the appropriate linear combination of normal coordinates and summing[38] over the index i, we obtain

$$\langle M(t)\rangle = -\left(\frac{2}{N+1}\right)^{1/2} m_0 \sum_{(p+N\,\text{even})}^{N} \frac{\sin\dfrac{p\pi}{N+1}}{1 + \cos\dfrac{p\pi}{N+1}} \xi_p(0) \exp\left(-t/\tau_p\right) \tag{80}$$

The summation is over all odd values of p from 1 to N if N is odd, or over even values of p if N is even. If an ensemble of chains is initially at equilibrium in the presence of an electric field which is shut off at $t = 0$, then

$$q_i(0) = (-1)^i \langle M(0)\rangle/Nm_0 \tag{81}$$

and

$$\xi_p(0) = -\left(\frac{2}{N+1}\right)^{1/2} \frac{\langle M(0)\rangle}{Nm_0} \frac{\sin\dfrac{p\pi}{N+1}}{1 + \cos\dfrac{p\pi}{N+1}} \tag{82}$$

Substitution for $\xi_p(0)$ in Eq. (80) leads to

$$\langle M(t)\rangle = \frac{2\langle M(0)\rangle}{N(N+1)} \sum_{(N+p\ \mathrm{even})} \left[\frac{\sin\dfrac{p\pi}{N+1}}{1+\cos\dfrac{p\pi}{N+1}} \right]^2 \exp\left(-t/\tau_p\right) \quad (83)$$

which is well approximated by

$$\langle M(t)\rangle/\langle M(0)\rangle = 8\pi^{-2} \sum_{(q\ \mathrm{odd})} q^{-2} \exp\left(-t/\tau_q\right)$$

$$q \equiv N+1-p \quad (84)$$

As has been pointed out before,[13, 14, 39] the important contributions to the dielectric relaxation are therefore from the fastest modes.

Acknowledgments

We thank the National Science Foundation for support of this work, and we thank William Gobush and Dewey K. Carpenter for valuable discussions.

References

1. P. E. Rouse, Jr., *J. Chem. Phys.*, **21**, 1272 (1953).
2. V. A. Kargin and G. L. Slonimskii, *Dokl. Akad. Nauk SSSR*, **62**, 239 (1948).
3. F. Bueche, *J. Chem. Phys.*, **22**, 603 (1954).
4. B. H. Zimm, *J. Chem. Phys.*, **24**, 269 (1956).
5. C. W. Pyun and M. Fixman, *J. Chem. Phys.*, **42**, 3838 (1965).
6. N. W. Tschoegl, *J. Chem. Phys.*, **39**, 149 (1963).
7. M. Fixman, *J. Chem. Phys.*, **45**, 785 (1966).
8. W. Kuhn and H. Kuhn, *Helv. Chim. Acta.*, **28**, 1533 (1945).
9. R. Cerf, (a) *J. Polymer Sci.*, **23**, 125 (1957); (b) *J. Phys. Radium*, **19**, 122 (1958).
10. J. D. Ferry, *Viscoelastic Properties of Polymers*, Wiley, New York, 1961.
11. A. Miyake, *Progr. Theoret. Phys. (Kyoto) Suppl.*, **10**, 56 (1959).
12. N. G. McCrum, B. E. Read, and G. Williams, *Anelastic and Dielectric Effects in Polymeric Solids*, Wiley, New York, 1967.
13. L. K. H. Van Beek and J. J. Hermans, *J. Polymer Sci.*, **23**, 211 (1957).
14. W. H. Stockmayer and M. E. Baur, *J. Am. Chem. Soc.*, **86**, 3485 (1964).
15. D. S. Thompson and S. J. Gill, *J. Chem. Phys.*, **47**, 5008 (1967).
16. R. Ullman, *J. Chem. Phys.*, **43**, 3161 (1965); ibid., **44**, 1558 (1966).
17. J. D. Ferry, L. A. Holmes, J. Lamb, and A. J. Matheson, *J. Phys. Chem.*, **70**, 1685 (1966).
18. A. Peterlin and C. Reinhold, *Trans. Soc. Rheol.*, **11**, 15 (1967).
19. A. V. Tobolsky and D. B. DuPré, *J. Polymer Sci.*, Part A-2, **6**, 1177 (1968).
20. (a) J. G. Kirkwood, *Rec. Trav. Chim.*, **68**, 649 (1949); (b) J. Riseman and J. G. Kirkwood in *Rheology*, Vol. I, F. Eirich, Ed., Academic, New York, 1956, pp. 495–523.

21. (a) N. Saito, *Bull. Kobayashi Inst. Phys. Res.*, **8**, 89 (1958); (b) K. Okano, *Busseiron Kenkyu* (II), **4**, 688 (1958).
22. W. H. Stockmayer, *Pure Appl. Chem.*, **15**, 539 (1967).
23. P. H. Verdier and W. H. Stockmayer, *J. Chem. Phys.*, **36**, 227 (1962).
24. P. H. Verdier, *J. Chem. Phys.*, **45**, 2118, 2122 (1966).
25. R. J. Glauber, *J. Math. Phys.*, **4**, 294 (1963).
26. D. E. Rutherford, *Proc. Roy. Soc.* (Edinburgh) *A* **62**, 229 (1947).
27. Recall that the σ_i are *bond* vectors and not the loci of beads with respect to a common origin. Thus we must choose sines rather than cosines as eigenfunctions for chains with free ends. Also, since Eq. (10) is concerned only with the averages of the bond vectors, there are only N normal modes, the translational diffusion mode being automatically excluded.
28. D. E. Rutherford, *Proc. Roy. Soc.* (Edinburgh) *A* **63**, 232 (1952).
29. J. D. Ferry, in *Die Physik der Hochpolymeren*, Vol. *4*, H. A. Stuart, Ed., Springer, Berlin, 1956, p. 96.
30. J. E. Frederick, N. W. Tschoegl, and J. D. Ferry, *J. Phys. Chem.*, **68**, 1974 (1964).
31. L. Monnerie, *IUPAC Symposium on Macromolecular Chemistry, Toronto, 1968*.
32. E. Dubois-Violette, P. G. deGennes and L. Monnerie, to appear in *J. chim. phys.*
33. N. Saito, K. Takahashi and Y. Yunoki, *J. Phys. Soc., Japan*, **22**, 219 (1967).
34. D. H. Reneker, *Am. Chem. Soc.*, Div. Polymer Chem., Preprints 3 (2), 60 (1962).
35. T. F. Schatzki, *Am. Chem. Soc.*, Div. Polymer Chem., Preprints 6 (2), 646 (1965).
36. R. N. Work and S. Fujita, *J. Chem. Phys.*, **45**, 3779 (1966).
37. J. S. Marsh, *Phys. Rev.*, **145**, 251 (1966).
38. L. B. W. Jolley, *Summation of Series*, 2nd ed., Dover Press, New York, 1961, Series Nos. 417 and 455.
39. F. Bueche, *J. Polymer Sci.*, **54**, 597 (1961).

LANGEVIN THEORY OF POLYMER DYNAMICS IN DILUTE SOLUTION*

ROBERT ZWANZIG

Institute for Fluid Dynamics and Applied Mathematics and Institute for Molecular Physics, University of Maryland, College Park, Maryland

CONTENTS

I. INTRODUCTION

As is well known, dynamic properties of polymer molecules in dilute solution are usually treated theoretically by Brownian motion methods. In particular, the standard approach is to use a Fokker-Planck (or Smoluchowski) equation for diffusion of the distribution function of the polymer molecule in its configuration space.

In recent articles[1,2] on the dynamics of stiff polymer chains, the Langevin version of Brownian motion theory was used instead of the more common Fokker-Planck approach. These investigations were made, however, only in the free-draining limit.

In a purely formal sense, Langevin and Fokker-Planck approaches to a problem are equivalent; but, as is often the case, one approach or the other may be preferable for practical reasons. In the Fokker-Planck method, one has to solve a partial differential equation in many variables. In the Langevin method, one has to solve coupled equations of motion for the same variables, under the influence of a random force. It is likely that this second approach will be most useful for performing computer experiments to simulate the actual motion of individual polymer molecules.

* This research was supported in part by National Science Foundation Grant NSF GP-7652.

The Fokker-Planck method was set forth in a series of papers by Kirkwood and collaborators.[3] After taking into account a certain error in the original formulation of this method,[4] the theory may be regarded as complete, in the sense that it provides a well-defined method of calculation. (There are reasons, however, for questioning the correctness of the model, i.e., point sources of friction in a hydrodynamic continuum, for which the theory was constructed. These reasons will be discussed in another place.)

Because of the formal equivalence of Fokker-Planck and Langevin methods, there is no intrinsic difficulty in translating Kirkwood's theory into Langevin terms. As far as I am aware, this has not yet been done. The main purpose of this article is to perform the translation.

In developing the Langevin theory of polymer dynamics in solution, an interesting complication arises from the phenomenon of hydrodynamic interaction. The fluctuating force on any individual segment of the polymer chain turns out to be correlated with the fluctuating force on other distant segments of the same chain. This correlation, which is not present in the free draining limit, may lead to practical difficulties in performing computer simulation experiments. Because of this, it seems worthwhile to discuss the effects of hydrodynamic interaction in some detail.

The plan of the article is as follows. First, we discuss the phenomenon of hydrodynamic interaction in general terms, and at the same time, we present some convenient notation. Then, we give the usual argument leading to the Fokker-Planck equation. After that we derive the Langevin equation that is formally equivalent to the Fokker-Planck equation, together with a statistical description of the fluctuating force.

II. HYDRODYNAMIC INTERACTION

We consider a single polymer molecule in solution. The solvent is treated as a viscous incompressible fluid. The polymer chain contains N monomer units or "beads," and each individual bead is regarded as a point source of friction in the solvent. This is the standard model.

In Kirkwood's original formulation of the Fokker-Planck theory, he took into account the possibility that various constraints might apply, e.g., constant bond length between adjacent beads. This led to the introduction of a "chain space" of lower dimensionality than the full $3N$-dimensional configuration space of the entire chain; and it led to a complicated machinery of Riemannian geometry, with covariant and contravariant tensors, etc.

In the present investigation we do not follow his procedure. Instead, we suppose that any constraints that might be imposed are maintained by appropriate intramolecular forces. This means that we can work in the Euclidean $3N$-dimensional space of the entire chain.

If desired, our results can be converted to chain space variables by the same methods that Kirkwood used. We shall not do this here.

Let $\mathbf{R}_j$ and $\dot{\mathbf{R}}_j$ be the position and velocity of the jth bead. This bead experiences a frictional force $\mathbf{F}_j$ due to its motion relative to the surrounding hydrodynamic continuum,

$$\mathbf{F}_j = -\rho(\dot{\mathbf{R}}_j - \mathbf{V}_j) \tag{1}$$

where ρ is a friction coefficient and $\mathbf{V}_j$ is the velocity that the fluid medium would have at the position $\mathbf{R}_j$ if that particular bead were not present.

The physical basis for the frictional force is not specified here; but it could arise, e.g., from Stokes' law friction on the bead.

Because $\mathbf{F}_j$ is the frictional force exerted on the bead by the medium, then $-\mathbf{F}_j$ is the force that the bead exerts on the medium. Now we recall that when a force (regarded as precisely localized at the position $\mathbf{R}_j$) is exerted on a viscous incompressible fluid, in steady motion at low Reynolds number, it produces an extra velocity field $\Delta\mathbf{V}(\mathbf{R})$ everywhere in the medium. This extra velocity field

$$\Delta\mathbf{V}(\mathbf{R}) = \mathbf{T}(\mathbf{R} - \mathbf{R}_j)\cdot(-\mathbf{F}_j) \tag{2}$$

is determined by the Oseen interaction tensor

$$\mathbf{T}(\mathbf{R}) = \frac{1}{8\pi\eta R}(\mathbf{1} + \mathbf{R}\mathbf{R}/R^2) \tag{3}$$

The viscosity of the medium is η, and $\mathbf{1}$ is the unit tensor. (The Oseen tensor is the Green's function for the Navier-Stokes equation under the conditions that the fluid is incompressible, convective effects can be neglected, and inertial effects coming from the time derivative can be neglected.)

Suppose that the velocity field in the absence of all beads is $\mathbf{V}^0(\mathbf{R})$. We will call this the unperturbed velocity field. Then the total velocity field at $\mathbf{R}_j$, due to the forces exerted on the fluid by all beads except the jth, is given by

$$\mathbf{V}_j = \mathbf{V}_j^0 - \sum_{k \neq j} \mathbf{T}(\mathbf{R}_j - \mathbf{R}_k)\cdot\mathbf{F}_k \tag{4}$$

To simplify equations we introduce the matrix

$$\mathbf{T}_{jk} = \mathbf{T}(\mathbf{R}_j - \mathbf{R}_k) \tag{5}$$

and impose the extra condition that it has no diagonal part, $T_{jj} = 0$. Then we can drop the restriction $j \neq k$ throughout all sums.

On combining Eqs. (1) and (4), we get a set of coupled equations for the velocity fields V_j,

$$V_j = V_j^{\,0} - \rho \sum_k T_{jk} \cdot (V_k - \dot{R}_k) \tag{6}$$

Our main interest is in the relative velocity of the bead and the fluid, so we subtract $\dot{R}_j$ from both sides of Eq. (6),

$$V_j - \dot{R}_j = V_j^{\,0} - \dot{R}_j - \rho \sum_k T_{jk} \cdot (V_k - \dot{R}_k) \tag{7}$$

and obtain coupled equations for the relative velocities.

The equations just derived are inhomogeneous simultaneous linear equations in $3N$ unknowns, the three cartesian components of each relative velocity $V_j - \dot{R}_j$. As such, they have the solution

$$V_j - \dot{R}_j = \frac{1}{\rho} \sum_k \zeta_{jk} \cdot (V_k^{\,0} - \dot{R}_k) \tag{8}$$

where the matrix ζ_{jk} is the inverse of the matrix $(1/\rho)\mathbf{1}\,\delta_{jk} + T_{jk}$. (The inverse exists provided that ρ is small enough; in another place we discuss the question whether this requirement is satisfied in usual applications.)

Equation (1) determines the frictional force on the jth bead. From Eq. (8), we obtain the explicit formula

$$F_j = -\sum_k \zeta_{jk} \cdot (\dot{R}_k - V_k^{\,0}) \tag{9}$$

Note that the *actual* velocity field $V(R)$ has been eliminated, and that only the unperturbed velocity field $V^0(R)$ remains.

Suppose for example that there is no unperturbed velocity field, $V^0(R) = 0$. Then the frictional force on the jth bead is determined by not only its own velocity $\dot{R}_j$, but also by the velocities $\dot{R}_k$ of all the other beads. The only exception can be when the friction tensor ζ_{jk} is strictly diagonal; and this may be expected to be true only in the complete absence of hydrodynamic interaction.

III. FOKKER-PLANCK EQUATION

Now we present the standard derivation of the Fokker-Planck equation for polymers in solution. (Terminology can often be confusing: in the present instance, the equation of interest is also called the Smoluchowski equation, and may be regarded as a limiting case of a more general Fokker-Planck equation, or a Kramers equation.)

Along with the frictional force on a bead, given by Eq. (9), there will be in general other forces F_j', derived in part from the potential energy U that holds the polymer chain together, and in part from external sources, e.g., electric or centrifugal fields. The total force on the jth bead is thus $F_j + F_j'$.

In the standard (or Smoluchowski) theory, it is assumed that inertial effects due to the mass of a bead have all relaxed away, and that a stationary flow in configuration space occurs. This flow is maintained by balancing the above total force by a "thermodynamic" force,

$$\mathbf{F}_j + \mathbf{F}_j' = k_B T \nabla_{R_j} \log P \qquad (10)$$

so that the net acceleration is zero. The thermodynamic force is of the type familiar in the theory of irreversible processes. If we were dealing with ordinary diffusion, then the driving force for a diffusion current would be represented by the gradient in chemical potential; this is analogous to what has just been done. The quantity P is the distribution function or density in configuration space, k_B is Boltzmann's constant, and T is absolute temperature.

If inertial effects were of interest, then we would introduce a distribution function in the *phase* space of the polymer chain, and we would be led to a Fokker-Planck equation of the Kramers type.

More explicitly, Eq. (10) is

$$-\sum_k \zeta_{jk} \cdot (\dot{\mathbf{R}}_k - \mathbf{V}_k^0) + \mathbf{F}_j' = k_B T \nabla_{\mathbf{R}_j} \log P \qquad (11)$$

This can be solved for the bead velocities,

$$\dot{\mathbf{R}}_j = \mathbf{V}_j^0 + \sum_k (\zeta^{-1})_{jk} \cdot [\mathbf{F}_k' - k_B T \nabla_{\mathbf{R}_k} \log P] \qquad (12)$$

The inverse $\{\zeta^{-1}\}_{jk}$ of the matrix ζ_{jk} is obviously the same as $(1/\rho)\mathbf{1}\,\delta_{jk} + \mathbf{T}_{jk}$. If, however, we use Kirkwood's chain space variables for a system with constraints, then the two quantities would have to be distinguished. The constraints would replace part of the internal force $\mathbf{F}'$, and the velocities associated with these constraints would vanish. This was a serious source of confusion in earlier versions of Kirkwood's theory; see Ref. 4 for further information on this point.

The current density along the jth coordinate axis in configuration space is

$$\mathbf{J}_j = \dot{\mathbf{R}}_j P \qquad (13)$$

According to the law of conservation of beads, the currents obey

$$\frac{\partial P}{\partial t} + \sum_j \nabla_{\mathbf{R}_j} \cdot \mathbf{J}_j = 0 \tag{14}$$

or

$$\frac{\partial P}{\partial t} = \sum_j \sum_k \nabla_{\mathbf{R}_j} \cdot \{ k_B T (\zeta^{-1})_{jk} \cdot \nabla_{\mathbf{R}_k} P - (\zeta^{-1})_{jk} \cdot \mathbf{F}_k' P - \delta_{jk} \mathbf{V}_k^0 P \} \tag{15}$$

This is the Fokker-Planck equation. Note that the quantity $k_B T \zeta^{-1}$ plays the role of a generalized diffusion coefficient.

IV. LANGEVIN EQUATION

The Langevin equation associated with the preceding Fokker-Planck equation can be found by standard methods. A fine review has been given by Lax[5]; we use his procedure and notation.

First we rewrite Eq. (15) in a canonical form,

$$\frac{\partial P}{\partial t} = -\sum_j \nabla_{\mathbf{R}_j} \cdot (\mathbf{A}_j P) + \sum_j \sum_k \nabla_{\mathbf{R}_j} \cdot \mathbf{D}_{jk} \cdot \nabla_{\mathbf{R}_k} P \tag{16}$$

where the diffusion tensor $\mathbf{D}_{jk}$ is

$$\mathbf{D}_{jk} = k_B T (\zeta^{-1})_{jk} = k_B T \left(\frac{1}{\rho} \delta_{jk} \mathbf{1} + \mathbf{T}_{jk} \right) \tag{17}$$

and the streaming term $\mathbf{A}_j$ is

$$\mathbf{A}_j = \frac{1}{k_B T} \sum_k (\mathbf{D}_{jk} \cdot \mathbf{F}_k' + \delta_{jk} \mathbf{V}_k^0) \tag{18}$$

According to Lax, the corresponding Langevin equations are

$$\frac{d\mathbf{R}_j}{d} = \mathbf{B}_j + \sum_m \sigma_{jm} f_m(t) \tag{19}$$

where $f_m(t)$ is a gaussian random variable with the first and second moments

$$\langle f_m(t) \rangle = 0 \tag{20}$$

and

$$\langle f_m(t_1) f_n(t_2) \rangle = 2 \, \delta_{mn} \, \delta(t_1 - t_2) \tag{21}$$

Because all higher moments of $f_m(t)$ are determined by these two, when $f_m(t)$ is a gaussian random variable, we do not have to specify them separately. Lax gives the general formula.

The diffusion tensor is related to the coefficients σ_{jm} by

$$\mathbf{D}_{jk} = \sum_m \sigma_{jm} \sigma_{km} \tag{22}$$

and the quantity $\mathbf{B}_j$ is related to $\mathbf{A}_j$ and to the coefficients σ_{jm} by

$$\mathbf{B}_j = \mathbf{A}_j - \sum_m \sum_k \sigma_{km} \cdot \nabla_{\mathbf{R}_k} \sigma_{jm} \tag{23}$$

Note that the quantities with which we are dealing are vectors and tensors in 3-space, so some care has to be taken with the ordering of subscripts.

The diffusion tensor $\mathbf{D}_{jk}$ is real and symmetric, and for small enough ρ it is positive definite. Therefore it possesses a real symmetric square root. From Eq. (22), we see that this square root is in fact the tensor σ_{jk}.

Equations (19)–(23) provide a complete translation of Kirkwood's Fokker-Planck theory into Langevin terms, when the entire $3N$-dimensional configuration space is used.

In Refs. 1 and 2, the Langevin equations included inertial terms. The procedure that we followed here, going from a Fokker-Planck (or Smoluchowski) equation in configuration space to Langevin equations in configuration space, can easily be generalized to make the translation from a Fokker-Planck (or Kramers) equation in phase space to the corresponding Langevin equations. (One may question, however, whether this more detailed theory is consistent with use of the usual Oseen tensor. Perhaps it will be necessary to introduce the more general Oseen tensor that includes inertial effects in the solvent.)

References

1. R. A. Harris and J. E. Hearst, *J. Chem. Phys.*, **44**, 2595 (1966); J. E. Hearst, R. A. Harris, and E. Beals, *ibid.*, **45**, 3106 (1966).
2. N. Saito, K. Takahashi, and Y. Yunoki, *J. Phys. Soc. Japan*, **22**, 219 (1967).
3. J. Riseman and J. G. Kirkwood, in *Rheology*, Academic Press, New York, 1956, Vol. I, Chap. 13, pp. 495–523; J. J. Erpenbeck and J. G. Kirkwood, *J. Chem. Phys.*, **29**, 909 (1958).
4. The error concerned an explicit formula for the translational diffusion coefficient. Kirkwood calculated the diffusion tensor as the projection onto chain space of the inverse of the complete friction tensor; he should have projected the friction tensor first, and then taken the inverse. This was pointed out by Y. Ikeda, *Kobayashi Rigaku Kenkyushu Hokoku*, **6**, 44 (1956); and also by J. J. Erpenbeck and J. G. Kirkwood, *J. Chem. Phys.*, **38**, 1023 (1963). An example of the effects of the error was given by R. Zwanzig, *J. Chem. Phys.*, **45**, 1858 (1966). In the present article this question does not come up because we use the complete configuration space.
5. M. Lax, *Rev. Mod. Phys.*, **38**, 541 (1966). See especially the material on pp. 546–657.

TOEPLITZ DETERMINANTS: SOME APPLICATIONS, THEOREMS, AND CONJECTURES

MICHAEL E. FISHER
and
ROBERT E. HARTWIG

Baker Laboratory, Cornell University, Ithaca, New York

CONTENTS

I. INTRODUCTION AND EXAMPLES

A Toeplitz matrix of order N has the form

$$\mathbf{C}_N = [c_{i-j}]_0^{N-1} = \begin{bmatrix} c_0 & c_{-1} & c_{-2} & \cdots & c_{-(N-1)} \\ c_1 & c_0 & c_{-1} & \cdots & c_{-(N-2)} \\ c_2 & c_1 & c_0 & \cdots & c_{-(N-3)} \\ \vdots & \vdots & \vdots & & \vdots \\ c_{N-1} & c_{N-2} & c_{N-3} & \cdots & c_0 \end{bmatrix} \quad (1)$$

Its elements c_n can be associated with the formal generating function

$$C(z) = \sum_{n=-\infty}^{\infty} c_n z^n \quad (2)$$

333

or, provided the elements decrease sufficiently fast for large $|n|$, with the function

$$c(\theta) = C(e^{i\theta}) = \sum_{n=-\infty}^{\infty} e^{in\theta} c_n \qquad (3)$$

Of frequent interest is the determinant

$$D_N(c) = \text{Det } \{\mathbf{C}_N\} = |c_{i-j}|_0^{N-1} \qquad (4)$$

Various applications of Toeplitz matrices and determinants have been discussed by Grenander and Szegö in their book[1] and, more recently, by Kac.[2] We will mention only a few examples arising in chemical physics and stochastic processes.

Ex. A. Random Walk

Consider a one-dimensional random walk on a lattice of N sites $j = 0, 1, 2, \ldots N - 1$ with absorbing barriers at $j = -1$ and $j = N$. Let $f_{j,l}$ denote the probability that the walker is at site j after l steps, $f_{j,0}$ being the initial probability distribution. Suppose that $P(j \to i) = P_{i-j}$ is the probability of making a step from site j to site i (ignoring the barriers). Then, taking account of the absorption, the distribution after l steps is easily seen to be given by

$$\mathbf{f}_l = (\mathbf{C}_N)^l \mathbf{f}_0, \qquad (5)$$

where $\mathbf{C}_N$ is the Toeplitz matrix $[P_{i-j}]_0^{N-1}$ and $\mathbf{f}_l$ is the column vector $[f_{i,l}]$. In the usual way the asymptotic properties of the distribution may be studied in terms of the eigenvalues and eigenvectors of $\mathbf{C}_N$. The determinant, of course, is equal to the product of the eigenvalues.

Ex. B. Prediction Theory

Suppose $\{X_n\}$ $n = 0, -1, -2, \ldots$ is a set of real, normalized random variables subject to a stationary distribution with covariance

$$\langle X_n X_m \rangle = \rho(m - n) = \rho(n - m) \qquad (6)$$
$$\langle X_m^2 \rangle = \rho(0) = 1$$

A linear predictor for the value of X_0 given the values of $X_{-1}, X_{-2}, \ldots X_{-N}$ is an expression of the form

$$Y_0 = \sum_{k=1}^{N} \alpha_k^{(N)} X_{-k} \qquad (7)$$

The "best" linear predictor will be provided by that set of $\alpha_k^{(N)}$ $(k = 1, 2, \ldots N)$ which minimize the expected square error

$$\mathscr{E}_N = \langle (X_0 - Y_0)^2 \rangle \tag{8}$$

One finds[2] that

$$\min_{\alpha} \mathscr{E}_N = D_N/D_{N-1} \tag{9}$$

where D_N is the determinant of the Toeplitz matrix with elements $c_n = \rho(n)$. If for some suitable covariance function the ratio D_N/D_{N-1} could approach zero as $N \to \infty$ then "perfect prediction" would become possible given an indefinitely long sample X_{-1} to $X_{-\infty}$.

Ex. C. Ising Model Correlation Functions

Consider a plane square lattice Ising model with a spin variable $s_{i,j} = \pm 1$ associated with the site (i, j) and interactions between nearest-neighbor sites. Kaufman and Onsager[3, 4] have shown how the spin–spin correlation functions in an infinite lattice,

$$\Gamma(i, j) = \langle s_{0,0} \, s_{i,j} \rangle \tag{10}$$

may be expressed in terms of Toeplitz determinants. Specifically one finds[3, 4]

$$\Gamma(0, N) = D_N(c) \qquad \text{and} \qquad \Gamma(N, N) = D_N(c_{B=0}) \tag{11}$$

where the generating function is

$$c(\theta) = \left(\frac{1 - Ae^{i\theta}}{1 - Ae^{-i\theta}} \right)^{1/2} \left(\frac{1 - Be^{-i\theta}}{1 - Be^{i\theta}} \right)^{1/2} \tag{12}$$

in which the parameters A and B are explicit, real functions of the temperature satisfying

$$
\begin{array}{lll}
|B| < A < 1 & \text{for } T < T_c & \\
|B| < A = 1 & \text{for } T = T_c & \quad (13) \\
|B| < A^{-1} < 1 & \text{for } T > T_c &
\end{array}
$$

The sign of the square root in Eq. (12) is to be chosen so that $c(\pi) > 0$.

For a wide range of other Ising lattices[5] the correlation functions for particular directions can be expressed in terms of precisely the *same* Toeplitz determinant although with different formulas for the parameters $A(T)$ and $B(T)$ [which nonetheless always satisfy Eq. (13)]. The behavior of the correlation functions for large separations of the spins is of particular interest for the study of critical phenomena.[6]

Ex. D. Dimers on a Plane Lattice

The adsorption of diatomic or dimeric molecules on a suitable cold crystalline surface can be quite realistically considered in terms of the "dimer model" in which dimers are represented by rigid rods which occupy the bonds (and associated terminal sites) of a plane lattice to the exclusion of other dimers. The partition function of a planar lattice of N sites *filled* with $\frac{1}{2}N$ dimers can be calculated exactly.[7] Now if a single dimer is removed from the lattice, one is left with two "monomers" or "holes" which may separate. The equilibrium correlation between the two monomers, however, is appreciable. As in the case of Ising models, the correlation functions for particular directions of monomer–monomer separation can be expressed exactly in terms of a Toeplitz determinant.[8] Although the structure of the basic generating functions is more complex than Eq. (12), the corresponding determinant for one direction has been reduced to an equally simple form.[9] One discovers that the correlations decay asymptotically only as $1/r^{1/2}$.

Other examples which we may mention in passing are: Dyson's Coulomb gas model in an external field[10] where the partition function itself is equal to a Toeplitz determinant; the one-dimensional Bose gas with delta function interactions where the occupation number of the ground state (the "density of the condensate") is expressed by a Toeplitz determinant of order equal to the number of particles[11]; the spin–spin correlation functions for a one-dimensional magnetic system of $S = \frac{1}{2}$ spins coupled by a nearest-neighbor "planar-Heisenberg" interaction (X–Y model), which are also equal to Toeplitz determinants[12]; finally, returning to planar Ising models, the interfacial tension between two regions of opposite order, the wall or boundary free energy and the free energy associated with a grain boundary can all be expressed in terms of the asymptotic properties of appropriate Toeplitz determinants.[13]

The above examples serve to indicate the usefulness of Toeplitz determinants and to illustrate the need for a knowledge of their asymptotic behavior for large order. This topic we now take up.

II. PREVIOUS RESULTS

One of the earliest results of interest to us is Szegö's theorem:[1]

THEOREM 1. *If the generating function $c(\theta)$ is the (almost everywhere existing) derivative of a real monotonically nondecreasing function and if*

$$k_0(c) = \frac{1}{2\pi} \int_0^{2\pi} \ln c(\theta) \, d\theta \qquad (14)$$

then

$$\lim_{N \to \infty} D_N(c)/D_{N-1}(c) = \exp [k_0(c)] \tag{15}$$

where the limit is approached from above. In case $\ln c(\theta)$ *is not Lebesgue integrable the limit is to be replaced by* 0.

This theorem has immediate application to Example B above since it shows that perfect prediction is possible only when the covariance function $\rho(n) = c_n$ is such that $\ln c(\theta)$ is not integrable (i.e., when the integral diverges to $-\infty$). When $k_0(c)$ exists Theorem 1 implies immediately that for large N one has $D_N \sim (e^{k_0})^N$ or $\ln D_N \approx Nk_0$. Our primary concern is with the higher order corrections to this asymptotic formula.

To obtain such higher order terms further restrictions on the elements c_n are needed. To introduce these we first note the identity

$$D_N(c) = |c_{i-j}| = \alpha^N |c_{i-j}/\alpha\rho_0^{i-j}| = D_N(c^\times) \tag{16}$$

where, for arbitrary nonzero α and ρ_0,

$$C^\times(z) = \alpha^{-1}C(z/\rho_0) \tag{17}$$

This identity is proved simply by multiplying the ith row of $D_N(c^\times)$ by ρ_0^i and the jth column by $\alpha^{-1}\rho_0^{-j}$. It shows that the elements c_n may be normalized in an arbitrary fashion. Next suppose that the large n behavior of the elements is characterized by

$$\lim_{n \to \infty} \inf |c_n|^{-1/n} = \rho_+$$
$$\lim_{n \to \infty} \inf |c_{-n}|^{-1/n} = \rho_-^{-1} \tag{18}$$

with the *restriction*

(a)
$$\rho_+ \geqq \rho_0 \geqq \rho_- \tag{19}$$

Then, without loss of generality, Eq. (16) shows that we may henceforth suppose that $\rho_0 = 1$.

In practice the following strong additional restriction often applies:

(b) as $n \to \infty$ $\quad |c_n| = O(\rho^n), \quad\quad |c_{-n}| = O(\sigma^n)$

with $\quad\quad 0 < \rho < 1, \quad\quad 0 < \sigma < 1 \tag{20}$

This restriction is included in the weaker condition (for suitable $\rho \geqq \rho_+^{-1}$ and $\sigma \geqq \rho_-$)

(c)
$$\sum_{n=-\infty}^{\infty} |c_n| < \infty \tag{21}$$

which we employ for our own further analysis.

Granted this last condition (c), we may extend Eq. (14) by defining the logarithmic Fourier coefficients

$$k_n = k_n(c) = \frac{1}{2\pi} \int_0^{2\pi} \ln c(\theta) e^{-in\theta} \, d\theta \qquad (22)$$

Notice that unless the change of the argument of $c(\theta)$ as θ runs from 0 to 2π vanishes identically $\ln c(\theta)$ will be discontinuous at the end of its range. It is natural, therefore, to require that the index ν of $c(\theta)$ satisfies the restriction

(d) $\qquad\qquad \nu(c) = (2\pi)^{-1}[\arg c(2\pi) - \arg c(0)] = 0 \qquad (23)$

Similarly, unless we impose the further condition

(e) $\qquad\qquad\qquad\qquad c(\theta) \neq 0 \qquad\qquad\qquad\qquad (24)$

the integrand $\ln c(\theta)$ in Eq. (22) might have one or more infinite singularities (which could well be nonintegrable). Under conditions (c), (d), and (e), however, we are assured that the Fourier series

$$\ln c(\theta) = \sum_{n=-\infty}^{\infty} k_n e^{in\theta} \qquad (25)$$

will converge absolutely.

We may now state the fundamental theorem of Szegö as extended by Kac, Baxter, and others[14] in a form due to Hirschman[15]:

THEOREM 2. *If the elements c_n satisfy conditions (c), (d), and (e) and, in addition,*

(f) $\qquad\qquad\qquad \sum_{n=-\infty}^{\infty} |n||c_n|^2 < \infty \qquad\qquad (26)$

then

$$\ln D_n(c) = Nk_0(c) + E_0(c) + E_{1,N}(c) \qquad (27)$$

where as $N \to \infty$ we have $E_{1,N}(c) = o(1)$ and

$$E_0(c) = \sum_{n=1}^{\infty} nk_n k_{-n} \qquad (28a)$$

$$= \frac{1}{8} \int_0^{2\pi} \frac{d\theta}{2\pi} \int_0^{2\pi} \frac{d\varphi}{2\pi} \left[\frac{\ln c(\theta) - \ln c(\varphi)}{\sin \frac{1}{2}(\theta - \varphi)} \right]^2 \qquad (28b)$$

The formula (27) is the central result of the theory. A convenient alternative form for the constant E_0 may be obtained by using auxiliary functions $p(\theta)$ and $q(\theta)$ defined in terms of the positive and negative Fourier coefficients of $\ln c(\theta)$ by

$$p(\theta) = \exp\left[\sum_{n=1}^{\infty} k_n e^{in\theta}\right] = 1 + \sum_{n=1}^{\infty} p_n e^{in\theta} \qquad (29)$$

$$q(\theta) = \exp\left[\sum_{n=1}^{\infty} k_{-n} e^{in\theta}\right] = 1 + \sum_{n=1}^{\infty} q_n e^{in\theta} \qquad (30)$$

In terms of these one has the factorization

$$c(\theta) = e^{k_0}/p(\theta)q(-\theta) \qquad (31)$$

One then finds easily that

$$E_0(c) = \frac{i}{2\pi} \int_0^{2\pi} \ln p(\theta) \frac{d}{d\theta} \ln q(-\theta)\, d\theta \qquad (32)$$

An immediate application of this theorem is to derive the Onsager-Yang formula for the spontaneous magnetization $M_0(T)$ of an Ising ferro-magnet.[4, 6] In terms of the correlation functions in Eq. (10), the "long-range order" $\Gamma(\infty)$, and hence $M_0(T)$ can be defined by

$$[M_0(T)]^2 = \Gamma(\infty) = \lim_{N\to\infty} \Gamma(0, N) \qquad (33)$$

From Eqs. (11), (12), and (13) one easily checks the validity of conditions (c) and (f) [and indeed (b)] provided $T \ne T_c$. Similarly, condition (e) is always satisfied; however, the index ν of $c(\theta)$ is zero, as required by condition (d), only for $T < T_c$. After an elementary calculation, which shows that $k_0(c) = 0$, one obtains from Eqs. (22), (27), and (28) the result

$$[M_0(T)]^2 = \Gamma(\infty) = (1 - A^2)^{1/4}(1 - B^2)^{1/4}(1 - AB)^{-1/2}$$
$$\text{for } T < T_c \qquad (34)$$

As $T \to T_c$ one has generally $(1 - A^2) \propto (T_c - T)$ so that the first factor yields the famous result[4, 6] $M_0(T) \sim (T_c - T)^{1/8}$ for T near T_c.

This example demonstrates the power of Theorem 2 but also highlights some of its inadequacies. In the first place, in order to obtain information on the rate of approach of the correlation functions to the limiting long-range order explicit estimates of the higher order term $E_{1, N}(c)$ in Eq. (27) are needed. Secondly, to discuss the decay of correlation above T_c where $A > 1$ and, in particular, to demonstrate the absence of long-range order there, the theorem must be extended at least to indices $\nu = \pm 1$. This can be seen by rewriting the generating function (12) in the form

$$c(\theta) = -e^{i\theta}\left(\frac{1 - A'e^{-i\theta}}{1 - A'e^{i\theta}}\right)^{1/2}\left(\frac{1 - Be^{-i\theta}}{1 - Be^{i\theta}}\right)^{1/2} \qquad (35)$$

where

$$A' = A^{-1} < 1, \qquad \text{for } T > T_c \qquad (36)$$

from which it is clear that the index is $+1$ when $T > T_c$. Thirdly, at the critical point itself one finds $v = \frac{1}{2}$ [so that $\ln c(\theta)$ is discontinuous at $\theta = 0$] and furthermore, conditions (c) and (f) are violated since $c_n \sim 1/n$ as $|n| \to \infty$. Lastly, in applications to the one-dimensional Bose gas[11] and elsewhere one also finds that $c(\theta)$ has zeros so that condition (e) is also violated.

In the next section we present some recently proved general theorems[17] inspired by the important work of T. T. Wu[18] on the Ising model correlation functions. These theorems give explicit expressions for the higher order term $E_{1,N}(c)$ and they also apply for arbitrary integral values of the index v. For the cases in which v is nonintegral and $c(\theta)$ is discontinuous or has zeros we discuss, in the last section, some plausible conjectures based on a few known exact results.

III. EXTENSIONS OF THE CLASSICAL THEOREM

Devinatz[16] has discussed the relaxation of condition (c), which requires the absolute convergence of the sum of the elements c_n. He replaces this by the more complex, but weaker condition

(c') $c(\theta)$ is continuous and there is a non-negative, continuous, doubly periodic function $m(\theta, \varphi)$ with $m(\theta, \theta) = 0$ and an $M > 0$ so that for every φ $(0 \leq \varphi \leq 2\pi)$

$$\int_0^{2\pi} \left| \frac{c(\theta) - c(\varphi)}{\theta - \varphi} \right| \frac{d\theta}{m(\theta, \varphi)} \leq M \qquad (37)$$

This condition is similar to that used by Onsager in his own unpublished derivation of the result, Eq. (34), for the spontaneous magnetization of the Ising model. It is to be noted, however, that Devinatz retains conditions (d), (e), and (f). In our theorems, on the contrary, we retain condition (c) but replace (f) by another (slightly stronger) condition on the auxiliary coefficients p_n and q_n defined in Eqs. (29) and (30). To state this we define the monotonically decreasing coefficients

$$\tilde{p}_l = \max_{n \geq l} |p_n| \qquad \text{and} \qquad \tilde{q}_l = \max_{n \geq l} |q_n| \qquad (38)$$

Our condition is then

$$(f') \qquad \eta_m = \sum_{l \geq m}^{\infty} \tilde{p}_l < \infty, \qquad \zeta_m = \sum_{l \geq m}^{\infty} \tilde{q}_l < \infty, \qquad (m \geq 0), \qquad (39)$$

which, incidentally, implies that η_m and ζ_m approach zero as $m \to \infty$. This condition is equivalent to the analogous condition constructed with the coefficients c_n and c_{-n} in place of p_n and q_n.

We may now state our direct extension of Theorem 2.

THEOREM 3. *If* $c(\theta)$ *satisfies conditions* (c), (d), (e) *and* (f') *[see Eqs. (21), (23), (24) and (39)] then*

$$\boxed{\ln D_N(c) = Nk_0(c) + E_0(c) + E_{1,N}(c) + E_{2,N}(c)} \tag{40}$$

where $k_0(c)$ *is given by Eq. (22),* $E_0(c)$ *by Eq. (28) and*

$$E_{1,N}(c) = - \sum_{n=1}^{\infty} n l_{N+n} m_{N+n} = O(\eta_N \zeta_N) \tag{41}$$

where $l_n(c)$ *and* $m_n(c)$ *are the Fourier coefficients of the functions* $l(\theta)$ *and* $m(\theta)$ *defined by*

$$\ln l(\theta) = -\ln m(-\theta) = \ln [p(\theta)/q(-\theta)] = \sum_{n=1}^{\infty} (k_{-n} e^{-in\theta} - k_n e^{in\theta}) \tag{42}$$

Finally the error term satisfies

$$E_{2,N}(c) = O(\rho_N \eta_N \zeta_N^2) \tag{43}$$

where

$$\rho_N = \sum_{l=0}^{N-1} \tilde{p}_l \sum_{j=N-l}^{\infty} |c_j| \to 0 \text{ as } N \to \infty| \tag{44}$$

Let us note immediately that when the coefficients $c_{\pm n}$ descrease exponentially in accordance with condition (b) [Eq. (20)] we have the simpler and useful order estimates

$$E_{1,N} = O(\rho^N \sigma^N), \qquad E_{2,N} = O(\rho^{2N} \sigma^{2N}) \tag{45}$$

These suggest the existence of an indefinite series of exponentially decreasing terms $E_{k,N}$ and, in fact, our method of proving the theorem[17] entails a matrix iterative procedure which would in principle yield a complete convergent expansion for $\ln D_N(c)$. An alternative integral expression for the leading correction term is

$$E_{1,N}(c) = \frac{1}{2} \int_0^{2\pi} \frac{d\theta}{2\pi} \int_0^{2\pi} \frac{d\varphi}{2\pi} \left[\frac{1 - e^{-iN(\theta-\varphi)}l(\theta)m(-\varphi)}{2 \sin^2 \frac{1}{2}(\theta - \varphi)} - \frac{il'(\theta)}{l(\theta)} - N \right] \tag{46}$$

where $l'(\theta) = dl/d\theta$.

As an application of this theorem let us calculate in leading order the decay of the Ising spin correlation function $\Gamma(0, N)$ to its limit $\Gamma(\infty)$ below T_c. From Eq. (12) and the definitions (42) we find easily

$$l(\theta) = \frac{1}{m(-\theta)} = \left[\frac{1 - 2B\cos\theta + B^2}{1 - 2A\cos\theta + A^2}\right]^{1/2} \qquad (47)$$

The asymptotic behavior of the coefficients l_n and m_n is determined by the singularities nearest to the real axis in the complex θ plane. These singularities are square root and inverse square root branch points at $i\theta = \pm \ln A$. From this it follows that

$$l_n \approx L_T A^n/n^{1/2}, \qquad m_n \approx -M_T A^n/n^{3/2}, \qquad (n \to \infty) \qquad (48)$$

where L_T and M_T are positive coefficients depending on A and B and, hence, on T. For $A < 1$ and large N the sum in Eq. (41) defining $E_{1,N}$ is easily seen to behave like its leading term $l_N m_N$. Finally, therefore, one obtains the result

$$\Gamma(0, N) = \Gamma(\infty)\{1 + F_T(A^{2N}/N^2)[1 + o(1)]\} \qquad \text{for } T < T_c \qquad (49)$$

This shows that the net correlation decays with separation distance r as $e^{-\kappa r}/r^2$ where the inverse range of correlation $\kappa(T)$ is $2\ln A^{-1}$. [The precise value of the amplitude F_T and expressions for the $o(1)$ terms of order $N^{-1}, N^{-2}, \ldots$ have been obtained by Wu.[18]] Ornstein-Zernike theory would predict a decay of $e^{-\kappa r}/r^{1/2}$ so the inverse square power of r in the decay law was somewhat surprising.[6b] However, by a perturbation argument appropriate to low temperatures one can see that the factor $1/r^2$ is peculiar to the two-dimensional Ising model with only nearest-neighbor coupling in directions normal to the direction of the correlation decay; with further neighbor interactions or in higher dimensions the Ornstein-Zernike result should be expected to hold asymptotically at fixed T less than T_c.

For many applications the monotonicity of the convergence of $D_N e^{-Nk_0}$ to its limit e^{E_0} will be of interest. For a real function $c(\theta)$ Theorem 1 shows that $D_N e^{-Nk_0}$ is nondecreasing so that the limit is approached from below. The Ising generating function (12), however, is of the form $\exp[i\delta(\theta)]$ with real δ. In such a case the limit may be approached from above as asserted by the following theorem.

THEOREM 4. *If the conditions of Theorem 3 are satisfied with real p_n and q_n and if*

$$p_n \geq p_{n+1} \geq 0, \qquad q_{n+1} \leq 0, \qquad \text{all } n \geq 0 \qquad (50)$$

and

$$r_{n+1} \leqq 0, \qquad s_n \geqq s_{n+1} \geqq 0, \qquad \text{all } n \geqq 0 \qquad (51)$$

where r_n and s_n are the Fourier coefficients of $r(\theta) = 1/p(\theta)$ and $s(\theta) = 1/q(\theta)$ then $\ln D_N(c) - Nk_0(c)$ decreases monotonically to the limit $E_0(c)$.

As shown in Appendix A, this theorem may be applied to the Ising model to prove that the spin–spin correlation functions $\Gamma(0, N)$ and $\Gamma(N, N)$ decrease monotonically with separation distance to the limiting long-range order $\Gamma(\infty)$.

Our next theorem deals with a generating function of index $\nu = \pm 1$ such as the Ising model generating function above T_c [see Eq. (35)]. As is evident from this example, any generating function of index unity may be reduced to one of index zero by multiplying by $e^{-i\theta}$. Conversely, the operation of multiplying by $e^{i\theta}$ simply has the effect of moving the matrix to the right or left by one column or, equivalently, by one diagonal. For convenience we introduce a minus sign and thus define a shifted determinant of index unity by

$$D_N^{(1)}(c) = D_N[e^{i(\theta - \pi)}c(\theta)] = (-)^N \begin{vmatrix} c_{-1} & c_{-2} & c_{-3} & \cdots & c_{-N} \\ c_0 & c_{-1} & c_{-2} & \cdots & c_{-(N-1)} \\ c_{+1} & c_0 & c_{-1} & & \\ \vdots & \vdots & \vdots & & \vdots \\ c_{N-2} & c_{N-3} & & \cdots & c_{-1} \end{vmatrix}$$

$$(52)$$

with a similar definition of $D_N^{(-1)}(c)$. These determinants may now be evaluated asymptotically in terms of the unshifted determinant with the aid of the following theorem.

THEOREM 5. *If $c(\theta)$ satisfies the conditions of Theorem 3 then*

$$D_N^{(1)}(c) = D_{N+1}(c)[l_N + \delta_N^{+}] \qquad (53)$$

$$D_N^{(-1)}(c) = D_{N+1}(c)[m_N + \delta_N^{-}] \qquad (54)$$

where

$$l_N(c) = O(\tilde{p}_N), \qquad m_N(c) = O(\tilde{q}_N) \qquad (55)$$

and

$$\delta_N^{+} = O[\sigma_N \tilde{p}_N(\rho_N + \eta_N)] \qquad \delta_N^{-} = O[\rho_N \tilde{q}_N(\sigma_N + \zeta_N)] \qquad (56)$$

where

$$\sigma_N = \sum_{l=0}^{N-1} \tilde{q}_l \sum_{j=N-l}^{\infty} |c_{-j}| \to 0 \qquad \text{as} \qquad N \to \infty \qquad (57)$$

As in the case of Theorem 3 the order estimates are simpler when the coefficients $c_{\pm n}$ decrease exponentially according to Eq. (20); we then have

$$l_N = O(\rho^N), \qquad m_N = O(\sigma^N) \qquad (58)$$

and

$$\delta_N{}^+ = O(\rho^{2N}\sigma^N), \qquad \delta_N{}^- = O(\rho^N\sigma^{2N}) \qquad (59)$$

A direct and important application of this theorem to the Ising model shows that there is no long-range order *above* T_c and, in fact, that the correlations decay like l_N. The estimates (48) apply above T_c if A is replaced by $A' = A^{-1}$. Accordingly, one has

$$\Gamma(0, N) = G_T(A^{-N}/N^{1/2})[1 + o(1)] \qquad (T > T_c) \qquad (60)$$

which implies a decay with distance as $e^{-\kappa r}/r^{1/2}$; this is now in accordance with the expectations of Ornstein-Zernike theory.[6b] [Explicit expressions for G_T and for the leading $o(1)$ terms have again been calculated by Wu.[18]] Another application of Theorem 5 is to the evaluation of the interfacial, wall and grain boundary free energies of the Ising model.[13]

For general integral index one may, as in the case of index unity, regard the generating function as derived from one of index zero by multiplication by $e^{-iv\theta}$). Equivalently, the determinant will be shifted by v diagonals from one to which Theorem 3 applies. The next theorem, which includes Theorem 5, expresses such a v-shifted determinant as a product of an unshifted determinant and of a "small" Toeplitz determinant of order v.

THEOREM 6. *If* $c(\theta)$ *satisfies the conditions of Theorem 3 then for* $v = 1, 2, 3, \ldots$

$$D_N^{(v)}(c) = D_N[e^{iv(\theta-\pi)}c(\theta)]$$

$$= \begin{vmatrix} d_0^{(N)} & d_{-1}^{(N)} & \cdots & d_{-v+1}^{(N)} \\ d_1^{(N)} & d_0^{(N)} & \cdots & d_{-v+2}^{(N)} \\ \cdot & \cdot & & \cdot \\ \cdot & \cdot & & \cdot \\ \cdot & \cdot & & \cdot \\ d_{v-1}^{(N)} & d_{v-2}^{(N)} & \cdots & d_0^{(N)} \end{vmatrix} D_{N+v}(c) \qquad (61)$$

where

$$d_j^{(N)} = l_{N+j} + \delta_N{}^+ \qquad (62)$$

in which $\delta_N{}^+$ *satisfies Eq.* (56).

A similar result, of course, holds for $D_N^{(-v)}(c)$ as is readily seen by transposing the original determinant and changing all the definitions accordingly.

The proofs of Theorems 3–6, which will be published elsewhere,[17] are fairly elementary, although a little lengthy. A principal step in the argument involves the construction of explicit asymptotic expressions for the elements of the inverse matrix $X_N = C_N^{-1}$ in terms of the coefficients p_n, q_n, l_n, and m_n. These formulas may themselves be useful in certain applications.

IV. SPECIAL RESULTS AND CONJECTURES

Theorems 5 and 6 of the previous section enable us to relax condition (d) on the index of $c(\theta)$. There remains, however, the question of dealing with generating functions which violate conditions (c) and (f) or (f') on the rate of decrease of $c_{\pm n}$, and condition (e) regarding the vanishing of $c(\theta)$. As an introduction consider the "singular generating function"

$$c(\theta) = t_\alpha(\theta) = \left(\frac{1 - e^{-i\theta}}{1 - e^{i\theta}}\right)^\alpha$$

$$= e^{-i\alpha(\pi - \theta)}, \qquad 0 \leq \theta < 2\pi \tag{63}$$

for which $\ln c(\theta)$ has a discontinuity of $2\pi\alpha$ at $\theta = 0$. [The index is evidently $\nu = \alpha$.] In fact when $\alpha = \frac{1}{2}$ this corresponds precisely to the Ising generating function (12) at $T = T_c$ and with $B = 0$ (as appropriate for the diagonal correlation function $\Gamma(N, N)$ on the square lattice). More generally we will suppose α is not zero, for which case $D_N(t_\alpha) = 1$, or an integer for which $D_N(t_{\pm m}) \equiv 0$. However, α may be allowed to take complex values.

For the elements of $D_N(t_\alpha)$ one finds easily

$$c_n(t_\alpha) = \frac{\sin \pi\alpha}{\pi(n + \alpha)} \tag{64}$$

so that conditions (c) and (f) are clearly violated. [In fact, (f') is also not satisfied.] Similarly one finds

$$k_0(t_\alpha) = 0, \qquad k_n(t_\alpha) = \alpha/n \qquad (n \neq 0) \tag{65}$$

from which it is evident that the sum (28a) defining the "constant" $E_0(t_\alpha)$ is logarithmically divergent. If, heuristically, we simply truncate this sum at some $N^\dagger = N\xi(\alpha)$ we replace $E_0(t_\alpha)$ by

$$E_{0,N}^\dagger(t_\alpha) = \sum_{n=1}^{N\dagger} n k_n(t_\alpha) k_{-n}(t_\alpha)$$

$$= \alpha^2 \ln \mu N - Z_\alpha + o(1) \tag{66}$$

where

$$\mu = \exp(1 + \gamma_E), \qquad Z_\alpha = \alpha^2[\ln \xi(\alpha) - 1] \tag{67}$$

in which $\gamma_E = 0.5772\ldots$ is Euler's constant. On the basis of Theorems 2 or 3 it is then natural to conjecture that as $N \to \infty$

$$\ln D_N(t_\alpha) = -\alpha^2 \ln \mu N - Z_\alpha + o(1) \tag{68}$$

so that $D_N \sim 1/N^{\alpha^2}$.

By a happy circumstance this conjecture can be verified. The elements of $D_N(t_\alpha)$ are of so-called Cauchy form, namely $c_{ij} = (a_i + b_j)^{-1}$, so that as shown in Appendix B, one finds explicitly

$$D_N(t_\alpha) = \left(\frac{\sin \pi\alpha}{\pi\alpha}\right)^N \prod_{m=1}^{N} \left(1 - \frac{\alpha^2}{m^2}\right)^{m-N} \tag{69}$$

A straightforward asymptotic analysis (presented in Appendix B) then confirms the conjecture (68) [provided $\alpha \neq \pm 1, \pm 2, \ldots$] and yields the formula

$$Z_\alpha = -\sum_{r=1}^{\infty} r\left[\ln\left(1 - \frac{\alpha^2}{r^2}\right) + \frac{\alpha^2}{r^2}\right] \tag{70}$$

in which the sum is convergent for all allowed α. The $o(1)$ terms in Eq. (66) turn out to be $-\frac{1}{12}\alpha^2(1 - \alpha^2)N^{-2} + O(N^{-4})$ and, in fact, the complete asymptotic expansion of $\ln D_N(t_\alpha)$ can be derived in terms of the Bernoulli polynomials $B_n(\alpha)$ (see Appendix B).

To extend this result to more general singular generating functions, such as the Ising generating function at $T = T_c$ ($A = 1$) with $B \neq 0$, consider

$$c(\theta) = t_\alpha(\theta)b(\theta) \tag{71}$$

where $b(\theta)$ is a "regular" generating function (i.e., its Fourier coefficients $c_n(b) = b_n$ satisfy the conditions of Theorems 2 or 3). Then we have

$$k_n(c) = k_n(t_\alpha) + k_n(b) \tag{72}$$

and truncating the sum of E_0 as before yields

$$E_{0,N}^\dagger(c) = E_{0,N}^\dagger(t_\alpha) + E_{0,N}^\dagger(b) - \alpha \sum_{n=1}^{N\dagger} [k_n(b) - k_{-n}(b)] \tag{73}$$

In the last two terms we may allow $N^\dagger$ to approach ∞ without fear of divergence. Then using Eq (66) and reexpressing the last term with the aid of Eq. (42) we are lead to:

CONJECTURE *If $t_\alpha(\theta)$ is defined by* Eq. (63) *with α non-integral and if $b(\theta)$ is regular then*

$$\ln D_N(t_\alpha b) = Nk_0(b) - \alpha^2 \ln \mu N - Z_\alpha(b) + o(1) \tag{74}$$

where μ is defined in Eq. (67) *and*

$$-Z_\alpha(b) = -Z_\alpha + E_0(b) + \alpha \ln l(b; 0) \tag{75}$$

in which $Z_\alpha = Z_\alpha(1)$ is defined by Eq. (70) *and $l(b; \theta)$ is defined in terms of the coefficients $k_n(b)$ via* Eq. (42).

Although we have not as yet made significant progress towards the proof of this conjecture a variety of detailed calculations[18, 19] for the case $\alpha = \frac{1}{2}$ and $b(\theta) = (1 - Be^{i\theta})^{1/2}(1 - Be^{-i\theta})^{-1/2}$ lend strong support to its validity. In particular, for the Ising model correlation functions the conjecture leads to

$$\Gamma(T_c, N) = \left(\frac{1 + B}{1 - B}\right)^{1/4} \frac{\exp(-Z_{1/2})}{N^{1/4}} [1 - o(1)] \tag{76}$$

This expression is consistent with the numerical data; it also indicates that the decay of correlation for large r is radially symmetric which is certainly expected on physical grounds.

By the same heuristic arguments we may extend the conjecture to cover generating functions with multiple singularities and zeros of the form

$$c(\theta) = b(\theta) \prod_{j=1}^{g} t_{\alpha_j}(\theta - \theta_j) u_{\beta_j}(\theta - \theta_j) \tag{77}$$

As before $b(\theta)$ is supposed regular, $t_\alpha(\theta)$ is defined by Eq. (63), and lastly, the "zero factors" $u_\beta(\theta)$ are defined by

$$u_\beta(\theta) = (1 - e^{-i\theta})^\beta (1 - e^{i\theta})^\beta = |2 \sin \tfrac{1}{2}\theta|^{2\beta} \tag{78}$$

From Eq. (77) we find for $n > 0$

$$k_{\pm n}(c) = k_{\pm n}(b) \pm \sum_{j=1}^{g} (\alpha_j \mp \beta_j)e^{\mp in\theta}/n \tag{79}$$

Truncating the sum for $E_0(c)$ at $N^\dagger = N\xi(\alpha_1 \ldots; \ldots \beta_g)$ leads after a few manipulations to the corresponding general conjecture

$$\ln D_N(c) = Nk_0(b) - \left[\sum_{j=1}^{g} (\alpha_j{}^2 - \beta_j{}^2)\right] \ln \mu N \\ - Z_{\alpha_1 \ldots; \ldots \beta_g}(b) + o(1) \tag{80}$$

where

$$Z_{\alpha_1 \dots; \dots \beta_g}(b) = Z_g(\alpha_1, \dots \alpha_g; \beta_1, \dots \beta_g; \theta_1, \dots \theta_g)$$

$$+ \sum_{j=1}^{g} \sum_{i=j}^{g} (\alpha_i + \beta_i)(\alpha_j - \beta_j) \ln [1 - e^{i(\theta_i - \theta_j)}]$$

$$- \sum_{j=1}^{g} [\alpha_j l(b; \theta_j) - \beta_j \ln b(\theta_j)] - E_0(b) \qquad (81)$$

We also require that $|\alpha_j + \beta_j|$ and $|\alpha_j - \beta_j|$ are nonintegral for all j. [Possibly further restrictions, such as the reality and positivity of the β_j, may be necessary.] The constant $Z_g(\alpha_1 \dots \theta_g)$ must reduce to the previously defined Z_α when $g = 1$, $\alpha_1 = \alpha$ and $\beta_1 = 0$.

In support of this conjecture we make the following observations. When $b = 1$, $\beta_j = 0$, $\alpha_1 = \alpha$, $\alpha_j = 0$ ($j > 1$) it is correct as discussed above. It is also trivially correct when $b = 1$ if $\alpha_j = \beta_j$ (all j) or $\alpha_j = -\beta_j$ (all j) since in these cases the determinant is triangular and equal to unity.

Following work by Lenard and Szegö[11, 20] we may also say something in the cases for which $\alpha_j = 0$ (all j). In particular, for general $b(\theta)$ and real positive β_j Lenard[20] has shown that the determinant has the bound

$$D_N\left(b \prod_j u_j\right) e^{-N k_0(b)} < K N^{\Sigma_j \beta_j^2} \qquad (82)$$

where K is a constant depending on the β_j. This upper bound is precisely of the form of Eq. (80). Furthermore, for the case $g = 2, b = 1, \theta_2 = \theta_1 + \pi$, this bound is achieved, thereby confirming the conjecture. Indeed, as with t_α, the determinant can be calculated explicitly in this case, with the result (for N even)

$$D_{2M}(u_\beta u_{\beta'}) = \prod_{l=0}^{M-1} [K_l(\beta, \beta')]^2 \qquad (\beta, \beta' > 0) \qquad (83)$$

where

$$K_l(\beta, \beta') = \frac{l! \Gamma(l + 1 + \beta + \beta') \Gamma(l + \frac{1}{2} + \beta) \Gamma(l + \frac{1}{2} + \beta')}{[\Gamma(l + 1 + \frac{1}{2}\beta + \frac{1}{2}\beta') \Gamma(l + \frac{1}{2} + \frac{1}{2}\beta + \frac{1}{2}\beta')]^2} \qquad (84)$$

From this (as in Appendix B) one readily checks the conjecture (80) and discovers that

$$Z_2(0, 0; \beta, \beta'; 0, \pi) = - \sum_{r=1}^{\infty} r\{2 \ln [1 + \Theta(r^{-1})] - (\beta^2 + \beta'^2) r^{-2}\} \qquad (85)$$

where

$$1 + \Theta(\tau) = \frac{[1 + \frac{1}{2}(\beta + \beta' - 1)\tau]^2 [1 + \frac{1}{2}(\beta + \beta')\tau]^2}{[1 + \frac{1}{2}(\beta - \frac{1}{2})\tau][1 + \frac{1}{2}(\beta' - \frac{1}{2})\tau][1 + (\beta + \beta')\tau]} \qquad (86)$$

Since $\Theta(r^{-1}) \sim r^{-2}$ for large r the form of (85) is strongly reminiscent of the formula (70) defining $Z_1(\alpha; 0) = Z_\alpha$. Indeed Eq. (85) can be rewritten as

$$Z_2(0, 0; \beta, \beta'; 0, \pi) = Z_{i\beta} + Z_{i\beta'} + Y(\beta, \beta') \qquad (87)$$

where the "interference term" is

$$Y(\beta, \beta') = \sum_{r=1}^{\infty} r \ln \frac{(1 - \beta^2 r^{-2})(1 - \beta'^2 r^{-2})}{[1 + \Theta(r^{-1})]^2} \qquad (88)$$

Kac[2] has discussed the cases $g = 1$, $\alpha = 0$, $\beta = \frac{1}{2}$ for general $b(\theta)$. His calculations, which can be extended to general β, confirm (after correction of a misprint) the two leading terms in Eq. (80). Finally, we remark that a generating function arising in the monomer–dimer problem (Example D), has a structure with $g = 2$ singularities corresponding to $\alpha_1 = \alpha_2 = \frac{1}{2}$ and $\beta_1 = \beta_2 = 0$. The corresponding determinant could be proved[9] to vary as $N^{-1/2}$ in accordance with the conjecture (80).

V. SUMMARY

We have reviewed known theorems on the asymptotic behavior of a Toeplitz determinant and presented new theorems which extend to the higher order corrections and to generating functions of nonzero but integral index. In certain cases monotonicity of the convergence may also be established. The proofs of the new theorems, which are to be presented elsewhere,[17] also yield asymptotic estimates of the elements of the inverse matrix. Existing theorems do not cover determinants for which the generating function is discontinuous, has nonintegral index or has zeros. Some special results and some general conjectures for these cases were reported.

Acknowledgments

We are grateful to Dr. A. Lenard for telling us of his work in Reference 20 and to Dr. G. A. Baker, Jr. for drawing our attention to Reference 2. The support of the National Science Foundation and of the Advanced Research Projects Agency through the Materials Science Center at Cornell University, is gratefully acknowledged.

APPENDIX A

Monotonicity of the Ising Model Correlation Functions

In order to apply Theorem 4 to prove that the Ising model spin correlation functions $\Gamma(0, N)$ and $\Gamma(N, N)$ [see Eq. (11)] decrease monotonically to the long-range order $\Gamma(\infty)$ we must study the coefficients p_n, q_n, r_n, and

s_n derived from the appropriate generating function, Eq. (12), namely,

$$c(\theta) = 1/p(\theta)q(-\theta) \tag{89}$$

where, as we easily find,

$$p(\theta) = 1/r(\theta) = \left(\frac{1 - Be^{i\theta}}{1 - Ae^{i\theta}}\right)^{1/2} = 1/q(\theta) = s(\theta) \tag{90}$$

Evidently, for this case $p_n = s_n$ and $r_n = q_n$. To use Theorem 4 we have to prove

$$p_n \geq p_{n+1} \geq 0 \qquad \text{and} \qquad q_{n+1} \leq 0 \qquad \text{all } n \geq 0 \tag{91}$$

Now by Cauchy's integral formula we can write

$$p_n = \frac{1}{2\pi i} \oint \left(\frac{1 - Bz^{-1}}{1 - Az^{-1}}\right)^{1/2} z^{n-1}\, dz \tag{92}$$

where the contour is the unit circle. The integrand has algebraic branch points on the positive real axis at $z = A$ and $z = B$. When $n = 0$ there is, in addition, a simple pole at the origin with residue $(B/A)^{1/2}$. Otherwise the integrand is analytic in the complex plane cut from $z = A$ to $z = B$. Accordingly, we may now shrink the contour until it runs around the branch point at $z = A$, along the branch cut from A to B, around the branch point B and back along the other side of the cut (remembering, when $n = 0$, to add the contribution from the pole at $z = 0$). For convenience we make the transformation $z = A\zeta$ and then obtain

$$p_n = (B/A)^{1/2} \delta_{n0} + \frac{A^n}{\pi} \int_{B/A}^{1} \left(\frac{\zeta - (B/A)}{1 - \zeta}\right)^{1/2} \zeta^{n-1}\, d\zeta + \Delta_n \tag{93}$$

where Δ_n is the contribution to the integral arising from the portions of the contracted contour which encircle the branch points. Since the singularities at both branch points are weaker than a simple pole this contribution vanishes in the limit that the contour shrinks down to the branch cut.

Now both factors in the integrand in Eq (93) are real and positive for ζ on the real axis between (B/A) and 1; so is the function $t^n(1 - At)$. It follows that $p_n \geq 0$ and $p_n - p_{n+1} \geq 0$; these imply the first inequality in Eq. (91). Incidentally, the positivity of $t^n(1 - t)$ and $t^n[1 - (B/A)t^{-1}]$ lead to the further inequalities

$$p_n > Ap_n > p_{n+1} > 0, \qquad p_n > Bp_{n-1}$$
$$(p_n - p_{n+1}) > A(p_n - p_{n+1}) > (p_{n+1} - p_{n+2}) > 0$$
$$(p_n - Bp_{n-1}) > A(p_n - Bp_{n-1}) > (p_{n+1} - Bp_n) > 0 \tag{94}$$

Indeed these inequalities remain valid *at* the critical point when $A = 1$ (while $B < 1$). [Note that the case $n = 0$ follows trivially by including the first term in Eq. (93).]

Consider now the coefficients q_n for which we find as above that

$$q_n = (A/B)^{1/2}\delta_{n0} - \frac{A^n}{\pi} \int_{B/A}^{1} \left(\frac{1-\zeta}{\zeta-(B/A)}\right)^{1/2} \zeta^{n-1}\, d\zeta \qquad (95)$$

When $B = 0$ this representation breaks down for $n = 0$ but it remains trivially true that $q_0 = 1$. As before, the positivity of the integrand ensures that $q_n \leq 0$ for all $n \geq 1$ as required in Eq. (90). In fact, $(-q_n)$ satisfies all the inequalities (94) for $n \geq 1$. Similarly, one may show that the elements c_{-n} for $n \geq 0$, and $(-c_n)$ for $n > 0$, satisfy Eq. (94). The inequalities also hold for a larger class of generating functions formed of products of factors $(1 - A_j e^{\pm i\theta})^{\alpha_j}$ with real A_j, provided the α_j satisfy suitable restrictions.

APPENDIX B

Asymptotic Evaluation of $D_N(t_\alpha)$

The determinant $D_N(t_\alpha)$ where t_α is defined by Eq. (63) has the coefficients

$$c_n = \frac{\sin \pi\alpha}{\pi(n + \alpha)} \qquad (\alpha\ \text{nonintegral}) \qquad (96)$$

so that

$$D_{N+1}(t_\alpha) = \left(\frac{\sin \pi\alpha}{\pi}\right)^{N+1} |(i - j + \alpha)^{-1}|_0^N \qquad (97)$$

where the last determinant, say $|d_{ij}|_0^N$, is of Cauchy form, namely,

$$d_{ij} = (a_i + b_j)^{-1} \quad \text{with} \quad a_i = i + \alpha, \qquad b_j = -j \qquad (98)$$

From the standard theory of a Cauchy determinant[21] one has

$$\frac{D_{N+1}}{D_N} = \left(\frac{\sin \pi\alpha}{\pi}\right) \frac{1}{a_N + b_N} \prod_{i=0}^{N-1} \frac{(a_N - a_i)(b_N - b_i)}{(a_N + b_i)(a_i + b_N)} \qquad (99)$$

and hence

$$D_N(t_\alpha) = \left(\frac{\sin \pi\alpha}{\pi\alpha}\right)^N \prod_{t=1}^{N-1} \left(1 - \frac{\alpha^2}{t^2}\right)^{t-N} \qquad (100)$$

By using the well-known result

$$\frac{\sin \pi\alpha}{\pi\alpha} = \prod_{t=1}^{\infty}\left(1 - \frac{z^2}{t^2}\right) \tag{101}$$

we obtain

$$\ln D_N(t_\alpha) = \sum_{t=1}^{N-1} t \ln\left(1 - \frac{\alpha^2}{t^2}\right) + N\sum_{t=N}^{\infty} \ln\left(1 - \frac{\alpha^2}{t^2}\right) \tag{102}$$

If we remove the divergent contribution of the first sum, extend its limit to ∞ and expand $\ln[1 - (\alpha^2/t^2)]$ which is justified for $N > |\alpha|$, we obtain

$$\ln D_N(t_\alpha) = -\alpha^2\psi(N) - \alpha^2\gamma_E - Z_\alpha - \alpha^2 N\zeta(2, N)$$

$$+ \sum_{r=2}^{\infty} r^{-1}[\zeta(2r - 1, N) - N\zeta(2r, N)]\alpha^{2r} \tag{103}$$

where $\psi(N)$ is the logarithmic derivative of the gamma function,[22a] γ_E is Euler's constant, the positive sum

$$Z_\alpha = \sum_{t=1}^{\infty} t\left[-\ln\left(1 - \frac{\alpha^2}{t^2}\right) - \frac{\alpha^2}{t^2}\right] \tag{104}$$

is absolutely convergent for all α (nonintegral), and the generalized zeta function[22b] is

$$\zeta(s, N) = \sum_{t=N}^{\infty} t^{-s}. \tag{105}$$

We may now utilize the asymptotic expansions[22c] of $\psi(N)$ and $\zeta(s, N)$ for large N in terms of Bernoulli numbers B_n. This leads to

$$\ln D_N(t_\alpha) = -\alpha^2 \ln N - \alpha^2(1 + \gamma_E) - Z_\alpha + \sum_{t=1}^{m-1} a_t N^{-2t} + O(N^{-2m}) \tag{106}$$

for $N > |\alpha|$ where

$$a_t = \sum_{l=0}^{t} \frac{(2t)!(1 - 2l)}{t(2l)!(2t - 2l + 2)!} B_{2l}\alpha^{2t-2l+2} \tag{107}$$

This is the result quoted in the text. From the formula (107) we find explicitly

$$a_1 = -\tfrac{1}{12}\alpha^2(1 - \alpha^2), \qquad a_2 = \tfrac{1}{120}\alpha^2(1 - \alpha^2)(3 - 2\alpha^2), \ \ldots \tag{108}$$

Finally these coefficients may be reexpressed more compactly in terms of Bernoulli polynomials[22d]

$$B_n(x) = \sum_{r=0}^{n}\binom{n}{r}B_n x^{n-r} = (-)^n[B_n(-x) + nx^{n-1}] \tag{109}$$

by writing the factor $(1 - 2l)$ in Eq. (107) as $(2t - 2l + 2) - (2t + 1)$. This leads to

$$a_t = t^{-1}(2t + 1)^{-1}\alpha B_{2t+1}(\alpha) - \tfrac{1}{2}t^{-1}(t + 1)^{-1}[B_{2t+2}(\alpha) - B_{2t+2}] \qquad (110)$$

When $|\alpha| < 1$ the rapidly convergent series

$$Z_\alpha = -\ln(1 - \alpha^2) - \alpha^2 + \sum_{r=2}^{\infty} r^{-1}[\zeta(2r - 1) - 1]\alpha^{2r} \qquad (111)$$

may be useful for numerical computation.[23]

References

1. U. Grenander and G. Szegö, *Toeplitz Forms and Their Applications*, University of California Press, Berkeley, California, 1958.
2. M. Kac, in *Summer Institute on Spectral Theory and Statistical Mechanics*, J. D. Pincus, Ed., Brookhaven Natl. Lab. Rept. BNL 993 (T-422) (1966).
3. B. Kaufman and L. Onsager, *Phys. Rev.*, **76**, 1244 (1949).
4. E. W. Montroll, R. B. Potts, and J. C. Ward, *J. Math. Phys.*, **4**, 308 (1963).
5. J. Stephenson, *J. Math. Phys.*, **5**, 1009 (1964); K. Kano, *Progr. Theoret. Phys. (Kyoto)*, **35**, 1 (1966); V. G. Vaks, A. I. Larkin, and Yu. N. Ovchinnikov, *Soviet Phys. JETP*, **22**, 820 (1966); and especially R. E. Hartwig and J. Stephenson, *J. Math. Phys.* **9**, 836 (1968).
6. See (a) L. P. Kadanoff *et al.*, *Rev. Mod. Phys.*, **39**, 395 (1967) and (b) M. E. Fisher, *Rept. Progr. Phys.*, **30**, 615 (1967).
7. M. E. Fisher and H. N. V. Temperley, *Phil. Mag.*, **6**, 1061 (1961); P. W. Kasteleyn, *Physica*, **27**, 1209 (1961); M. E. Fisher, *Phys. Rev.*, **124**, 1664 (1961).
8. M. E. Fisher and J. Stephenson, *Phys. Rev.*, **132**, 1411 (1963).
9. R. E. Hartwig, *J. Math. Phys.*, **7**, 286 (1966).
10. F. J. Dyson, *J. Math. Phys.*, **3**, 157 (1962).
11. A. Lenard, *J. Math. Phys.*, **5**, 930 (1964).
12. E. Lieb, T. Schultz, and D. Mattis, *Ann. Phys. (N.Y.)*, **16**, 407 (1961).
13. M. E. Fisher and A. E. Ferdinand, *Phys. Rev. Letters*, **19**, 169 (1967).
14. See, for example, the lectures by Hirschman in Ref. 2.
15. I. I. Hirschman, *J. d'Analyse Math.*, **14**, 225 (1965).
16. A. Devinatz, *Illinois J. Math.*, **11**, 160 (1967).
17. R. E. Hartwig and M. E. Fisher, *Arch. Ratl. Mech. Anal.*, (1969) [in press].
18. T. T. Wu, *Phys. Rev.*, **149**, 380 (1966).
19. R. E. Hartwig, Ph.D. thesis, University of Adelaide, Australia, 1966; see also Hartwig and Stephenson, Ref. 5.
20. See A. Lenard, *Some Remarks on Large Toeplitz Determinants* (unpublished).
21. See, for example, T. Muir, *A Treatise on the Theory of Determinants*, Dover Press, New York, 1960, Sections 323–4, p. 353.
22. A. Erdélyi, *Higher Transcendental Functions*, Vol. 1, McGraw-Hill, London, 1953, (a) p. 15, (b) p. 24, (c) pp. 47–48, (d) pp. 35–38.
23. See, e.g., M. E. Fisher and R. J. Burford, *Phys. Rev.*, **156**, 583 (1967), Section 5.1.

A NEW SERIES EXPANSION FOR PATH INTEGRALS IN STATISTICAL MECHANICS*

TERENCE BURKE

*Department of Physics, Boston University,
Boston, Massachusetts*

and

ARMAND SIEGEL†

*Service de Physique Théorique, Saclay, France and Department of
Physics, Boston University, Boston, Massachusetts*

The use of path or functional integration techniques in physics offers many apparent simplifications especially in statistical mechanics. However, in practice it is usually impossible to make an explicit evaluation of the path integrals one meets. Here we shall give a very condensed account of a possible approximation scheme for the calculation of a particular class of path integrals.

The functional integral

$$K(X, \beta; X_0, 0) \equiv \int \exp\left\{-\int_0^\beta V[x(t)]dt\right\} d_{w(0,X_0;\ \beta,X)}x \qquad (1)$$

$$\equiv \int \exp\left(-\int_0^\beta \left\{\frac{1}{2}\left[\frac{dx(t)}{dt}\right]^2 + V[x(t)]\right\}dt\right) \delta(x(\beta) - X)$$

$$\times \prod_{0 < t < \beta} \frac{\delta x(t)}{(2\pi\, dt)^{1/2}} \qquad (2)$$

is an expectation value over Wiener measure

$$\prod_{0 < t \le \beta} \exp\left\{-\frac{1}{2}\left[\frac{dx(t)}{dt}\right]^2\right\} \frac{\delta x(t)}{(2\pi\, dt)^{1/2}} \qquad (3)$$

conditional on $x(0) = X_0$, of the functional $V(x(\cdot))$ of $x(t)$, where $x(t)$ is

---

* Work supported by the U.S. Air Force Office of Scientific Research, Grant No. AF-AFOSR 557-67.

† Present address: Department of Physics, Boston University.

defined over $0 < t \le \beta$, in the sense that

$$K(X, \beta; X_0, 0) = E_{(0, \beta]}\left(\exp\left\{-\int_0^\beta V[x(t)]dt\right\}\delta(x(\beta) - X) \mid X_0\right) \quad (4)$$

In writing the above, we are leaning heavily on various published and other available treatments of the subject. In Eq. (1) we use the notation of Brush[1]; the notation of Eqs. (2), (3), and (4) is from an informally distributed set of lecture notes by Siegel.[2]

The functional defined above is also the Green's function[2,3] or propagator of the equation

$$\frac{\partial \psi}{\partial t} = \left[\frac{1}{2}\frac{\partial^2}{\partial x^2} - V(x)\right]\psi = H\psi \quad (5)$$

for $\psi(x, 0) = \delta(x - X_0)$. The one-dimensional Bloch-Schrödinger equation

$$\frac{\partial \Psi}{\partial \theta} = \left[\frac{\hbar^2}{2m}\frac{\partial^2}{\partial y^2} - U(y)\right]\Psi = \mathscr{H}\Psi \quad (6)$$

goes into the dimensionless form (5) under the following substitutions:

$$x = \frac{y}{l}; \quad t = \hbar\omega\theta; \quad H(x) = \frac{\mathscr{H}(y(x))}{\hbar\omega}; \quad \Psi(x) = \sqrt{l}\,\psi(y(x)) \quad (7)$$

which makes use of the basic length and energy parameters

$\hbar\omega$ = energy of ground state of system obeying Eq. (6)

$l = (\hbar/m\omega)^{1/2}$ = width of the ground-state wave function of Eq. (6)   (8)

The Bloch equation is Eq. (6) as it stands; the Schrödinger equation is Eq. (6) with $\theta = i \times$ time; Wiener measure goes into Feynman measure under the latter transformation. We shall speak throughout in the language of the Bloch equation and Wiener measure. Our results are, at least formally, transformable into the Schrödinger-Feynman situation.

Wiener integrals in general, often useful in statistical mechanics[1,4], can be expressed in terms of the propagator in Eq. (4). In particular, putting $\theta = 1/kT$, $\beta = \hbar\omega/kT$, we have for the partition function of the particle obeying Eq. (6)

$$Z(\beta) \equiv \int P_W[x(\beta) \mid x(0)]\mid_{x(\beta) = x(0) = x_0}$$

$$\times E_{(0, \beta)}^W\left(\exp\left\{-\int_0^\beta V[x(t)]\,dt\right\}x(0) = x(\beta) = x_0\right) dx_0 \quad (9)$$

where $P_W[x(\beta) \,|\, x(0)]$ is the Wiener probability density of $x(\beta)$ given $x(0)$, and E^W is the expectation value with respect to the Wiener probability.

By way of completing this compressed presentation of the ideas we propose mainly to work on, we wish to present the Uhlenbeck-Ornstein integral.[2, 5] To use this, we must take ω in Eq. (8) as the frequency associated with the harmonic part of $U(y)$ only, i.e., we assume

$$U(y) = \frac{K}{2} y^2 + \frac{1}{3!} U'''(0)y^2 + \cdots \tag{10}$$

and define

$$\omega = (K/m)^{1/2}, \qquad l = (\hbar/2m\omega)^{1/2} \tag{11}$$

With these definitions, both differing from Eqs. (8), we can still transform variables and functions according to Eq. (7). (The reason for the change from Eq. (8) to Eq. (11) is that we want the Uhlenbeck-Ornstein weighting to come out in standard form). The result is [2]

$$\frac{\partial \psi}{\partial t} = \left[\frac{\partial^2}{\partial x^2} - \frac{x^2}{4} - V'(x) \right] \psi \tag{12}$$

where

$$V'(x) = V[y(x)]/\hbar\omega - x^2/4 \tag{13}$$

is the transformed potential *minus the harmonic part*.

One further functional transformation is needed before we can have the Uhlenbeck-Ornstein integral in the needed standard form: Put

$$\varphi(x) = e^{-t/2} e^{-x^2/4} \psi(x) \tag{14}$$

Then Eq. (12) becomes

$$\frac{\partial \varphi}{\partial t} = \left[-H_{F-P} + V'(x) \right] \varphi \tag{15}$$

where

$$H_{F-P} = -\frac{\partial}{\partial x} \left(x + \frac{\partial}{\partial x} \right) \tag{16}$$

is the Fokker-Planck operator. The Green's function of this operator alone i.e., the solution of

$$\frac{\partial P[x(t) \,|\, x(0)]}{\partial t} = H_{F-P} P[x(t) \,|\, x(0)] \tag{17}$$

for $P(x(t)\,|\,x(0)) \underset{t\to 0}{\longrightarrow} \delta[x(t) - x(0)]$, is the Uhlenbeck-Ornstein function

$$P_{U-O}[x(t)\,|\,x(0)] = [2\pi(1 - e^{-2t})]^{-1/2} \exp\left\{-\frac{[x(t) - x(0)e^{-t}]^2}{2(1 - e^{-2t})}\right\} \quad (18)$$

This function is in every sense a conditional probability analogous to the Wiener probability

$$P_W[x(t)\,|\,x(0)] = (2\pi t)^{-1/2} \exp\left\{-\frac{[x(t) - x(0)]^2}{2t}\right\} \quad (19)$$

which serves as basis of the Wiener weighting (3). It follows that the propagator in Eq. (4) can be taken over as the full Green's function of Eq. (15), if $V(x)$ is replaced by $V'(x)$ and $E_{[0,\beta]}$ is taken with respect to the Uhlenbeck-Ornstein weighting.

The usefulness of the Uhlenbeck-Ornstein weighting lies in situations where $U(y)$ contains a substantial harmonic part; $V'(x)$ is then considerably smaller than $V(x)$, and an approximation scheme based on any sort of expansion with respect to $V'(x)$ is therefore much closer to its goal than one based on $V(x)$ and the Wiener weighting.

It can be shown that the partition function when based on the Unlenbeck-Ornstein scheme becomes

$$Z(\beta) = e^{-\beta/2} \int P_{U-O}[x(\beta)\,|\,x(0)]|_{x(\beta)=x(0)=x0}$$
$$E_{(0,\,\beta)}^{U-O}\left(\exp\left\{-\int_0^\beta V'[x(t)]dt\right\}x(0) = x(\beta) = x_0\right) dx_0 \quad (20)$$

An exact evaluation of the functional integral (4) with either the Wiener or the Uhlenbeck-Ornstein weighting, can not be made except in the case where $V(x)$ either vanishes or is a harmonic oscillator potential. Approximations used in the past chiefly involved: (a) Subdivision of the time axis (cf. Kac[3]), and (b) expansion with respect to moments of the random function $x(t)$ (Gel'fand and Yaglom[6]). We here propose an expansion with respect to moments of the random function $V[x(t)]$, which should in general give higher accuracy. As in the expansion of Ref. 6, in each term the functional integration reduces to a product of ordinary integrations. We do this in four ways, since (1) the expansion is applied to Eq. (4); (2) it is applied to the partition function in conjunction with a suggestion of Feynman and Hibbs[4]; four expressions in all are obtained, by using the Wiener and the Uhlenbeck-Ornstein weighting in each of (1) and (2).

We first define the normalized average of a functional $f[x(t)]$ by

$$\langle f[x(t)]\rangle = E_{(0,\,\beta)}\{f[x(t)]\,|\,x(\beta) = X, x(0) = X_0\} \quad (21)$$

Then for either Wiener or Uhlenbeck-Ornstein weighting

$$K(X, \beta; X_0, 0) = P[x(\beta)|x(0)]|_{x(0)=X_0,\ x(\beta)=X}\left\langle \exp\left\{-\int_0^\beta dt V[x(t)]\right\}\right\rangle$$

$$= P[x(\beta)|x(0)]|_{x(0)=X_0,\ x(\beta)=X} \cdot \exp\left\{-\int_0^\beta dt\langle V[x(t)]\rangle\right\}$$

$$\times \left\langle \exp\left(-\int_0^\beta dt\{V[x(t)] - \langle V[x(t)]\rangle\}\right)\right\rangle$$

$$= P[x(\beta)|x(0)]|_{x(0)=X_0,\ x(\beta)=X} \cdot \exp\left\{-\int_0^\beta dt\langle V[x(t)]\rangle\right\}$$

$$\times \left(1 + \sum_{n=2}^\infty \frac{(-1)^n}{n!} \int_0^\beta dt_n \cdots \int_0^\beta dt_1\right.$$

$$\times \left\langle \{V[x(t_1)] - \langle V[x(t_1)]\rangle\} \cdots \right.$$

$$\left.\left.\{V[x(t_n)] - \langle V[x(t_n)]\rangle\}\right\rangle\right) \qquad (23)$$

If we define

$$F[x(t)] = V[x(t)] - \langle V[x(t)]\rangle$$

the nth term in the expansion is written in the form

$$K_n = (-1)^n P[x(\beta)|x(0)]|_{x(0)=X_0, x(\beta)=X}$$

$$\cdot \exp\left[-\int_{-\infty}^\infty dy V(y) \int_0^\beta d\tau P(x(\tau), x(\beta)|x(0))\right]\Bigg|_{\substack{x(0)=X_0, x(\beta)=X, \\ x(\tau)=y}}$$

$$\cdot \int_0^\beta dt_n \int_0^{t_n} dt_{n-1} \cdots \int_0^{t_2} dt_1 \int_{-\infty}^\infty dy_n \cdots \int_{-\infty}^\infty dy_1 F(y_n)\cdots F(y_1)$$

$$\cdot P(x(t_1), x(t_2), \cdots x(t_n), x(\beta)|x(0))\Bigg|_{\substack{x(0)=X_0, x(\beta)=X \\ x(t_i)=y_i \quad i=1,\ldots,n}} \qquad (24)$$

Because of the Markovian nature of the two processes, this joint probability depending on $(n + 2)$ points $x(0)$, $y(t_1)$, $y(t_2)$, ..., $y(t_n)$, $x(\beta)$ can be expressed as the product

$$P(y(t_1), y(t_2), \ldots, y(t_n), x(\beta) \mid x(0))$$

$$= P(y(t_1) \mid x(0)) \cdot P(y(t_2) \mid y(t_1)) \cdots P(x(\beta) \mid y(t_n)) \quad (25)$$

On substitution of Eqs. (18) and (19), K_n is obtained in closed form for the Uhlenbeck-Ornstein and Wiener processes, respectively. For example, for the partition function the lowest order approximation based on the Uhlenbeck-Ornstein process is

$$Z_1(\beta) = \frac{1}{2(\pi \cosh \beta)^{1/2}} \int_{-\infty}^{\infty} dx_0 \exp\left[-\frac{x_0^2}{2} \tanh(\beta/2) \right]$$

$$\times \exp\left[-\int_0^\beta \left[\frac{\cosh \beta}{4\pi \cosh \tau \cosh(\beta - \tau)} \right]^{1/2} \int_{-\infty}^{\infty} V(y) \right.$$

$$\times \left. \exp\left\{ -\frac{\cosh \beta}{4 \cosh \tau \cosh(\beta - \tau)} \left[y - \frac{\cosh(\beta/2 - \tau)}{\cosh(\beta/2)} x_0 \right]^2 \right\} dy \, d\tau \right]$$

$$(26)$$

We now give a brief description of a new expansion which is more accurate for $Z(\beta)$. It is based on a suggestion of Feynman and Hibbs[4] who calculated the Wiener integral corresponding to the first term in this expansion. Our method of calculation uses probability techniques and treats both the Wiener and Uhlenbeck-Ornstein processes. In the latter case we first rewrite Eq. (20) in the form

$$Z(\beta) = e^{-\beta/2} \int_{-\infty}^{\infty} d\bar{x} \int_{-\infty}^{\infty} dx_0 \, P_{U-O}[x(\beta); \bar{x}|x(0)]\Big|_{x(\beta)=x(0)=x_0}$$

$$\times E_{(0,\beta)}^{U-O}\left(\exp\left\{ -\int_0^\beta dt V'[x(t)] \right\} | \bar{x}; x(\beta) = x(0) = x_0 \right) \quad (27)$$

in which the functional averages are restricted to paths with fixed mean $\bar{x}$

$$\bar{x} = \frac{1}{\beta} \int_0^\beta x(t) \, dt \tag{28}$$

Introduction of the new normalized average

$$\langle f[x(t)] \rangle_x = \frac{\displaystyle\int_{-\infty}^{\infty} dx_0 \, P_{U-O}[x(\beta); \bar{x}|x(0)]|_{x(\beta)=x(0)=x_0} \times E_{(0,\beta)}^{U-O}\{f[x(t)]|\bar{x}; x(\beta) = x(0) = x_0\}}{\displaystyle\int_{-\infty}^{\infty} dx_0 \, P_{U-O}[x(\beta); \bar{x}|x(0)]|_{x(\beta)=x(0)=x_0} E_{(0,\beta)}^{U-O}}$$

$$\{1|\bar{x}; x(\beta) = x(0) = x_0\}$$

$$(29)$$

gives

$$Z(\beta) = e^{-\beta/2} \int_{-\infty}^{\infty} d\bar{x} \left\{ \int_{-\infty}^{\infty} d\bar{x}_0 \, P_{U-o}[x(\beta); \bar{x} \,|\, x(0)]|_{x(\beta)=x(0)=x_0} \right.$$

$$\left. \times E^{U-o}_{(0,\beta)} \left[1\,|\,\bar{x}; x(\beta) = x(0) = x_0 \right] \right\} \cdot \left\langle \exp\left\{ -\int_0^{\beta} dt \, V'[x(t)] \right\} \right\rangle_{\bar{x}} \quad (30)$$

$$= e^{-\beta/2} \int_{-\infty}^{\infty} d\bar{x} \left\{ \int_{-\infty}^{\infty} dx_0 \, P_{U-o}[x(\beta); \bar{x} \,|\, x(0)]|_{x(\beta)=x(0)=x_0} \, E^{U-o}_{(0,\beta)} \right.$$

$$\times \left[1\,|\,\bar{x}; x(\beta) = x(0) = x_0 \right] \exp\left\{ -\int_0^{\beta} dt \langle V'[x(t)] \rangle_{\bar{x}} \right\}$$

$$\times \left\{ 1 + \sum_{n=2}^{\infty} \frac{(-1)^n}{n!} \int_0^{\beta} dt_n \cdots \int_0^{\beta} dt_1 \langle F[x(t_1)] \cdots F[x(t_n)] \rangle_{\bar{x}} \right\} \quad (31)$$

where

$$F[x(t)] = V'[x(t)] - \langle V'[x(t)] \rangle_{\bar{x}}$$

In the evaluation of the first term in Eq. (31) we write

$$\int_0^{\beta} dt \langle V'(x(t)) \rangle_{\bar{x}}$$

$$= \frac{\int_0^{\beta} d\tau \int_{-\infty}^{\infty} dy \, V'(y) \int dx_0 \, P_{U-o}[x(\tau), x(\beta); \bar{x}|x(0)]\Big|_{\substack{x(\beta)=x(0)=x_0 \\ x(\tau)=y}}}{\int_{-\infty}^{\infty} dx_0 \, P_{U-o}[x(\beta); \bar{x}|x(0)]|_{x(\beta)=x(0)=x_0}} \quad (32)$$

and use a theorem which follows from the theory of Gaussian Markov processes

$$\int_{-\infty}^{\infty} dx_0 \, P_{U-o}[x(\tau), x(\beta); \bar{x}|x(0)]\Big|_{\substack{x(\beta)=x(0)=x_0 \\ x(\tau)=y}}$$

$$= P_{U-o}[x(\beta); \bar{x}|x(0)]|_{x(\beta)=x(0)=y} \quad (33)$$

so that the expression in Eq. (32) becomes

$$\frac{\beta \int dy \, V'(y) P_{U-o}[x(\beta); \bar{x}|x(0)]|_{x(\beta)=x(0)=y}}{\int dy \, P_{U-o}[x(\beta); \bar{x}|x(0)]|_{x(\beta)=x(0)=y}} \quad (34)$$

The first term in Eq. (31) is easy to evaluate explicitly and in the case of the

Uhlenbeck-Ornstein process[7] Eq. (31) can be written as

$$Z_1(\beta) = \frac{1}{2\pi} \left[\frac{\pi\beta}{\cosh\beta - 1} \right]^{1/2} \int_{-\infty}^{\infty} d\bar{x}\, e^{-(\beta\bar{x}^2)/2}$$

$$\times \exp\left[-\beta\left(\frac{\beta}{2\pi[(\beta/2)\coth(\beta/2) - 1]} \right)^{1/2} \int_{-\infty}^{\infty} dy\, V'(y) \right.$$

$$\times \exp\left\{ -\frac{\beta(y - \bar{x})^2}{2[(\beta/2)\coth(\beta/2) - 1]} \right\} \right] \left\{ 1 + \sum_{n=2}^{\infty} \frac{(-1)^n}{n!} S_n(\bar{x}) \right\}$$

A similar procedure gives the corresponding result for the Wiener process the first term of which was obtained by Feynman and Hibbs[4] using a path integral approach.

Higher terms in the expansion for $Z(\beta)$ can be straightforwardly calculated using the theory of Gaussian Markov processes. For example in the case of the Wiener process we obtain for the first term inside the summation of Eq. (35)

$$S_2(\bar{x}) = \int_0^\beta d\mu \int_0^\mu d\tau\, \frac{3}{2\pi} \left\{ \frac{\beta}{6\pi\tau(\beta - \tau)[\beta^2 - 3\tau(\beta - \tau)]} \right\}^{1/2}$$

$$\times \int_{-\infty}^{\infty} dY \int_{-\infty}^{\infty} dy\, F\left(Y + \frac{y}{2} \right) F\left(Y - \frac{y}{2} \right)$$

$$\times \exp\left[-\frac{\beta y^2}{2\tau(\beta - \tau)} \right] \exp\left\{ -\frac{6\beta[Y - \bar{x}]^2}{\beta^2 - 3\tau(\beta - \tau)} \right\} \tag{36}$$

Feynman and Hibbs[4] showed that in the case when $U(x)$ is a harmonic oscillator potential their result gave a good approximation to the partition function. We hope the first few terms in the above expansion will be amenable to numerical evaluation in the case of simple potentials.

References

1. S. G. Brush, *Rev. Mod. Phys.*, **33**, 79 (1961).
2. A. Siegel, "Introduction à la Théorie des Intégrales Fonctionnelles," and "Intégrales Fonctionnelles en Mécanique Statistique." (Lectures given at C.E.N., Saclay, France, June, 1966).
3. M. Kac, *Probability and Related Topics in Physical Sciences*, Interscience, New York, 1959.
4. R. P. Feynman and A. Hibbs, *Quantum Mechanics and Path Integrals*, McGraw-Hill, New York, 1965.
5. D. Falkoff, *Ann. Phys.*, **4**, 325 (1958).
6. I. M. Gel'fand and A. M. Yaglom, *J. Math. Phys.*, **1**, 48 (1960).
7. S. Newman and A. Siegel, unpublished.

BROWNIAN MOTION AND
INDETERMINACY RELATIONS

EUGENE GUTH

Oak Ridge National Laboratory,
*Oak Ridge, Tennessee**

Introduction. The theory of Brownian motion, originated by Einstein and Smoluchowski, is not only one of the most beautiful subjects in classical physics,[1] but it had also a great heuristic role in the development of quantum physics. Einstein's work on photons in particular, and the laws of radiation in general, was greatly stimulated by his investigation of Brownian motion.[2] More recently, for Feynman's space–time formulation of quantum mechanics the formulation of Einstein's theory of Brownian motion was very suggestive. Wiener's work on integration in function spaces had its origin in a comment by Perrin in his book, *Les Atoms*, on the analogy of the very irregular curves followed by particles in the Brownian motion and the supposed continuous nondifferentiable curves of the mathematicians. This is one of the many cases of abstract mathematical theories which had their origin in physics.

It is, perhaps, less known that the concepts of complementarity and indeterminacy also arise naturally in the theory of Brownian motion. In fact, position and apparent velocity of a Brownian particle are complementary in the sense of Bohr; they are subject to an indeterminacy relation *formally* similar to that of quantum mechanics, but *physically* of a different origin. Position and apparent velocity are not conjugate variables in the sense of mechanics. The indeterminacy is due to the statistical character of the apparent velocity, which, incidentally, obeys a non-linear (Burgers') equation. This is discussed in part I.

The original theory of Brownian motion by Einstein was based on the diffusion equation and was valid for long times. Later, a more general formulism including short times also, has been developed. Instead of the diffusion equation, the telegrapher's equation enters. Again, an indeterminacy relation results, which, for short times, gives determinacy as a limit. Physically, this simply means that a Brownian particle's

---

* Operated by Union Carbide Corporation for the U.S. Atomic Energy Commission.

indeterminacy is due to the multiple collisions with the atoms of its surrounding. For short times, before the occurrence of these multiple collisions, we have determinacy. This is elaborated in part II.

I

We start from the (one-dimensional) system

$$\frac{\partial n}{\partial t} + \frac{\partial j}{\partial q} = 0 \tag{1}$$

$$j = nv_d = -D\frac{\partial n}{\partial q} \tag{2}$$

Here n designates the density or distribution function; j the diffusion current; v_d the apparent velocity, namely, the drift velocity, of a Brownian particle; and D the diffusion constant. Equation (1) is a continuity equation while Eq. (2) is simply Fick's law augmented by a definition of v_d.

Elimination of j gives the diffusion equation

$$\frac{\partial n}{\partial t} = D\frac{\partial^2 n}{\partial q^2} \tag{3}$$

Elimination of n can be carried out by first integrating Eq. (2)

$$n = \exp\left(-\frac{1}{D}\int dq\, v_d\right) \tag{4}$$

Substitution into Eq. (1) and simultaneous replacement of j by nv_d in the same equation gives the nonlinear equation[3]

$$\frac{\partial v_d}{\partial t} + 2v_d\frac{\partial v_d}{\partial q} = D\frac{\partial^2 v_d}{\partial q^2} \tag{5}$$

This is precisely of the form of the equation Burgers[4] used for his model of turbulence. Equation (5), slightly generalized, also describes approximately the flow through a shock wave in a viscous compressible fluid (v_d represents then the excess of flow velocity over sonic velocity). Furthermore, Eq. (5), again slightly generalized, occurs in the theory of moving concentration boundaries as shown by Stockmayer.[5] Similar reducible nonlinear equations enter the nonstationary operation of separating cascades as discussed by Montroll and Newell.[6]

It was shown by Hopf[7] and Cole,[8] independently, that the solution of Eq. (5) can be reduced to that of Eq. (3). However, in all this work only Eq. (5) is of physical interest, while (2) or (4) appear as mathematical tricks and n is devoid of any physical significance. On the contrary, in our problem, we start with the system of Eqs. (1), (2), and (3) in which *both* n and j and consequently n and v_d have clear physical significance. Equation (2) which connects Eq. (5) with Eqs. (1), (3), and (4) follows from physics and is not just a mathematical trick.

From Eq. (3) follows immediately Einstein's relation,

$$(\Delta q)^2 = \overline{q^2} = 2Dt; \qquad \text{or } \Delta q = (2Dt)^{1/2}; \qquad (\bar{q} = 0) \qquad (6)$$

For the drift velocity we obtain

$$\Delta v_d = \frac{\partial}{\partial t}(\Delta q) = (D/2t)^{1/2}; \quad (\bar{v_d} = 0) \qquad (7)$$

From Eqs. (6) and (7), it follows

$$\Delta q \, \Delta v_d = D \qquad (8)$$

The equality sign in Eq. (8) instead of the more general "larger or equal" sign is due to implication of the fundamental solution of the diffusion equation, namely,

$$n(q, t) = (2\pi Dt)^{-1/2} \, e^{-q^2/4Dt} = (\pi \overline{q^2})^{-1/2} \, e^{-q^2/\overline{2q^2}} \qquad (9)$$

For a more general result, we have with n as our distribution function, [see Eq. (4)], (assuming again $\bar{v}_d = \bar{q} = 0$)

$$\Delta v_d \, \Delta q = \left[D^2 \int dq \, \frac{1}{n} \left(\frac{\partial n}{\partial q} \right)^2 \right]^{1/2} \left[\int dq \, q^2 n \right]^{1/2} \qquad (10)$$

Applying

$$\left[\int dq \, F^2 \int dq \, G^2 \right]^{1/2} \geq \int dq \, FG \qquad (11)$$

to Eq. (10), we obtain

$$\Delta v_d \, \Delta q \geq D \qquad (12)$$

This is the generalization of Eq. (8), first obtained by Fürth[9] in 1933. Our derivation [10] is, of course, equivalent to his, but perhaps a little more direct by explicit reference to the Schwarz inequality, Eq. (11).

Clearly, the physical reason for the indeterminacy relations of Eqs. (12) and (8) is due to the statistical character of the drift velocity v_d as defined by Eq. (2) through the statistical distribution function n. Thereby, v_d becomes complementary to q.

Formally, replacing v_d by v and D by $\hbar/2m$, Eq. (12) goes over into the quantum-mechanical indeterminacy relation. However, the same substitution does not transform the diffusion equation into the Schrödinger equation, but only if the time or the mass is made imaginary. This last difference reflects the fact that the *diffusion equation describes an irreversible process*, while the *Schrödinger equation concerns a reversible situation.*

Incidentally, there is a classical analog to the relation

$$\Delta E \, \Delta t \sim \hbar \tag{12a}$$

One has to replace $\hbar \to -k$ (Boltzmann's constant) and $t \to 1/T$ (T being absolute temperature) to obtain

$$\Delta E \, \Delta(1/T) = -k \quad \text{or} \quad \Delta E \, \Delta T \sim kT^2 \tag{12b}$$

This replacement is, of course, the same which carries over the unitary operator $e^{(i/\hbar)Ht}$ into the Boltzmann factor $e^{-H/kT}$, or the Schrödinger into the Bloch equation.

II

The diffusion treatment of Brownian motion in general, Einstein's relation (Eq. (6)) in particular is valid only after the Brownian particle had multiple collisions with the surrounding atoms. For short times, before any collisions occur, there is no statistics; we have determinacy.

We consider[11] the slowing down of a Brownian particle as described by the Kramers equation (p, momentum; m, mass)

$$\frac{\partial f}{\partial t} + \frac{p}{m} \frac{\partial f}{\partial q} - \frac{1}{\tau}(pf) = 0 \tag{13}$$

The third term is due to "frictional forces":

$$\tau = m/\mu$$

where μ is the "frictional constant" and τ a relaxation time. Taking the first two moments with respect to p of Eq. (13), we obtain a system of two first-order differential equations

$$\frac{\partial n}{\partial t} + \frac{\partial j}{\partial q} = 0 \tag{14}$$

$$\tau \frac{\partial j}{\partial t} + D \frac{\partial n}{\partial q} + j = 0 \tag{15}$$

Here we put

$$n(q, t) = \int f \, dp; \quad j(q, t) = \int \frac{pf \, dp}{m}; \quad D = \frac{\tau}{m^2} \int \frac{p^2 f \, dp}{n} \tag{16}$$

and the (approximate) assumption has been made that the second factor of D is independent of q. Equation (14) is identical with Eq. (1), but Fick's law is "generalized" by Eq. (15).

Both n and j satisfy the telegrapher's equation in the form

$$\left[\tau \frac{\partial^2}{\partial t^2} + \frac{\partial}{\partial t} - D \frac{\partial^2}{\partial q^2} \right] \begin{bmatrix} n \\ j \end{bmatrix} = 0 \tag{17}$$

[For the three-dimensional case the system, [Eqs. (14) and (15)], applies also if in the first equation $\partial j/\partial q$ is replaced by div $\mathbf{j}$ ($\mathbf{j}$ being a vector) and in the second equation $\partial n/\partial q$ is replaced by grad n. We have then

$$\frac{\partial n}{\partial t} + \text{div } \mathbf{j} = 0 \tag{14a}$$

$$\tau \frac{\partial j}{\partial t} + D \text{ grad } n + \mathbf{j} = 0 \tag{15a}$$

Here only n satisfies the telegrapher's equation, while j obeys a somewhat different equation because div grad $\neq$ grad div.]

The definition of v_d is still given by the first of the double equation (2). Thus, in Eq. (10) we just replace the first factor using $v_d = j/n$, and obtain

$$\Delta v_d \, \Delta q = \left[\int dq (j^2/n^2) n \right]^{1/2} \left[\int dq \, qn \right]^{1/2} \tag{18}$$

Application of the Schwarz inequality, Eq. (11) gives

$$\Delta v_d \Delta_q \geq \int dq \, jq \tag{19}$$

Now the integral $I = \int dq jq$ obeys the differential equation

$$\tau(\partial I/\partial t) + I - D = 0 \tag{20}$$

from which, with $I(0) = 0$,

$$I = D(1 - e^{-t/\tau}) \tag{21}$$

Hence we obtain as our final result

$$\Delta v_d \, \Delta q \geq D(1 - e^{-t/\tau}) \tag{22}$$

The choice $I(0) = 0$ is necessary, because we know that $t \to 0$, $\Delta v_d \, \Delta q \to 0$, giving determinacy. For long times $(t \gg \tau)$ Eq. (22) reduces to Eq. (12), while for short times $(t \ll \tau)$, of course, it gives zero.

Now D is inversely proportional to a macroscopic (transport) cross section which itself is proportional to Avogadro's number N. Hence, D and the product of indeterminacy is proportional to $1/N$. This feature is characteristic of classical uncertainty relations. N molecules form, so to speak, a critical domain.

For $(\Delta q)^2 = \overline{q^2}$, we obtain Ornstein's relation[12]

$$\overline{q^2} = 2D\tau[t/\tau - 1 + e^{-t/\tau}] \tag{23}$$

which reduces for long times $[t \gg \tau]$ to Einstein's relation, Eq. (6), while for short times $(t \ll \tau)$ it gives

$$\overline{q^2} = (D/\tau)t^2 \tag{24}$$

as one should expect. Equation (23) follows from the (exact) Kramers equation, [Eq. (13)] if one averages over the initial positions and velocities. The higher moments will be, of course, different for Eq. (13) and our approximate system Eqs. (14) and (15).

Incidentally, the telegrapher's equation (17) with $\tau = i\hbar/2mc^2$ is satisfied by the Klein-Gordon (also Dirac) wavefunction for a free particle, if the factor $\exp[-(i/\hbar)mc^2 t]$ is split off from it. Thus, the time lag according to relativity corresponds to an imaginary relaxation time τ.

References

1. See for example, M. C. Wang and G. E. Uhlenbeck, *Rev. Mod. Phys.*, **17**, 327 (1945).
2a. W. Pauli, in *Albert Einstein, Philosopher-Scientist*, P. A. Schilpp, Ed. Tudor, New York, 1949, p. 155 speaks of Einstein's general derivation of Planck's law "as the ripe fruit of his earlier work on the Brownian movement."
2b. R. P. Feynman, *Rev. Mod. Phys.*, **20**, 367 (1948) derives the Schrödinger equation from an integral relation which, for a free particle, is an analytic continuation of the integral relation from which Einstein, *Ann. Physik*, **17**, 549 (1905), derived the diffusion equation.
3. I have been familiar with this result for a long time. It does not seem to have been stated *explicitly* in the literature before.
4. J. M. Burgers, *Proc. Acad. Sci. Amsterdam.* **43**, 2 (1940); **53**, 247 (1950).
5. W. H. Stockmayer, *Trans. N.Y. Acad. Sci.*, Ser 2, **13**, 266 (1950–51).
6. E. W. Montroll and G. F. Newell, *J. Appl. Phys.*, **23**, 184 (1952).
7. E. Hopf, *Commun. Pure Appl. Math.*, **3**, 20 (1950).
8. J. D. Cole, *Quart. Appl. Math.*, **9**, 225 (1951).
9. R. Fürth, *Z. Physik.*, **81**, 143 (1933).

10. E. Guth, *Phys. Rev.*, **26**, 213 (1962). It might be of interest to remark that the relation $(\Delta q)^2 > 2D\,\Delta t$, giving the condition for the convergence of the solutions of the difference equation (obtained by introducing differences Δq and Δt) toward the solutions of the diffusion equation (3) is closely related to Einstein's relation, Eq. (6) and can, in fact, be obtained by random walk considerations; cf. R. Courant, K. Friedrichs, and H. Levy, *Math. Ann.*, **100**, 32 (1928); *IBM J.*, **11**, 215, 231 (1967).

11. The following development, leading to Eq. (22) has been first explicitly given in Ref. 10. The system of Eqs. (14) and (15) can also be derived from a random walk problem initiated by G. I. Taylor and developed by S. Goldstein in the context of fluid dynamics.

12. L. S. Ornstein, *Proc. Acad. Sci., Amsterdam*, **21**, 96 (1918).

AUTHOR INDEX

Numbers in parentheses are reference numbers and show that an author's work is referred to although his name is not mentioned in the text. Numbers in *italics* indicate the pages on which the full references appear.

A

Akheizer, N. I., 84(15), *98*
Alder, B. J., 80(4), *98*
Alexandrowicz, Z., 255(35), *259*
Alfrey, T., Jr., 168(79), *183*
Allnatt, A. R., 150(50), 176, 177, 179, *182*
Amemiya, A., 150(31,32), *182*
Anderson, J. R., 150(61), *182*
Anderson, P. W., 103(2), 105(6), 112(6), *126*
Andres, R. P., 150(51), 176, *182*
Ardente, V., 129(2), *136*
Arends, C. B., 168(80), *183*
Ashkin, J., 270(7), *280*
Atchison, W. F., 234(8), 236(8), 240(8), *258*
Avrami, J., 179, 180, *183*

B

Bagdassarian, 177, 179
Bailey, N., 275(11), *280*
Bak, T. A., 219
Balescu, R., 15(1), *34*
Baranger, M., 120(17), 121(17), *127*
Bartholomay, A. F., 150, 157, 159, *181*
Bartlett, M. S., 137(3), *148*
Barton, G., 19(2), *34*
Barut, A., 19(3), 20, *34*
Baur, M. E., 305(14), 323(14), *323*
Bazley, N. W., 150(45), *182*
Beals, E., 325(1), 331(1), *331*
Bernard, W., 67(1), 73(19), 75(19), *76*, 77
Berne, B. J., 129, 130, *136*
Bharucha-Reid, A. T., 150, 165(62), *182*
Blackman, M., 93(36), 96(36), *99*
Blok, J., 73(17), 77
Blume, M., 124, 125, *127*
Boguliubov, N. N., 199, 218, *218*
Boon, J. P., 129, 130, *136*
Born, M., 207(16), *218*

Boudart, M., 150(51), 176, *182*
Bourbaki, N., 45(10), *63*
Brout, R., 200(11), *218*
Bruce, C. R., 88(24), *99*
Brush, S. G., 356, *362*
Bueche, F., 305(3), 323(39), *323*, 324
Burford, R. J., 252, *258*, 353(23), *353*
Burgers, J. M., 364, *368*
Burke, T., 355
Burr, J. G., 172, 175, *183*
Burton, M., 150(40), *182*
Byers Brown, W., 91(30), *99*

C

Callen, H. B., 67(1), 73(19), 75(19), *76*, 77
Carrier, G., 157, *182*
Cassassa, E. F., 229(1), *257*
Cerf, R., 305(9), 319(9), *323*
Chakraverty, B. K., 150(52), *182*
Chandrasekhar, S., 121(19), *127*, 137(2), 139(2), 143(2), *148*
Chapman, S., 40(5), 41(5), 50(5), 54(5), 61(5), *62*
Chebycheff, P., 89(25), *99*
Chen, S. H., 131(6), 132(6,9), 136(6), *136*
Cohen, E. G. D., 39(3), *62*, 68(6), 74(6), *76*
Cohen, E. R., 150(24), 166, 168, *181*
Cole, J. D., 364, *368*
Cook, J. G., 73(17), 77
Courant, R., 365(10), *369*
Courtney, W. G., 150(53), 176, *182*
Cowling, T. G., 40(5), 41(5), 50(5), 54(5), 61(5), *62*

D

Dalgarno, A., 91(30), *99*
Dalton, N. W., 254(33), *259*
Damle, P. S., 129(2), *136*
Darvey, I. G., 150, 160, 164, *181*

CUMULATIVE INDEX TO VOLUMES I-XIII AND XV

Authors of Articles

Numerals in bold type are volume numbers

Titles of Articles